Iron-Sulfur Proteins

VOLUME II

Molecular Properties

MOLECULAR BIOLOGY

An International Series of Monographs and Textbooks

Editors: BERNARD HORECKER, NATHAN O. KAPLAN, JULIUS MARMUR, AND HAROLD A. SCHERAGA

A complete list of titles in this series appears at the end of this volume.

Iron-Sulfur Proteins

VOLUME II
Molecular Properties

Edited by *Walter Lovenberg*

SECTION ON BIOCHEMICAL PHARMACOLOGY
EXPERIMENTAL THERAPEUTICS BRANCH
NATIONAL HEART AND LUNG INSTITUTE
NATIONAL INSTITUTES OF HEALTH
BETHESDA, MARYLAND

ACADEMIC PRESS New York and London   1973

A Subsidiary of Harcourt Brace Jovanovich, Publishers

ACADEMIC PRESS, INC.
111 Fifth Avenue, New York, New York 10003

United Kingdom Edition published by
ACADEMIC PRESS, INC. (LONDON) LTD.
24/28 Oval Road, London NW1

Library of Congress Cataloging in Publication Data

Lovenberg, Walter.
    Iron-sulfur proteins.

    (Molecular biology)
    Includes bibliographies.
    1. Iron-sulfur proteins.   I.   Title.   II.   Series:
Molecular biology; an international series of monographs
and textbooks.
QP552.I7L69   574.1'9245   72-13613
ISBN 0–12–456002–4 (v. 2)

Contents

1. The Chemical Properties of Ferredoxins

Richard Malkin

2. The Types, Distribution in Nature, Structure-Function, and Evolutionary Data of the Iron–Sulfur Proteins

Kerry T. Yasunobu and Masaru Tanaka

   William A. Eaton and Walter Lovenberg

     I. Introduction   131
    II. Chemical Properties   132
   III. Stereochemistry and Electronic Structure   136
    IV. Summary and Conclusions   157
         References   160

4. Crystal and Molecular Structure of Rubredoxin from
    Clostridium pasteurianum

   L. H. Jensen

     I. Theory   164
    II. Experimental Procedure   174
   III. Determination of the Structure   177
    IV. Addendum   189
         References   193

5. Probing Iron–Sulfur Proteins with EPR and ENDOR
    Spectroscopy

   W. H. Orme-Johnson and R. H. Sands

     I. Introduction   195
    II. The EPR Phenomenon   196
   III. The Phenomenon of ENDOR   204
    IV. The Physics of Iron in Proteins   208
     V. Rubredoxins   211
    VI. Two-Iron (Plant-Type) Ferredoxins   214
   VII. Iron–Sulfur Proteins with Four Iron Atoms   222
  VIII. Eight-Iron (Clostridial-Type) Ferredoxins   224
    IX. EPR in More Complex Iron–Sulfur Proteins   227
         References   235

6. Mössbauer Spectroscopy of Iron–Sulfur Proteins

   Alan J. Bearden and W. R. Dunham

     I. The Mössbauer Spectroscopic Method   239
    II. Mössbauer Data   244
         References   251

7. NMR Spectroscopy of the Iron–Sulfur Proteins

   W. D. Phillips and Martin Poe

     I. Introduction   255   II. Paramagnetism and NMR   256

8.   Current Insights into the Active Center of Spinach Ferredoxin and Other Iron–Sulfur Proteins

Graham Palmer

List of Contributors

Numbers in parentheses indicate the pages on which the authors' contributors begin.

ALAN J. BEARDEN (239), *Donner Laboratory, University of California, Berkeley, California*

W. R. DUNHAM (239), *Biophysics Research Division, Institute of Science and Technology, The University of Michigan, Ann Arbor, Michigan*

WILLIAM A. EATON (131), *Laboratory of Chemical Physics, National Institute of Arthritis, Metabolism, and Digestive Diseases, National Institutes of Health, Bethesda, Maryland*

L. H. JENSEN (163), *Department of Biological Structure, University of Washington, Seattle, Washington*

WALTER LOVENBERG (131), *Section of Biochemical Pharmacology, Experimental Therapeutics Branch, National Heart and Lung Institute, National Institutes of Health, Bethesda, Maryland*

RICHARD MALKIN (1), *Department of Cell Physiology, University of California, Berkeley, California*

W. H. ORME-JOHNSON (195), *Department of Biochemistry, College of Agricultural and Life Sciences, and Institute for Enzyme Research, University of Wisconsin, Madison, Wisconsin*

GRAHAM PALMER (285), *Biophysics Research Division, Institute of Science and Technology, and Department of Biological Chemistry, The University of Michigan, Ann Arbor, Michigan*

W. D. PHILLIPS (255), *Central Research Department, Experimental Station, E. I. du Pont de Nemours and Company, Wilmington, Delaware*

MARTIN POE (255), *Merck Institute for Therapeutic Research, Rahway, New Jersey*

ix

MASARU TANAKA (27), *Department of Biochemistry-Biophysics, University of Hawaii, Honolulu, Hawaii*

R. H. SANDS (195), *Biophysics Research Division, Institute of Science and Technology, The University of Michigan, Ann Arbor, Michigan*

KERRY T. YASUNOBU (27), *Department of Biochemistry-Biophysics, University of Hawaii, Honolulu, Hawaii*

Preface

Our understanding of the biological role and molecular properties of iron–sulfur proteins has grown rapidly during the past decade. In fact, from the time that this treatise was first conceived (about three years ago), our knowledge on detailed structure has proceeded from a meager level to a reasonably sophisticated one; but even this level may seem meager within several years.

The objective of this two-volume treatise is to present a detailed account by outstanding scientists of the biological importance and the physical and chemical properties of this group of proteins. While it is meaningless to compare the relative importance of any group of molecules in complex biological systems, it should be noted that iron–sulfur proteins provide the cornerstone for such fundamentally important processes as nitrogen fixation and photosynthesis at the same time they participate in innumerable key reactions in nature, ranging from the most primitive bacterium to man. It is for this reason that students and/or investigators in all biological disciplines will find valuable information in this work.

Volume II provides an in-depth analysis of the chemical and physical properties of many of the iron–sulfur proteins. Particular emphasis is placed on the theory and use of physicochemical techniques in the study of metalloproteins. The chemical properties of the ferredoxins and a very complete structural and genetic analysis of iron–sulfur electron carriers are presented in individual chapters. Subsequent chapters are then devoted to the theory and use in iron–sulfur protein research of the following techniques: optical spectroscopy, electron paramagnetic resonance and electron nuclear double resonance spectroscopy, X-ray crystallography, proton magnetic resonance spectroscopy, and Mossbauer spectroscopy. The volume is concluded by a detailed discussion of our current knowledge on the active centers of each type of iron–sulfur protein.

The presentations have not been changed to conform to a particular style. It is hoped that the individualistic nature of each chapter will give the reader an idea of the approaches being pursued in some of the major laboratories.

Volume I of "Iron–Sulfur Proteins" deals largely with the biological properties of these proteins; Volume II deals with the molecular properties. This division is somewhat arbitrary since many of the authors are deeply involved in investigating both aspects of these molecules, and it was the intent that all chapters represent the interests and philosophies of the individual laboratories.

In Chapter 1 of Volume I, Dr. Beinert presents a historical review of the subject and some details on the extremely important role played by electron paramagnetic resonance in developing our understanding of iron–sulfur proteins. Other chapters are devoted to the role of ferredoxin in nitrogen fixation and to the general aspects of bacterial metabolism. Two contributions deal with the role of iron–sulfur proteins in the photosynthetic process. Three chapters are concerned with the mechanism of hydroxylation reactions that require iron–sulfur proteins, specifically rubredoxin and alkane hydroxylation, putidaredoxin and camphor hydroxylation, and adrenodoxin and steroid hydroxylation. This first volume also includes very complete review chapters on complex iron–sulfur proteins.

WALTER LOVENBERG

Contents of Volume I

CHAPTER 1

The Chemical Properties of Ferredoxins

RICHARD MALKIN

I. INTRODUCTION

Chemical characterization of iron–sulfur proteins, in particular the ferredoxins, has been an extremely active area of investigation since 1962 when the ferredoxin from *C. pasteurianum* was first described (Mortenson *et al.*, 1962). Early studies were primarily concerned with isolation of the ferredoxins in a pure state, but subsequent work has been directed toward elucidating the nature of the active site in these proteins by both chemical and physical methods. This chapter will be limited to a discussion of the chemical properties of the simple iron–sulfur proteins with particular emphasis on chloroplast and bacterial-type ferredoxins and the information derived from these studies on the nature of the active site in the ferredoxins. Several reviews concerned with related topics have

1

TABLE I

Some Properties of Ferredoxins and Related Proteins

Protein	Molecular weight	Visible absorption bands (nm) (oxidized form)	Ext. coefficient (major visible band) per gm-atom iron	Reference
I. Two-iron protein				
A. Photosynthetic organisms: chloroplast ferredoxin	12,000	420, 463, 515(sh)	4800	Matsubara and Sasaki (1968), Tagawa and Arnon (1962, 1968)
B. Nonphotosynthetic organisms				
1. Adrenodoxin	13,000	414, 455, 515(sh)	4900	Tanaka et al. (1970), Kimura and Suzuki (1967), and Kimura (1968)
2. Putidaredoxin	12,000	415, 455, 560(sh)	3875	Cushman et al. (1967) and Tsibris and Woody (1970)
3. A. vinelandii protein 1	21,000	420, 460, 550	4730	Shethna et al. (1968)
4. A. vinelandii protein 2	24,000	420, 460, 550	6970	Shethna et al. (1968)
5. C. pasteurianum paramagnetic protein	24,000	425, 463, 550	~3500	Hardy et al. (1965)
6. Mitochondrial nonheme iron protein	26,000	460, 575	—	Rieske et al. (1964)
II. Four-iron proteins: high-potential iron protein	10,000	375	—	Bartsch (1963) and Dus et al. (1967)
III. Eight-iron proteins: bacterial ferredoxins				
A. Photosynthetic organisms				
1. Chromatium ferredoxin	10,000	390	3850	Bachofen and Arnon (1966) and Matsubara et al. (1970)
2. Chlorobium ferredoxin	6,000	380	—	Buchanan et al. (1969)
B. Nonphotosynthetic organisms				
1. Clostridial ferredoxin	6,000	390	3850	Lovenberg et al. (1963) and Hong and Rabinowitz (1970a)
2. Azotobacter ferredoxin	15,000	400	4400	Yoch et al. (1969) and Shethna (1970)

been published (Buchanan, 1966; Malkin and Rabinowitz, 1967a; Kimura, 1968; Hall and Evans, 1969; Buchanan and Arnon, 1970; Tsibris and Woody, 1970).

For the purpose of the following discussion, it is convenient to classify the simple iron–sulfur proteins. As shown in Table I, these proteins may be divided into three major groups on the basis of their iron content. Thus, proteins with two iron atoms, four iron atoms, and eight iron atoms per mole of protein have been isolated. Rubredoxin, a protein containing one iron atom, and the high molecular weight, conjugated iron–sulfur proteins will be considered in other chapters in this volume.

The two-iron proteins may be subdivided into the chloroplast ferredoxins and a second group of proteins, such as adrenodoxin and putidaredoxin, found in a variety of nonphotosynthetic systems. Only one four-iron protein has been isolated—the high-potential iron protein. Evidence of the distribution of this protein has thus far been confined to the class of purple photosynthetic bacteria. The eight-iron proteins (bacterial-type ferredoxins) have only been found in bacteria, where their distribution is in both photosynthetic and nonphotosynthetic organisms.

II. CHEMICAL CHARACTERISTICS OF FERREDOXINS

A. Spectral Properties

The two-iron proteins are generally reddish in color in the oxidized state. The absorption spectrum of spinach ferredoxin, representative of this group, is shown in Fig. 1. The spectrum shows peaks in the visible region at 420 and 463 nm, a near-ultraviolet absorption peak at 330 nm, and a protein peak at 276 nm. In general, all two-iron proteins have an absorption spectrum similar to that of spinach ferredoxin (see Table I). In contrast to this group of proteins, iron–sulfur proteins having more than two iron atoms per molecule are brown in color in the oxidized form with a broad absorbance band in the 380- to 400-nm region; the absorption spectrum of the ferredoxin from *Clostridium acidi-urici*, shown in Fig. 2, is an example of the type found in these proteins.

The extinction coefficient of the major visible absorbance band of the oxidized proteins expressed per atom of iron is essentially the same for all the two-iron proteins (Table I). The values for the bacterial-type ferredoxins are also close to those of the two-iron proteins, suggesting that the nature of the iron bonding in all of these proteins is similar even though the proteins have diverse functions and have been isolated from a variety of different sources.

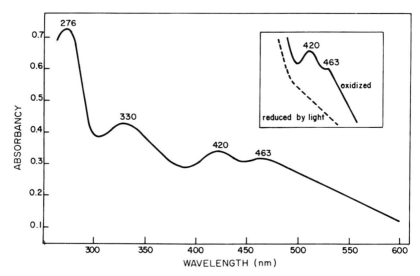

Fig. 1. The absorption spectrum of the chloroplast-type ferredoxin from spinach.

All ferredoxins undergo a partial bleaching on reduction, as shown for the spinach and clostridial ferredoxins in Figs. 1 and 2. Figure 2 also indicates two convenient methods of reducing ferredoxins: chemically with sodium hydrosulfite and enzymatically with hydrogen gas and hydrogenase. The extent of reduction clearly varies with different reductants,

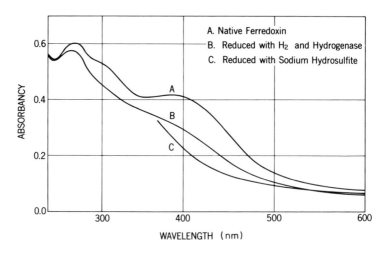

Fig. 2. The absorption spectrum of the bacterial-type ferredoxin from *Clostridium acidi-urici.*

so that one must carefully evaluate any conclusions drawn from the extent of reduction by one method alone. This decrease in absorbance is the opposite of that found in the other large group of proteins containing iron, the hemoproteins. As shown in Figs. 1 and 2, the reduced iron–sulfur proteins are not colorless; detailed spectral studies (Palmer *et al.*, 1967a; Wilson, 1967) have shown that distinguishable absorbance bands are present in the visible region even in the reduced state.

In contrast to all other iron–sulfur proteins, the high-potential iron protein shows an increase in absorption upon reduction. The reduced protein has a broad absorption band at approximately 388 nm of slightly greater intensity than that of the oxidized protein (Bartsch, 1963; Flatmark and Dus, 1969).

Extensive optical rotary dispersion (ORD) and circular dichroism (CD) measurements have been made of many of the iron–sulfur proteins (Ulmer and Vallee, 1963; Gillard *et al.*, 1965; Palmer *et al.*, 1967a; Atherton *et al.*, 1966; Lovenberg, 1966). One general conclusion from these measurements is that the bonding of the chromophoric groups in these proteins is associated with optically active environments. In addition, it has been concluded that reduction changes the environment of the chromophore.

One striking feature of the CD spectra of several different two-iron proteins is the great degree of similarity over the entire visible region. A comparative study of spinach ferredoxin and adrenodoxin, two proteins with different biological functions, has shown that in the oxidized and reduced states the CD transitions are almost identical (Palmer *et al.*, 1967a). Thus this CD study has confirmed the conclusion, drawn from the absorption spectra, that the chromophoric bonding in these two-iron proteins is very similar.

The CD spectrum of the oxidized high-potential iron protein (a four-iron protein) shows four optically active transitions of relatively weak rotary strength (Flatmark and Dus, 1969), even though the optical absorbance spectrum shows only one broad absorption band in this region. The reduced spectrum of this protein also shows optical activity, although the changes upon reduction are not as striking as those found with the two-iron proteins (Flatmark and Dus, 1969).

Gillard *et al.* (1965) first reported the ORD spectra of bacterial ferredoxins from two clostridial species and a related bacterium, *Peptostreptococcus elsdenii*. The data indicated the presence of two optically active transitions (at 490 and 570 nm) underlying the diffuse absorption tail of the visible optical absorbance spectrum. In the same report, these workers showed the ORD spectrum of rubredoxin from *P. elsdenii* and commented upon the similarity of this spectrum to that of the bacterial ferredoxins. However, Lovenberg (1966) compared the ORD spectra of *C. pasteurianum* ferredoxin and rubredoxin, finding that the rotary strength of clostridial rubredoxin was much greater than that of clostridial ferredoxin, and suggested that the qualitative similarity discussed by Gillard *et al.* (1965) was caused by a rubredoxin contamination in the ferredoxin samples used. Atherton *et al.* (1966) reinvestigated this question by examining the CD spectra of clostridial ferredoxin and rubredoxin. The CD spectra of the two oxidized proteins showed clear differences at most points in the visible region but, again, some similarities were observed. In the reduced state, the CD spectra were clearly different; these workers maintained that their study confirmed some similarity in the chromaphoric centers of ferredoxin and rubredoxin.

Optical rotary dispersion spectra of three clostridial ferredoxins in the ultraviolet region have been described (Devanathan *et al.*, 1969), and the ORD parameters from the Moffit equation have been calculated. These parameters were found to be indicative of a random coil conformation, indicating little secondary structure or helix content.

B. Molecular Weights and Amino Acid Composition

Ferredoxins are relatively small proteins (Table I). The clostridial ferredoxins have a molecular weight of 6000 (Lovenberg *et al.*, 1963) as does the bacterial-type ferredoxin from *Chlorobium* (Buchanan *et al.*, 1969). However, the ferredoxins from both *Chromatium* and *Azotobacter* are larger than the other bacterial ferredoxins, with molecular weights of 10,000 and 15,000, respectively (Matsubara *et al.*, 1970; Yoch and Arnon, 1972).

The chloroplast ferredoxins have molecular weights of 12,000 (Sugeno and Matsubara, 1969; Benson and Yasunobu, 1969; Keresztes-Nagy *et al.*, 1969; Rao and Matsubara, 1970), similar to the values reported for adrenodoxin and putidaredoxin (Tanaka *et al.*, 1970; Cushman *et al.*, 1967). The remaining two-iron proteins are significantly larger, with molecular weights in the range of 24,000.

The amino acid compositions of the clostridial ferredoxins are quite unusual. The composition of the ferredoxin from *C. pasteurianum* is given in Table II (Tanaka *et al.*, 1966). The protein has 55 amino acid residues, of which twelve are aspartate and glutamate. Only one basic residue is present, and the protein has a very low content of the aromatic residues. No histidine, methionine, or tryptophan residues are found. Of particular interest is the cysteine content: This protein and all clostridial ferredoxins have eight cysteine residues per mole of protein (Lovenberg *et al.*, 1963).

TABLE II

AMINO ACID COMPOSITION OF FERREDOXINS

Amino acid	Clostridium pasteurianum[a]	Chloropseudomonas ethylicum[b]	Chromatium[c]	Azotobacter vinelandii[d]	Spinach[e]
Lysine	1	0	2	6	4
Histidine	0	0	2	2	1
Arginine	0	0	2	1	1
Tryptophan	0	0	0	1	1
Aspartic acid	8	6–7	8	15	13
Threonine	1	4	6	4	8
Serine	5	2	4	2	7
Glutamic acid	4	9	16	20	13
Proline	3	3	5	9	4
Glycine	4	4	5	4	6
Alanine	8	8	3	8	9
Half-cystine	8	8	9	8	5
Valine	6	5	6	10	7
Methionine	0	0	1	1	0
Isoleucine	5	4	6	7	4
Leucine	0	2	3	8	8
Tyrosine	1	3	3	2	4
Phenylalanine	1	0	0	5	2
Total	55	58–59	81	113	97

[a] Tanaka et al. (1966).
[b] Rao et al. (1969).
[c] Matsubara et al. (1970).
[d] Yoch and Arnon (1972).
[e] Matsubara and Sasaki (1968).

Also included in Table II are the amino acid compositions of the bacterial ferredoxins from two photosynthetic bacteria and from an aerobic organism, *Azotobacter vinelandii*. The ferredoxin from the green sulfur bacterium, *Chloropseudomonas*, resembles clostridial ferredoxin in having approximately 55 amino acid residues, a low basic residue content, and, in addition, a lack of several residues, as is the case with the clostridial ferredoxins (Rao et al., 1969). The ferredoxins from *Chromatium* and *Azotobacter* have the full complement of amino acid residues (Matsubara et al., 1970; Yoch and Arnon, 1972). All the bacterial ferredoxins, in common with the clostridial ferredoxins, also have at least eight cysteine residues per mole of protein.

The chloroplast ferredoxins have 96–97 amino acid residues per mole of protein and contain the full complement of amino acids, as shown in Table II for spinach ferredoxin. These proteins are also highly acidic owing to a preponderance of aspartate and glutamate groups; of the chloroplast ferredoxins examined thus far all have had at least five cysteine residues per mole of protein.

The amino acid sequence studies of the ferredoxins and of other iron–sulfur proteins will be discussed in Chapter 2 of this volume.

C. Nonheme Iron and Inorganic Sulfide Content

Ferredoxins have been recognized as iron-containing proteins since their initial characterization (Mortenson et al., 1962). The iron in these proteins is known *not* to be bound in an iron–porphyrin complex, as in the hemoproteins, but is bound directly by the amino acid residues of the protein without the intervention of any cofactor group, such as the heme moiety.

In contrast to the straightforward characterization of the iron content of chloroplast ferredoxins (Fry and San Pietro, 1962; Tagawa and Arnon, 1962), a wide range of values is found in the early literature for the bacterial-type ferredoxins. Values of from five to eight iron atoms per mole of clostridial ferredoxin have been reported (Lovenberg et al., 1963; Palmer et al., 1966; Mortenson, 1964; Malkin and Rabinowitz, 1966a). However, a more recent, critical examination of the iron content and molar extinction coefficient has clearly shown that clostridial ferredoxin (Hong and Rabinowitz, 1970a) contains eight atoms of iron per mole of protein. The other bacterial-type ferredoxins, initially reported to have less than eight atoms of iron per mole, have also been found to contain eight iron atoms (Table II). Thus, as previously stated, iron–sulfur proteins with only two, four, or eight iron atoms per mole of protein have been characterized; the models to explain certain properties of these proteins must take into account this multiple two-iron observation.

In addition to containing iron, ferredoxins are characterized by having an unusual form of sulfur, referred to as either "acid-labile" or "inorganic" sulfide. The origin of these terms is the observation first reported by Massey (1957) with succinic dehydrogenase that acidification of iron–sulfur proteins results in a release of H_2S. This release of inorganic sulfide has been measured by a sensitive colorimetric assay (Fogo and Popowsky, 1949) based on methylene blue formation [Eqs. (1) and (2)].

$$(1)$$

$$\text{(structure)} \xrightarrow[\text{oxidation}]{+H_2S} \text{(structure)} \quad (2)$$

Methylene blue

The amount of inorganic sulfide detected in all well-characterized ferredoxins has always been equivalent to the amount of nonheme iron present.

Although H_2S is released from ferredoxins on acidification, the origin of this sulfur has been questioned. Several groups proposed that the sulfide in the ferredoxins arises directly from the cysteine residues in the protein by a β-elimination reaction (Bayer *et al.*, 1965; Gersonde and Druskeit, 1968) [Eq. (3)].

$$B^{\ominus} + \overset{\frown}{\underset{\substack{CH-NH-C-R' \\ | \quad\quad \| \\ C=O \quad O \\ | \\ R}}{CH_2-SH}} \longrightarrow \underset{\substack{C-NH-C-R' \\ | \quad\quad \| \\ C=O \quad O \\ | \\ R}}{\overset{CH_2}{\|}} + SH^- \quad (3)$$

One observation leading to this proposal was the finding that H_2S could be liberated from iron–cysteine complexes under basic conditions (Bayer *et al.*, 1965; Bayer and Parr, 1966). However, most workers now agree that the studies of the origin of the H_2S in ferredoxins by Malkin and Rabinowitz (1966a), Jeng and Mortenson (1968), and Hong *et al.* (1969), in addition to the requirements for the reconstitution of ferredoxins (Section IV,B), have shown that the H_2S does not arise from the cysteine residues. In particular, two groups (Jeng and Mortenson, 1968; Hong *et al.*, 1969) isolated ferredoxin from bacterial cultures grown in the presence of ^{35}S to prepare uniformly labeled [^{35}S]ferredoxin. Acidification of the protein to release H_2S resulted in a 50% loss of radioactivity. A total sulfur analysis of clostridial ferredoxin also indicated that the ferredoxin contained more sulfur atoms than could be accounted for by the cysteine residues alone. Studies on the reaction of ferredoxins with mercurials and on the reconstitution of ferredoxins (Sections II,A, IV,A, and IV,B) are also consistent with the view that all ferredoxins contain two different forms of sulfur: the acid-labile sulfide and the sulfur of the cysteine residues of the polypeptide chain.

D. Oxidation–Reduction Properties

One of the most striking features of the ferredoxins is an extremely electronegative oxidation–reduction potential. Most of the proteins have potentials lower than those of the pyridine nucleotide system (-320 mV

TABLE III
Oxidation–Reduction Properties of Ferredoxins and Related Proteins

Protein	E_0' (mV)	Total number of electrons transferred	Reference
Spinach ferredoxin	−420	1	Tagawa and Arnon (1962)
Adrenodoxin	−350	1	Orme-Johnson (unpublished)
Putidaredoxin	−250	1	Tsibris and Woody (1970)
A. vinelandii protein 1	∼−350	1	Orme-Johnson (unpublished)
A. vinelandii protein 2	∼−350	1	Orme-Johnson (unpublished)
C. pasteurianum paramagnetic protein	∼−350	1	Orme-Johnson (unpublished)
High-potential iron protein	+350	1	Bartch (1963) and Dus et al. (1967)
Chromatium ferredoxin	−490	2	Bachofen and Arnon (1966)
Clostridial ferredoxin	−390 to −420	2	Tagawa and Arnon (1962), Sobel and Lovenberg (1966), and Eisenstein and Wang (1969)
A. vinelandii ferredoxin	−420	?	Yoch and Arnon (1972)

at pH 7) (Table III), replacing pyridine nucleotides as the most electro-negative group of electron carriers so far demonstrated in biological systems.

For the two-iron proteins, Tagawa and Arnon (1962) first reported the oxidation–reduction potential of spinach ferredoxin to be −420 mV at pH 7, equivalent to that of the hydrogen electrode. It was also shown that spinach ferredoxin functions as a one-electron carrier. Using different techniques, several groups (Evans *et al.*, 1968; Mayhew *et al.*, 1969; Moss *et al.*, 1969; Moleski *et al.*, 1970; Orme-Johnson and Beinert, 1969a) have found that all the iron–sulfur proteins which contain two atoms of iron act as one-electron carriers in electron transfer reactions, although there is some variation in their oxidation–reduction potentials.

Of the bacterial-type ferredoxins, the clostridial type have been studied the most extensively as regards oxidation–reduction characteristics. Al-though the oxidation–reduction potential of this protein has been found by several groups to be approximately −400 mV (Tagawa and Arnon, 1962; Sobel and Lovenberg, 1966), the number of electrons transferred by clostridial ferredoxin has been a subject of controversy. In their initial studies on *C. pasteurianum* ferredoxin, Tagawa and Arnon (1962) re-ported the protein acts as a one-electron carrier, whereas Sobel and Lovenberg (1966) reported the protein as a two-electron carrier. In a reinvestigation, Tagawa and Arnon (1968) again found the protein to be a one-electron carrier; values of two were reported by other groups for clostridial ferredoxin and for another bacterial-type protein, the fer-redoxin from *Chromatium* (Evans *et al.*, 1968; Mayhew *et al.*, 1969). A more recent investigation has led to a possible explanation for these conflicting results. Eisenstein and Wang (1969) found that the clostridial ferredoxin molecule can accommodate two electrons in two independent sites, one having a potential of −367 mV and the second −398 mV at pH 7; thus the protein acts as a two-electron carrier, even though it is actually mediating one-electron transfers. On the basis of these results, it would appear that the bacterial-type ferredoxins, although having eight iron atoms, can accommodate only two electrons. This result is in agree-ment with an electron paramagnetic resonance study of this ferredoxin (Orme-Johnson and Beinert, 1969b).

One striking exception in the oxidation–reduction characterization of the iron–sulfur proteins is the high-potential iron protein, a one-electron carrier, which was found to have an oxidation–reduction potential of +350 mV (Bartsch, 1963; Dus *et al.*, 1967; Flatmark and Dus, 1969). This high oxidation–reduction potential suggests that the bonding of the iron and sulfide in high-potential iron protein must be fundamentally different from that found in other iron–sulfur proteins. Evidence supporting this conclusion is also based on electron paramagnetic resonance studies (Palmer *et al.*, 1967b).

III. THE CHEMICAL REACTIVITY OF FERREDOXINS

A. Reactivity toward Mercurials and Other Sulfhydryl Reagents

Studies of the reaction of ferredoxins with mercurials have been useful in both the chemical characterization of these proteins and the preparation of apoprotein derivatives, free of both iron and sulfide, which could be converted to give reconstituted ferredoxin molecules (Section IV,A).

Fry and San Pietro (1963) reacted the mercurial, *p*-chloromercuribenzoate (PCMB), with spinach ferredoxin and observed a parallel decrease of all the visible absorption bands. The amount of PCMB necessary to completely titrate the protein was found to be nine equivalents per mole of spinach ferredoxin. The same stoichiometry has been reported for the reaction of alfalfa ferredoxin with sodium mersalyl (Keresztes-Nagy and Margoliash, 1966) and for the reaction of spinach ferredoxin with phenylmercuriacetate (Petering and Palmer, 1970).

Clostridial ferredoxins also react with mercurials. Lovenberg *et al.* (1963) found that the ferredoxin from *C. pasteurianum* reacts with approximately twenty moles of PCMB. Sodium mersalyl was also found to lead to a loss of visible absorbance of the clostridial ferredoxins.

The stoichiometries of the reactions of PCMB with spinach and clostridial ferredoxins are summarized in Table IV. The observed titration results are compatible with the known sulfur composition of these proteins when it is realized that two moles of PCMB react with one mole

TABLE IV
THE REACTION OF PCMB WITH FERREDOXINS

	Clostridial ferredoxin[a,b]			Spinach ferredoxin[a,c]		
	Cysteine	Sulfide	Total	Cysteine	Sulfide	Total
Sulfur atoms	8	8	16	5	2	7
Expected PCMB reacting	8	16	24	5	4	9
Observed PCMB reacting	—	—	~21	—	—	9

[a] Measured in moles per mole of protein.
[b] Lovenberg *et al.* (1963).
[c] Fry and San Pietro (1963).

of inorganic sulfide. These results indicate that in both these ferredoxins all the sulfur is in a form which reacts directly with PCMB without prior reduction of the protein and have been interpreted as an indication that the ferredoxins do not contain disulfide bonds.

Although most ferredoxins have been assumed to react very rapidly with mercurials, few systematic kinetic studies on the rate of reaction of a mercurial with any individual protein have been reported. The results of one such study (Fig. 3) compare the rates of reaction of PCMB with three different ferredoxins. Reaction with spinach ferredoxin is very rapid, while that with clostridial ferredoxin is significantly slower. The ferredoxin from *Azotobacter,* in contrast to the other two ferredoxins, is extremely sluggish in its reaction with PCMB. The behavior of the latter protein is similar to that reported for the high-potential iron protein from *Chromatium* (Flatmark and Dus, 1969), where PCMB does not completely react with all the sulfur in the protein, even after a 16-hour reaction period. These kinetic studies are a reflection of the availability of the sulfur groups to the added mercurials but they cannot simply be correlated with size of the protein or number of sulfur groups present.

The reaction of ferredoxins with a second group of sulfhydryl reagents, the alkylating reagents (iodoacetate and iodoacetamide), has also been studied. No alkylation of the native proteins occurs in clostridial or spinach ferredoxins, even over a time period of several hours (Lovenberg *et al.,* 1963; Petering and Palmer, 1970). With *C. pasteurianum* ferre-

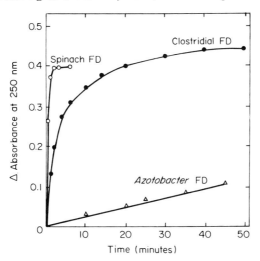

Fig. 3. The rate of reaction of PCMB with the ferredoxins from spinach, *Clostridium pasteurianum,* and *Azotobacter vinelandii* (from Yoch and Arnon, 1972).

doxin, however, it was found that reduction of the protein in the presence of urea led to a complete alkylation of the eight cysteine residues in the molecule (Lovenberg et al., 1963). This result indicates that the cysteine groups were not present as free sulfhydryl groups but were blocked, presumably by the iron atoms in the molecule. In contrast to the clostridial protein, almost all of the cysteine residues of spinach ferredoxin could be alkylated in the presence of 8 M urea without the addition of any reductant, although this reaction took several hours to go to completion.

In studies on the reaction of clostridial ferredoxin with other sulfhydryl reagents, N-ethylmaleimide or 5,5'-dithiobis(2-nitrobenzoic acid) (DTNB), neither reagent reacted with the native protein (Lovenberg et al., 1963; Malkin and Rabinowitz, 1966a). The latter reagent does react with the cysteine sulfhydryl groups after reduction of the protein in urea. In addition, DTNB reacts rapidly with clostridial ferredoxin in the presence of 4 M guanidine hydrochloride but not in the presence of 6.4 M urea. The results with DTNB again indicate that the cysteine residues in the protein are unavailable for direct reaction. The addition of the denaturant guanidine hydrochloride destroys the active site of these molecules, resulting in a rapid reaction with DTNB.

Observations on the nature of reactivity of both the sulfide and cysteine sulfur groups gave early indications that the cysteine sulfhydryl groups, the iron atoms, and the inorganic sulfide moieties are closely interrelated at the active center of the ferredoxins. The chemical evidence has been confirmed by extensive physical measurements, in particular, electron paramagnetic resonance studies made on these proteins.

B. Reactivity toward Iron Chelating Agents

The presence of iron in the ferredoxins led to several investigations on the effect of iron chelating agents on the proteins and to studies to determine the iron valence.

In general, although ferredoxins are low molecular weight proteins with relatively large amounts of iron and thus might be expected to have the iron atoms exposed, the iron in most native ferredoxins reacts slowly with ferric or ferrous chelating agents. Fry and San Pietro (1962) found that, in a 90-minute period, only half the iron in spinach ferredoxin reacted with the ferrous chelating agent, o-phenanthroline. The reaction of o-phenanthroline with the iron in clostridial ferredoxin was also extremely slow (Malkin and Rabinowitz, 1967b); the ferric chelating agent, Tiron, did not react with clostridial ferredoxin at a significant rate over a 1-hour period (Malkin and Rabinowitz, 1967b).

In the presence of denaturants, such as urea or guanidine hydrochloride, the reaction of the iron in ferredoxins with chelating agents is rapid (Malkin and Rabinowitz, 1967b; Petering and Palmer, 1967). These findings suggest that the iron atoms in both spinach and clostridial ferredoxin are buried in the interior structure of the molecule and are only exposed after denaturation.

Fry and San Pietro (1963) studied the reaction of spinach ferredoxin with Tiron or o-phenanthroline in the presence of a mercurial to block sulfhydryl groups under anaerobic conditions in an attempt to determine the valence of the metal ions. Essentially all the iron could react with the ferric chelating agent and little reacted with the ferrous chelating agent, a result confirmed independently by Palmer and Sands (1966) and by Palmer et al. (1967b). It is concluded that all the iron in native spinach ferredoxin is in the ferric state.

Early investigations on the valence state of the iron in clostridial ferredoxins were equivocal. Buchanan et al. (1963) found, under the standard conditions for assay of ferrous iron with o-phenanthroline, ferric iron was rapidly reduced to the ferrous state when added to ferredoxin solutions. Not surprisingly, all the iron in ferredoxin also appeared in the ferrous state under these conditions. In a later study (Lovenberg et al., 1963), it was shown by the same group that the reduction of added ferric iron was inhibited by glacial acetic acid.

It seems probable that the reduction of at least some of the iron occurs during the acid treatment required to liberate the iron for assay. Blomstrom et al. (1964) attempted to prevent this reduction by the addition of a mercurial which would block sulfhydryl reducing groups. Using this technique, these workers concluded there were a minimum of two ferric atoms in clostridial ferredoxin. Using similar methods, Sobel and Lovenberg (1966) and Palmer et al. (1966) found that approximately half the iron in the ferredoxin from C. pasteurianum was in the ferric state.

Studies on the reaction of clostridial ferredoxin with the ferric chelating agent, Tiron, shown in Fig. 4, also indicate that half the iron in ferredoxin is in the ferric state. Neither the native protein nor the protein in the presence of urea (Fig. 4A and B, respectively) reacted with Tiron. However, in the presence of guanidine hydrochloride and oxygen (Fig. 4D). all the iron reacted with the ferric chelating agent. Under anaerobic conditions, in the presence of guanidine hydrochloride, only half the iron reacted as ferric iron, indicating that oxygen was responsible for the oxidation of half the iron to the ferric state under aerobic conditions. It had previously been found (Malkin and Rabinowitz, 1967b) that clos-

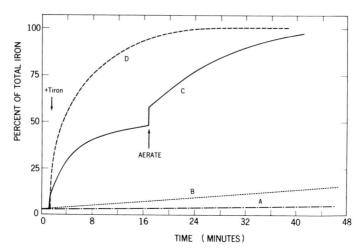

Fig. 4. The reaction of Tiron with clostridial ferredoxin. (A) Native ferredoxin; (B) ferredoxin in 6.4 M urea; (C) ferredoxin in 4 M guanidine hydrochloride under anaerobic conditions; (D) ferredoxin in 4 M guanidine hydrochloride under aerobic conditions (from Malkin and Rabinowitz, 1967b).

tridial ferredoxin was relatively stable in guanidine hydrochloride solutions under anaerobic conditions.

All the chemical methods discussed in the determination of the iron valence state necessarily involve the release of the bound metal ion from the protein by addition of either a denaturant or a mercurial, and it is evident that changes in oxidation state can occur during or after release of the metal ion. Although these methods indicate that at least part of the iron in native clostridial ferredoxin and all of the iron in native spinach ferredoxin may be in the ferric state, the physical measurements on these and related iron–sulfur proteins (discussed in separate chapters of this volume) have led to the conclusion that the iron bonding in iron–sulfur proteins involves degrees of electron sharing with ligand atoms, presumably sulfur, which make the assignment of normal valencies and oxidation state virtually impossible.

In most ferredoxins, the loss of sulfide from the protein is usually accompanied by a loss of iron, suggesting a close association in the binding of these two components. A parallel loss of iron and sulfide from spinach ferredoxin after treatment with an iron-chelating agent has been found (Fry and San Pietro, 1962). A similar experiment with clostridial ferredoxin (Fig. 5) indicates that treatment of this ferredoxin with hydrosulfite and the iron-chelating agent, dipyridyl, leads to a release of both iron and sulfide from the protein. The kinetics of the release of these

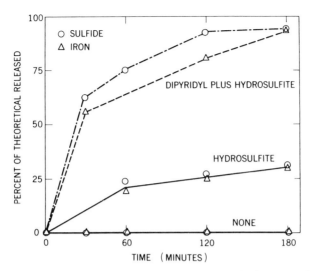

Fig. 5. The reaction of dipyridyl with clostridial ferredoxin (from Malkin and Rabinowitz, 1966a).

two components were identical, and both elements were released quantitatively under the conditions used.

In contrast to the behavior of the ferredoxins, the high-potential iron protein shows some anomalous reactions (Dus et al., 1967). When the protein was aminoethylated by a procedure which leads to a loss of H_2S, there was no change in the iron content of the molecule. In addition, treatment of the high-potential iron protein with 8 M urea caused a loss of the visible absorption spectrum and a loss of H_2S, but the iron remained firmly bound to the protein and was nondialyzable even after chelation with o-phenanthroline. It would appear that this protein has groups other than the sulfur moieties with a strong tendency to chelate the iron.

C. Iron and Sulfide Exchange Studies

The nature of the bonding of the iron and sulfide in the clostridial ferredoxins has been examined by studies of the exchange of iron and sulfide. Lovenberg et al. (1963) found that ^{59}Fe would not exchange with untreated C. pasteurianum ferredoxin at pH 7.4 but that a rapid exchange occurred when the protein was treated with mersalyl prior to the addition of the ^{59}Fe (Fig. 6). Under comparable conditions, the iron in the small peptide, ferrichrome (considered to be ionically coordinated) was found to undergo a relatively rapid exchange with the added ^{59}Fe.

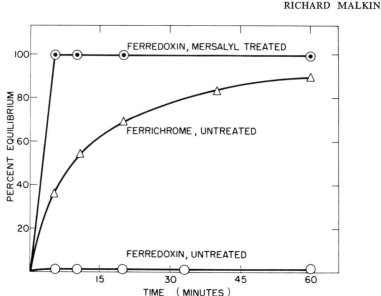

Fig. 6. Exchange of ^{59}Fe with clostridial ferredoxin and ferrichrome (from Lovenberg *et al.,* 1963).

When the analogous experiment was carried out with sodium [^{35}S] sulfide, no exchange could be observed with either the untreated protein or the mersalyl-treated protein.

In a subsequent study of the iron and sulfide exchange properties of clostridial ferredoxin, Hong and Rabinowitz (1970c) found that under anaerobic conditions sulfide and iron exchange with untreated ferredoxin could be observed at alkaline pH values. The exchange of sulfide and iron was found to proceed approximately 100 times faster in the presence of urea, but the recovery of ferredoxin in the presence of urea was much less than in its absence, indicating degradation had occurred.

Although these results indicate that both the iron and sulfide in ferredoxin can exchange with added iron or sulfide under suitable conditions, the initial observation of Lovenberg *et al.* (1963) of the absence of sulfide exchange with mersalyl-treated ferredoxin has not been adequately explained.

In addition to these chemical exchange reactions, Jeng and Mortenson (1968) described an enzymic reaction in which sodium [^{35}S] sulfide is exchanged with the sulfide of *C. pasteurianum* ferredoxin. The extent of exchange in the enzyme-catalyzed reaction was only 8.7%. The authors suggested the possibility that only one of the eight sulfides present in the molecule underwent this enzymic exchange. The enzymic properties of this reaction have not been studied in detail.

D. Oxygen Sensitivity

Ferredoxins and other iron–sulfur proteins have been found to be sensitive to oxygen, the interaction with oxygen being related to the inorganic sulfide present in these proteins.

During the initial purification of several ferredoxins from different clostridial species (Lovenberg *et al.*, 1963), it was reported that there was a significant difference in the stability of the ferredoxins and that some clostridial ferredoxins underwent severe deterioration in a matter of hours after purification. The first well-documented discussion of this type of deterioration process was presented by Keresztes-Nagy and Margoliash (1966) in their description of the chloroplast ferredoxin from alfalfa. This ferredoxin was found to deteriorate rapidly in air, while storage under N_2 markedly increased the stability of the protein. Further characterization of this deterioration process showed that the inorganic sulfide group was released from the ferredoxin in the presence of O_2, indicating that oxidation of this form of sulfur was critical to the deterioration process.

Malkin and Rabinowitz (1967b) also found that the presence of oxygen led to a rapid destruction of clostridial ferredoxin, while the protein was relatively stable under anaerobic conditions. In the presence of guanidine hydrochloride, under anaerobic conditions, there was little deterioration of clostridial ferredoxin in a 75-minute period; under aerobic conditions, in the presence of the same concentration of guanidine hydrochloride, there was a rapid decrease of the visible absorbance spectrum, indicating deterioration of the iron–sulfide chromophoric center. Further studies with the clostridial ferredoxins (Malkin and Rabinowitz, 1967b) also suggested the oxygen-sensitive group in the protein was the inorganic sulfide moiety.

A more extensive study of the oxygen sensitivity of spinach ferredoxin and other iron–sulfur proteins (Petering *et al.*, 1971) details some of the reactions which occur under oxidative denaturing conditions. It was found that destruction of spinach ferredoxin by O_2 or ferricyanide leads to a loss of iron but that the inorganic sulfide became covalently attached to the resulting apoprotein. These unusual reactions are clearly a consequence of the presence of the inorganic sulfide and must be a function of the type of bonding which is involved in the active site of these proteins.

Although the mechanism of the oxidative denaturation of the iron–sulfur proteins may vary from protein to protein, it is obvious from these studies that anaerobic handling and storage of the proteins is advisable at all times.

IV. RECONSTITUTION STUDIES WITH FERREDOXINS

A. Preparation of Reconstitutable Apoproteins

The successful reconstitution of ferredoxins from apoproteins devoid of iron and sulfide has been an important step in chemical and physical studies with these proteins.

Early attempts to reconstitute clostridial ferredoxin completely from an isolated apoferredoxin were unsuccessful (Lovenberg et al., 1963); the addition of ferric chloride and sodium sulfide to an apoferredoxin prepared by mercurial treatment did not lead to the reconstitution of ferredoxin. However, if the reaction mixture containing the bleached protein obtained by mercurial treatment was treated directly with 2-mercaptoethanol without prior separation of the protein from the mercurial, the ferredoxin color could be restored. This regenerated protein was reisolated and shown to be identical to the native material with respect to its optical absorbance spectrum, enzymic activity, and iron and sulfide content. Although this technique did not result in a complete reconstitution of clostridial ferredoxin, it was a method which allowed an incorporation of different isotopes of iron ([57]Fe, ^{59}Fe) into the protein and led to more detailed electron paramagnetic resonance and Mössbauer measurements.

Subsequent to this work, reconstitution of clostridial ferredoxin from an isolated apoprotein, iron, and inorganic sulfide was demonstrated (Malkin and Rabinowitz, 1966b). The apoferredoxin was prepared by treatment of the native material with the mercurial, sodium mersalyl, and was first purified on Chelex-100 and then on Sephadex G-25. The protein fraction isolated from the Chelex column contained no iron but still contained sulfide. The protein obtained from the Chelex column was converted to ferredoxin by the addition of only iron and 2-mercaptoethanol, indicating the sulfide was still present in the protein fraction. The apoprotein from the Sephadex column was free of both iron and sulfide. This protein was converted to ferredoxin by the addition of iron, inorganic sulfide, and 2-mercaptoethanol. The reconstituted protein was indistinguishable from the native protein with respect to enzymic activity, spectral properties, and iron and sulfide content.

Another method for the preparation of apoferredoxins which could be converted to ferredoxin involved the removal of the iron and sulfide from the protein by treatment with trichloroacetic acid (Hong and Rabinowitz, 1967). The properties of the apoproteins prepared by acid treatment are slightly different from those of the mercurial-treated protein, but the reconstitution of this apoprotein leads to a ferredoxin which is indistinguishable from the native material.

The methods used for the preparation of reconstitutable bacterial apoferredoxin have been successfully applied to several other iron–sulfur proteins: spinach ferredoxin (Bayer et al., 1967), adrenodoxin (Suzuki, 1967), and putidaredoxin (Tsibris et al., 1968).

B. Characteristics of the Reconstitution Reaction

1. REQUIREMENTS

Reconstitution of both clostridial and spinach ferredoxin has been shown to require iron and inorganic sulfide (Malkin and Rabinowitz, 1966b; Hong and Rabinowitz, 1967; Bayer et al., 1967). In conjunction with the results previously discussed, the requirement for inorganic sulfide in the reconstitution of ferredoxin clearly demonstrates that the sulfide is an independent moiety in the iron–sulfur proteins.

The optimal conditions for reconstitution of clostridial ferredoxins have been studied by Hong and Rabinowitz (1970b). The recovery of native ferredoxin was increased by addition of either sulfide or iron above the stoichiometric amount necessary for reconstitution, possibly because of the removal of some of the added iron and sulfide as insoluble complexes.

In contrast to these reports with clostridial ferredoxin, Petering et al. (1971) found an unusual reconstitution reaction with a spinach ferredoxin system. Treatment of this ferredoxin with urea in the presence of O_2 led to the preparation of an apoprotein which had no iron but retained the inorganic sulfide in a bound form (Section III,D). Reconstitution of the active ferredoxin required only the addition of iron and a suitable reductant. The nature of the bound form of sulfide in the apoprotein was not identified, although it was suggested that the sulfide was bound in the form of a trisulfide (RSSSR).

It is possible to replace the inorganic sulfide in the reconstitution of various iron–sulfur proteins with selenide, as first reported with putidaredoxin by Tsibris et al. (1968). The iron–selenide putidaredoxin had a biological activity comparable to that of the corresponding iron–sulfur protein. The general shape of the visible absorbance spectrum of the selenide protein was the same as in the corresponding iron–sulfur protein, although the peaks had shifted about 20 nm to longer wavelengths in the selenide protein. The incorporation of selenide for sulfide has allowed the use of several selenium isotopes during the reconstitution and has led to the preparation of iron–selenide protein derivatives which have been extremely useful in electron paramagnetic resonance studies with this protein (Tsibris et al., 1968; Orme-Johnson et al., 1968).

2. The "All-or-None" Nature of the Iron–Sulfide Bonding in
Clostridial Ferredoxin

In their study of the chemical characterization of the clostridial ferredoxins, Lovenberg *et al.* (1963) observed that the addition of a small
amount of mercurial to ferredoxin led to the formation of only two elec-
trophoretically distinguishable species: native ferredoxin and apoferredoxin. No ferredoxin species having less than the full complement of
iron and sulfide was formed during the reaction, suggesting that the loss
of iron and sulfide from native ferredoxin occurred by a type of cooperative process.

With the preparation of apoferredoxins which could be reconverted to
the native protein, further investigations on the cooperative nature of
the iron bonding in the clostridial ferredoxins have been carried out by
Hong and Rabinowitz (1970b). These workers have attempted to prepare
ferredoxin molecules with less than eight atoms of iron and sulfide by
reconstitution of clostridial ferredoxin in the presence of a limiting
amount of either iron or sulfide. Extensive purification of the reconstituted ferredoxins was found to be essential before any conclusions could
be drawn concerning the nature of the product, and it was found that
a ferredoxin deficient in either iron or sulfide could not be prepared under
a variety of conditions tested. These workers concluded that the incorporation of all the iron and sulfide into the apoprotein occurs by a cooperative process in which the binding of the first atom of iron facilitates
the binding of the remaining chromophoric group.

This "all-or-none" nature of the iron and sulfide bonding in clostridial
ferredoxins was further tested by an attempt to remove a portion of the
iron in the protein (Hong and Rabinowitz, 1970b). Clostridial ferredoxin
was treated with limiting amounts of either dipyridyl or a mercurial,
and the protein derivatives resulting from this treatment were isolated
and extensively purified. No ferredoxin molecule was isolated after any
treatment which contained less than eight atoms of iron and eight moles
of sulfide.

Although the studies of the reconstitution of clostridial ferredoxin have
given strong evidence for the cooperative bonding of all the iron and
sulfide in the protein, electron paramagnetic resonance studies (Orme-
Johnson and Beinert, 1969b) and the detailed study of the oxidation–reduction properties of clostridial ferredoxin (Eisenstein and Wang, 1969)
indicate that clostridial ferredoxin may contain two discrete sets of iron
atoms, each acting as an independent electron transfer center. On the
basis of the latter results, one might expect to be able to prepare a clostridial ferredoxin derivative with only one four-iron center. However,

until the nature of the iron–sulfide bonding in these ferredoxins has been detailed by crystallographic measurements, the relationship between these two groups of iron atoms and the properties of the protein which result in the "all-or-none" cooperative binding will remain uncertain.

NOTE ADDED IN PROOF. Recent findings in several laboratories (Laishley et al., 1969; Shethna et al., 1971; Yoch and Valentine, 1972; Orme-Johnson et al., 1972) have demonstrated the existence of bacterial-type ferredoxins containing four iron atoms and four acid-labile sulfur atoms per mole of protein. Thus, the ferredoxin from Desulfovibrio gigas has a molecular weight of 6600 and an iron content of four atoms per mole of protein (Laishley et al., 1969). The ferredoxin from Bacillus polymyxa has been found to contain four iron atoms per molecule and to have a higher molecular weight (8800) than that of the Desulfovibrio ferredoxin (Yoch and Valentine, 1972; Orme-Johnson et al., 1972). Both of these ferredoxins are characterized by a broad absorption band in the 400-nm region, a spectral property similar to that of bacterial-type ferredoxins having eight iron atoms. The oxidation–reduction potential of the Bacillus ferredoxin has been found to be approximately -380 mV (Yoch and Valentine, 1972; Orme-Johnson et al., 1972) and the protein accepts one electron per four iron atoms. The amino acid compositions of the two ferredoxins have also been reported (Laishley et al., 1969; Yoch and Valentine, 1972).

A recent developement in the study of bacterial-type ferredoxins is the demonstration of the existence of two chemically distinguishable ferredoxins in the cells of several organisms. Thus, the photosynthetic bacterium Rhodospirillum rubrum contains two ferredoxins, one containing approximately two iron atoms and a second containing approximately six iron atoms (Shanmugam et al., 1972). Azotobacter vinelandii cells have been found to have two ferredoxins (Yoch and Arnon, 1972) as has Bacillus polymyxa (Yoch, 1973). The properties of several of these ferredoxins have been described in the cited references, but evidence for a functional relationship between these multiple forms of ferredoxin has not yet been obtained.

REFERENCES

Atherton, N. M., Garbett, K., Gillard, R. D., Mason, R., Mayhew, S. J., Peel, J. L., and Stangroom, J. E. (1966). Nature (London) 212, 590.
Bachofen, R., and Arnon, D. I. (1966). Biochim. Biophys. Acta 120, 259.
Bartsch, R. G. (1963). In "Bacterial Photosynthesis" (H. Gest, A. San Pietro, and L. P. Vernon, eds.), pp. 315–326. Antioch Press, Yellow Springs, Ohio.

Bayer, E., and Parr, W. (1966). *Angew. Chem.* **78**, 824.

Bayer, E., Parr, W., and Kazmaier, B. (1965). *Arch. Pharm.* **298**, 196.

Bayer, E., Josef, D., Krauss, P., Hagenmaier, H., Röder, A., and Trebst, A. (1967). *Biochim. Biophys. Acta* **143**, 435.

Benson, A. M., and Yasunobu, K. T. (1969). *J. Biol. Chem.* **244**, 955.

Blomstrom, D. C., Knight, E., Jr., Phillips, W. D., and Weiher, J. F. (1964). *Proc. Nat. Acad. Sci. U.S.* **51**, 1085.

Buchanan, B. B. (1966). *Struct. Bonding* **1**, 109.

Buchanan, B. B., and Arnon, D. I. (1970). *Advan. Enzymol.* **33**, 119.

Buchanan, B. B., Lovenberg, W., and Rabinowitz, J. C. (1963). *Proc. Nat. Acad. Sci. U.S.* **49**, 345.

Buchanan, B. B., Matsubara, H., and Evans, M. C. W. (1969). *Biochim. Biophys. Acta* **189**, 46.

Cushman, D. W., Tsai, R. L., and Gunsalus, I. C. (1967). *Biochem. Biophys. Res. Commun.* **26**, 577.

Devanathan, T., Akagi, J. M., Hersh, R. T., and Himes, R. H. (1969). *J. Biol. Chem.* **244**, 2846.

Dus, K., DeKlerk, H., Sletten, K., and Bartsch, R. (1967). *Biochim. Biophys. Acta* **140**, 291.

Eisenstein, K. K., and Wang, J. H. (1969). *J. Biol. Chem.* **244**, 1720.

Evans, M. C. W., Hall, D. O., Bothe, H., and Whatley, F. R. (1968). *Biochem. J.* **110**, 485.

Flatmark, T., and Dus, K. (1969). *Biochim. Biophys. Acta.* **180**, 377.

Fogo, J. K., and Popowsky, M. (1949). *Anal. Chem.* **21**, 732.

Fry, K. T., and San Pietro, A. (1962). *Biochem. Biophys. Res. Commun.* **9**, 218.

Fry, K. T., and San Pietro, A. (1963). *In* "Photosynthetic Mechanisms of Green Plants" (B. Kok and A. T. Jagendorf, eds.), pp. 252–261. Nat. Acad. Sci.-Natl. Res. Council., Washington, D.C.

Gersonde, K., and Druskeit, W. (1968). *Eur. J. Biochem.* **4**, 391.

Gillard, R. D., McKenzie, E. D., Mason, R., Mayhew, S. G., Peel, J. L., and Stangroom, J. E. (1965). *Nature (London)* **208**, 769.

Hall, D. O., and Evans, M. C. W. (1969). *Nature (London)* **223**, 1342.

Hardy, R. W. F., Knight, E., Jr., McDonald, C. C., and D'Eustachio, A. J. (1965). *In* "Non-Heme Iron Proteins: Role in Energy Conversion" (A. San Pietro, ed.), pp. 275–282. Antioch Press, Yellow Springs, Ohio.

Hong, J.-S., and Rabinowitz, J. C. (1967). *Biochem. Biophys. Res. Commun.* **29**, 246.

Hong, J.-S., and Rabinowitz, J. C. (1970a). *J. Biol. Chem.* **245**, 4982.

Hong, J.-S., and Rabinowitz, J. C. (1970b). *J. Biol. Chem.* **245**, 6574.

Hong, J.-S., and Rabinowitz, J. C. (1970c). *J. Biol. Chem.* **245**, 6582.

Hong, J.-S., Champion, A. B., and Rabinowitz, J. C. (1969). *Eur. J. Biochem.* **8**, 307.

Jeng, S. D., and Mortenson, L. E. (1968). *Biochem. Biophys. Res. Commun.* **32**, 984.

Keresztes-Nagy, S., and Margoliash, E. (1966). *J. Biol. Chem.* **241**, 5955.

Keresztes-Nagy, S., Perini, F., and Margoliash, E. (1969). *J. Biol. Chem.* **244**, 981.

Kimura, T. (1968). *Struct. Bonding* **5**, 1.

Kimura, T., and Suzuki, K. (1967). *J. Biol. Chem.* **242**, 485.

Laishley, E. J., Travis, J., and Peck, H. D., Jr. (1969). *J. Bacteriol.* **98**, 302.

Lovenberg, W. (1966). In "Protides of the Biological Fluids" (H. Peeters, ed.), pp. 165–172. Elsevier, Amsterdam.

Lovenberg, W., Buchanan, B. B., and Rabinowitz, J. C. (1963). J. Biol. Chem. 238, 3899.

Malkin, R., and Rabinowitz, J. C. (1966a). Biochemistry 5, 1262.

Malkin, R., and Rabinowitz, J. C. (1966b). Biochem. Biophys. Res. Commun. 23, 822.

Malkin, R., and Rabinowitz, J. C. (1967a). Annu. Rev. Biochem. 36, 113.

Malkin, R., and Rabinowitz, J. C. (1967b). Biochemistry 6, 3880.

Massey, V. (1957). J. Biol. Chem. 229, 763.

Matsubara, H., and Sasaki, R. M. (1968). J. Biol. Chem. 243, 1732.

Matsubara, H., Sasaki, R. M., Tsuchiya, D. K., and Evans, M. C. W. (1970). J. Biol. Chem. 245, 2121.

Mayhew, S. G., Petering, D., Palmer, G., and Foust, G. P. (1969). J. Biol. Chem. 244, 2830.

Moleski, C., Moss, T. H., Orme-Johnson, W. H., and Tsibris, J. C. M. (1970). Biochim. Biophys. Acta 214, 548.

Mortenson, L. E. (1964). Biochim. Biophys. Acta 81, 71.

Mortenson, L. E., Valentine, R. C., and Carnahan, J. E. (1962). Biochem. Biophys. Res. Commun. 7, 448.

Moss, T. H., Petering, D., and Palmer, G. (1969). J. Biol. Chem. 244, 2275.

Orme-Johnson, W. H., and Beinert, H. (1969a). J. Biol. Chem. 244, 6143.

Orme-Johnson, W. H., and Beinert, H. (1969b). Biochem. Biophys. Res. Commun. 36, 337.

Orme-Johnson, W. H., Hansen, R. E., Beinert, H., Tsibris, J. C. M., Bartholomaus, R. C., and Gunsalus, I. C. (1968). Proc. Nat. Acad. Sci. U.S. 60, 368.

Orme-Johnson, W. H., Stombaugh, N. A., and Burris, R. H. (1972). Fed. Proc. 31, 448.

Palmer, G., and Sands, R. H. (1966). J. Biol. Chem. 241, 253.

Palmer, G., Sands, R. H., and Mortenson, L. E. (1966). Biochem. Biophys. Res. Commun. 23, 357.

Palmer, G., Brintzinger, H., and Estabrook, R. W. (1967a). Biochemistry 6, 1658.

Palmer, G., Brintzinger, H., Estabrook, R. W., and Sands, R. H. (1967b). In "Magnetic Resonance in Biological Systems" (A. Ehrenberg, B. G. Malmström, and T. Vänngård, eds.), pp. 159–171. Pergamon, Oxford.

Petering, D. H., and Palmer, G. (1967). Fed. Proc. 26, 731.

Petering, D. H., and Palmer, G. (1970). Arch. Biochem. Biophys. 141, 456.

Petering, D., Fee, J. A., and Palmer, G. (1971). J. Biol. Chem. 246, 643.

Rao, K. K., and Matsubara, H. (1970). Biochem. Biophys. Res. Commun. 38, 500.

Rao, K. K., Matsubara, H., Buchanan, B. B., and Evans, M. C. W. (1969). J. Bacteriol. 100, 1411.

Rieske, J. S., MacLennan, D. H., and Coleman, R. (1964). Biochem. Biophys. Res. Commun. 15, 338.

Shanmugam, K. T., Buchanan, B. B., and Arnon, D. I. (1972). Biochim. Biophys. Acta 256, 477.

Shethna, Y. I. (1970). Biochim. Biophys. Acta 205, 58.

Shethna, Y. I., DerVertanian, D. V., and Beinert, H. (1968). Biochem. Biophys. Res. Commun. 31, 862.

Shethna, Y. I., Stombaugh, N. A., and Burris, R. H. (1971). Biochem. Biophys. Res. Commun. 42, 1108.

Sobel, B. E., and Lovenberg, W. (1966). *Biochemistry* **5**, 6.

Sugeno, K., and Matsubara, H. (1969). *J. Biol. Chem.* **244**, 2979.

Suzuki, V. (1967). *Biochemistry* **6**, 1335.

Tagawa, K., and Arnon, D. I. (1962). *Nature (London)* **195**, 537.

Tagawa, K., and Arnon, D. I. (1968). *Biochim. Biophys. Acta* **153**, 602.

Tanaka, M., Nakashima, T., Benson, A., Mower, H., and Yasunobu, K. T. (1966). *Biochemistry* **5**, 1666.

Tanaka, M., Haniu, M., and Yasunobu, K. T. (1970). *Biochem. Biophys. Res. Commun.* **39**, 1182.

Tsibris, J. C. M., and Woody, R. W. (1970). *Coord. Chem. Rev.* **5**, 417.

Tsibris, J. C. M., Namtvedt, M. J., and Gunsalus, I. C. (1968). *Biochem. Biophys. Res. Commun.* **30**, 323.

Ulmer, D. D., and Vallee, B. L. (1963). *Biochemistry* **2**, 1335.

Wilson, D. F. (1967). *Arch. Biochem. Biophys.* **122**, 254.

Yoch, D. C. (1973). *Arch. Biochem. Biophys.* In press.

Yoch, D. C., and Arnon, D. I. (1972). *J. Biol. Chem.* **247**, 4514.

Yoch, D. C., and Valentine, R. C. (1972). *J. Bacteriol.* **100**, 1211.

Yoch, D. C., Benemann, J. R., Valentine, R. C., and Arnon, D. I. (1969). *Proc. Nat. Acad. Sci. U.S.* **64**, 1404.

CHAPTER 2

The Types, Distribution In Nature, Structure‑ Function, and Evolutionary Data Of the Iron‑Sulfur Proteins

KERRY T. YASUNOBU and MASARU TANAKA

27

I. INTRODUCTION

A detailed review of the research which led to the isolation of the various types of iron–sulfur proteins will not be attempted in this article. This aspect is admirably covered in numerous review articles (Valentine, 1964; Buchanan, 1966; San Pietro, 1965; Malkin and Rabinowitz, 1967; Hardy and Burns, 1968; Kimura, 1968) and they should be consulted for specific details.

However, credit should be given to Davenport (1960), Hill and Bendall (1960), and San Pietro and Lang (1958) for their initial characterization of the plant ferredoxins. The major credit for the discovery of the first iron–sulfur protein goes to Mortenson *et al.* (1962), Valentine *et al.* (1962a,b), and Wolfe *et al.* (1963) who showed the presence of the *C. pasteurianum* ferredoxin. Tagawa and Arnon (1962) demonstrated that the plant and bacterial ferredoxins were interchangeable and were both capable of catalyzing the photoreduction of NADP, and they coined the term ferredoxin for this group of iron–sulfur proteins. The importance of these investigations was that they indicated a new type of protein containing nonheme iron and sulfide exists in nature. Buchanan *et al.* (1963) and Mortenson (1964) noted the presence of a red protein fraction in their dark-brown ferredoxin preparations. Lovenberg and Sobel (1965) crystallized and characterized this protein from *C. pasteurianum* and showed that a new type of iron–sulfur protein exists in nature, one in which the iron is chelated to the sulfur of the cysteine residues. Since that time, numerous other types of iron–sulfur proteins have been isolated.

The present chapter will be concerned with the distribution of the various types of iron–sulfur proteins in nature, the structure-function relationships, and the primary structures of the various iron–sulfur proteins. From the latter, evolutionary and genetic data of the organisms containing the iron–sulfur proteins are abstracted.

A. Classification and Types of Iron–Sulfur Proteins

In Chapter 1 of Volume I of this treatise Beinert has classified various iron–sulfur proteins. However, in the present chapter, a slightly different classification that has been designed for comparing the primary structures of the various proteins (Table I).

B. Distribution of Iron–Sulfur Proteins in Nature

Protein chemists interested in protein evolution must isolate the various iron–sulfur proteins for their investigations. To assist investigators, the sources of most of the iron–sulfur proteins characterized are summarized in Section XVI. In some cases, the investigators have actually isolated the protein, but in other cases, it was simply shown to be present by an assay method. Wherever possible the report leading to the isolation of the pure protein is cited. Furthermore, the choice of a particular species is important if one wants to obtain maximum amount of an iron–sulfur protein. For example, rubredoxin can be isolated from various clostridial species. However, the maximum producer of rubredoxin is the *C. pasteurianum* in which case about 10 mg of the pure protein can be isolated from about 1 kg of wet cells (Lovenberg, 1972). The yield from the other clostridial species is much lower (A. M. Benson, H. Mower, and K. T. Yasunobu, unpublished results).

II. THE PRIMARY STRUCTURES OF THE IRON–SULFUR PROTEINS

A limited number of laboratories have been involved in the primary structure determination of iron–sulfur proteins. The two main groups have been our research team at the University of Hawaii and Matsubara's group at the Space Science Laboratories, Berkeley, California. Cole's group at the University of California at Berkeley determined the sequence of two anaerobic bacterial ferredoxins. Dus *et al.* (1971) determined the sequence of the *Chromatium* high-potential iron protein. Keresztes-Nagy *et al.* (1969) determined the amino acid sequence of alfalfa ferredoxin. Recently, Travis *et al.* (1971) determined the amino acid sequence of the *Desulfovibrio gigas* ferredoxin and McCarthy and Lovenberg (1972) determined the primary structure of the *C. pasteurianum* rubredoxin.

The first iron–sulfur protein to be sequenced was the ferredoxin from *C. pasteurianum* which was reported by our laboratory (Tanaka *et al.*, 1964). It was discovered later that two weeks after the report appeared

TABLE I

TYPES OF IRON–SULFUR PROTEINS

Type I. Proteins containing both iron and sulfide
  Class I. Ferredoxins active in anaerobic fermentation, nitrogen fixation and hydrogen metabolism.
    Subclass I. The clostridial or anaerobic type contain 8 Fe–8 S^{2-} per 6000 daltons. Absorption maxima at 280, 300, and 390 nm. $E_0 = -420$ mV.
    Subclass II. The *Desulfovibrio* type of ferredoxin contains 4 Fe–4 S^{2-} per 6000 daltons. Active in sulfite reduction which produces ATP.
  Class II. Photosynthetic ferredoxins
    Subclass I. Ferredoxin from the photosynthetic purple bacteria *Chromatium* type which contains 5–6 Fe and 5–6 S^{2-} per 10,100 daltons. Absorption maxima at 280, 310, and 385 nm. $E_0 = -490$ mV.
    Subclass II. Ferredoxin from photosynthetic green bacteria iron and sulfide content unreported. Molecular weight about 7200 daltons. Absorption maxima at 280, 300, and 385 nm.
  Class III. Algal and plant ferredoxins includes blue-green algae (procaryote) as well as high algae and plants. Contains 2 Fe and 2 S^{2-} per 11,500 daltons. Absorption maxima at 275, 330, 420, and 465 nm. $E_0 = -420$ mV.
  Class IV. Nonferredoxin proteins containing Fe and S^{2-}.
    Subclass I. Adrenodoxin and adrenodoxin-like proteins contains 2 Fe–2 S^{2-} per 12,638 daltons. Absorption maxima at 276, 320, 414, and 455 nm. $E_0 = -325$ mV. Includes related proteins testerodoxin and iron–sulfur protein from ovary. All are active in steroid hydroxylation.
    Subclass II. Putidaredoxin type contains 2 Fe–2 S^{2-} per 11,594 daltons. Absorption maxima at 280, 320, 415, and 455 nm. $E_0 \cong 96$ mV. Involved in camphor hydroxylation in *Pseudomonas putida*.
    Subclass III. *Euglena* iron–sulfur protein contains 2 Fe–2 S^{2-} per 20,000 daltons. Absorption maxima at 278, 310, 425, and 470 nm. Active in a fatty acid desaturase.
    Subclass IV. *Azotobacter* iron–sulfur proteins I and II both contain 2 Fe–2 S^{2-} per 21,000 and 24,000 daltons. Both show similar absorption maxima at 280, 331–334, 418–419, 460, and 550 nm. Both proteins probably involved in nitrogen fixation.
    Subclass V. *B. polymyxa* iron–sulfur protein contain 2 Fe–2 S^{2-} per 20,000 daltons.
    Subclass VI. Iron–sulfur protein from complex III of mitochondria contains 2 Fe–2 S^{2-} per 26,000 daltons. $E_0 = 220$ mV. Probably involved in oxidative phosphorylation.
    Subclass VII. *Chromatium* type of high-potential iron protein contains 4 Fe–4 S^{2-} per 10,000 daltons. Absorption maxima at 276, 320, 415, and 455 nm. $E_0 = 350$ mV.
    Subclass VIII. Enzymes which contain Fe and S^{2-} included in this category are enzymes such as succinic dehydrogenase, xanthine oxidase, dihydrorotic acid dehydrogenase, NADH dehydrogenase, aldehyde oxidase, nitrogenase, etc.
Type II. Proteins containing iron but no sulfide.
  Class I. Clostridial or anaerobic type of rubredoxin contains one molecule of iron per approximately 6000 daltons. Absorption maxima at 280, 380, and 490 nm. $E_0 = -0.057$ V. Function unknown.
  Class II. *Pseudomonas oleovorans* (aerobic) type of rubredoxin. Contains one to two molecules of iron per 20,000 daltons. Absorption maxima at 497, 380, and 280 nm. Component of a redox system which hydroxylates alkanes and fatty acids.

TABLE II
IRON–SULFUR PROTEINS WHOSE SEQUENCES ARE
BEING DETERMINED OR ARE COMPLETED

Protein	Status	Reference
C. pasteurianum Fd	Completed	Tanaka et al. (1966)
C. butyricum Fd	Completed	Benson et al. (1967)
M. aerogenes Fd	Completed	Tsunoda et al. (1968)
C acidi-urici Fd	Completed	Rall et al. (1969)
C tartarivorum Fd	Completed	Tanaka et al. (1971b)
P. elsdenii Fd	Completed	Azari et al. (1970)
C thermosaccharolyticum Fd	Completed	Tanaka et al. (1973b)
D. gigas Fd	Completed	Travis et al. (1971)
Chromatium Fd	Completed	Matsubara et al. (1970)
Photosynthetic green bacteria Fd	In progress	M. Tanaka, H. Haniu, K. T. Yasunobu (unpublished)
Microcystis Fd	In progress	Tanaka et al. (1972b)
Spinach Fd	Completed	Matsubara et al. (1967, 1968)
Alfalfa Fd	Completed	Keresztes-Nagy et al. (1969)
Scenedesmus Fd	Completed	Sugeno and Matsubara (1969)
Koa Fd	Completed	Benson and Yasunobu (1969)
Equisetum Fd	In progress	Aggarwal et al. (1971)
Taro Fd	Completed	Rao and Matsubara (1970)
M. aerogenes Ru	Completed	Bachmayer et al. (1968a)
P. elsdenii Ru	Completed	Bachmayer et al. (1968b)
C. pasteurianum Ru	Completed	McCarthy (1972)
D. gigas Ru	In progress	Travis et al. (1971)
P. oleovorans Ru	Near completion	Benson et al. (1971)
Chromatium high-potential iron protein	Completed	Dus et al. (1971)
Putidaredoxin	In progress	Tsai et al. (1971)
	Completed	Tanaka et al. (1973c)
Adrenodoxin (beef)	Completed	Tanaka et al. (1971b)
		Tanaka et al. (1973a)

Cole's laboratory independently arrived at the same sequence. In an attempt to prevent such duplication of effort by several laboratories, Table II lists the various iron–sulfur proteins which have been already sequenced or are in the process of being sequenced.

A. Preparation of Apoprotein and Derivatives

Since the iron–sulfur proteins contain iron in all cases and in some cases iron and sulfide, it is necessary first to prepare the apoprotein. The procedure most commonly used is to take a solution of the native protein (10 mg/ml) and add trichloroacetic acid (10% final concentration) at 4°C. The addition of 1 mg of ethylenediaminetetraacetic acid per 10 mg of protein greatly accelerated the removal of the iron from the protein. The protein is quite stable under these conditions and can be kept as a suspension in the trichloroacetic acid solution for at least three days at 4°C. Usually after standing overnight, the mixture is centrifuged and the supernatant removed. A small amount of protein is found in the supernatant solution, but it can be recovered after removing the trichloroacetic acid by ether extraction. The protein can be washed in absolute ethanol, in ether, and then dried. However, if a derivative is to be made immediately, there is no need to go through the drying procedure.

The clostridial type of rubredoxin is quite stable, and therefore it is difficult to remove the iron. McCarthy and Lovenberg (1972) removed the iron by heating the trichloroacetic acid suspension of rubredoxin to 50°C for 15 minutes. The aporubredoxin is further treated with a solution of 0.05% o-phenanthroline in 70% ethanol to remove the iron. The aporubredoxin is further washed with ethanol. These same investigators found a more gentle procedure for preparing the apoprotein. The rubredoxin is dissolved in 1.3 M mercaptoethanol and o-phenanthroline is added. The pH of the solution is brought to 9.5, and the solution is heated to 60°C and is left standing for several hours. The reagents are removed from the mixture by passing the solution through a Sephadex column.

Usually, one of two derivatives is prepared. A useful derivative in the case of the anaerobic bacterial ferredoxins has been the β-aminoethylcysteine derivative (Tanaka et al., 1966; Bachmayer et al., 1968a). The introduction of the aminoethylcysteine residues gives additional points in the protein which are susceptible to cleavage by trypsin (Raftery and Cole, 1963). Another useful derivative is the carboxymethylcysteine derivative. The procedure has been discussed in detail by Crestfield et al. (1963) and need not be detailed here. In the case of ferredoxins from anaerobic bacteria, due to their low molecular weight, they will pass through the dialysis tubing, and, therefore, one must pass the reaction mixtures through a Sephadex G-25 column to remove excess reagents. In the case of the ferredoxins, during Sephadex sieving, invariably there are some low molecular weight contaminants which are eluted after the protein peak and which contain amino acids. Accurate amino acid compositions can only be obtained with the derivatives which have been purified in this manner. Margoliash and co-workers developed a one-step method for preparing the carboxymethylcysteine derivative without going through a step involving the isolation of the apoprotein (Keresztes-Nagy and Margoliash, 1966). The method was applied to alfalfa ferredoxin and gave excellent results. We have recently tried this procedure with the *Peptostreptococcus elsdenii* ferredoxin (MW 6000) with excellent results. Presumably, this one-step method would also be satisfactory for the preparation of the aminoethylcysteine derivatives of other iron–sulfur proteins.

B. Reconstitution of Apoproteins

The apoproteins can be reconstituted to the holo forms by the addition of iron or iron and inorganic sulfide depending upon the prosthetic groups of the particular iron–sulfur protein. In the case of the clostridial ferredoxins, Malkin and Rabinowitz (1966) and Hong and Rabinowitz (1967) detailed the conditions necessary for maximum conversion of the apoferredoxin to the reconstituted form. The conditions require excess mercaptoethanol to reduce the cysteine residues of the protein and to keep the iron and sulfide which are added at pH 8.5 in solution. The excess reagents are removed by Sephadex G-25 and by a DEAE cellulose chromatography step. The yields can be as high at 70%, and Malkin and Rabinowitz (1966) and Hong and Rabinowitz (1970) could find no difference in the properties of reconstituted *C. acidi-urici* ferredoxin and the native form of the protein.

Aporubredoxin can be reconstituted by treatment with an excess of mercaptoethanol and Fe^{3+} or Fe^{2+} (Lovenberg and Williams, 1969) at pH 9.5. The reconstituted rubredoxin shows an absorption spectrum which is identical to that of the native *C. pasteurianum* rubredoxin. Lode and Coon (1971) reported that the *P. oleovorans* aporubredoxin can be reactivated by a similar procedure to yield reconstituted rubredoxin.

C. Sequence Determination of the Proteins

The main approach to date has been the classical one in which the protein derivatives are hydrolyzed by trypsin, chymotrypsin, or thermolysin in separate experiments. The peptides are separated by the use of ion exchange, partition chromatography, and electrophoretic methods. However, with the production of the protein sequencer by Beckman and several other commercial organizations, it is possible to alter the approach to sequence work. Thus far, we have been able to determine the NH_2-terminal sequence of several of the nonheme iron proteins in the Beckman protein sequencer. In the case of the *Clostridium tartarivorum* ferredoxin, the *Peptostreptococcus elsdenii* ferredoxin, and the *Pseudomonas oleovorans* rubredoxin, we were able to determine 27, 32, and 40 amino acid residues, respectively, from the NH_2-terminal end of these proteins. The major difficulty is that the proteins are extracted by the solvents used for extraction of the excess reagents. Better results have been obtained with the cysteic acid derivative, and ten additional residues have been determined with some ferredoxins. The methods of primary sequence determination of the iron–sulfur proteins will change drastically in the future and will depend more on the use of the protein sequencer, resulting in a shortening of the time required to sequence these proteins.

III. A CONSIDERATION OF THE INDIVIDUAL IRON–SULFUR PROTEINS

A. The Clostridial or Anaerobic Type of Ferredoxins

The first iron–sulfur protein to be characterized was the ferredoxin from *C. pasteurianum* in 1962. Within a short time, a large number of ferredoxins of this type were isolated, and the general properties of the clostridial ferredoxins were known. Some of the physicochemical properties of the ferredoxins of this type are summarized in Table III. Owing to the high iron and sulfide content, the crystals of the protein are dark black. Some of the interesting features of the ferredoxins of this class include the characteristic absorption maxima and the very negative oxidation–reduction potentials, which are about the same as the hydrogen electrode (about −420 mV).

1. BIOLOGICAL ROLE OF THE "ANAEROBIC" FERREDOXINS

The various biological roles of ferredoxin in the anaerobic bacteria have been described in detail in the review articles of Valentine (1964) and Buchanan (1966). In addition, Mortenson and Nakos have discussed the function of ferredoxin in Chapter 2 of Volume I of this treatise. In these reactions, ferredoxin acts as a redox protein. It is interesting to note that besides its role in the fermentation of organic compounds, it is required for nitrogen fixation and H_2 metabolism.

Very few studies have been made to determine the specific activity of the different ferredoxins. There is a report in which several of the ferredoxins were tested in the phosphoroclastic cleavage of pyruvate (Lovenberg *et al.*, 1963; and Table IV). It is interesting to note that the *C. butyricum* ferredoxin is the most active. In addition, as will be discussed in greater detail later, it is possible to draw a line of symmetry in the ferredoxin molecule, and when the two halves of the various ferredoxin molecules are compared, the ferredoxin from *C. butyricum* shows the greatest similarity between the two halves of the molecule.

TABLE III

SOME PHYSICOCHEMICAL PROPERTIES OF THE 8 FE–8 S^{2-}
OR CLOSTRIDIAL TYPE OF FERREDOXIN

Property	Values
Molecular weight	
Sedimentation equilibrium	$6,000^a$
Amino acid analysis	$6,012^a$
$s_{20,w}$	$1.4 \, S \pm 0.1 \, S^a$
Isoelectric point	about 3.7^a
Mobility at pH 8.2 and 4.0	$-5.1 \times 10^{-5} \, \text{cm}^2 \, \text{V}^{-1} \, \text{sec}^{-1}$
	$-2.8 \times 10^{-5} \, \text{cm}^2 \, \text{V}^{-1} \, \text{sec}^{-1}$
Partial specific volume	$0.63 \, \text{cm}^3/\text{gm}^a$
Moles of Fe and S^{2-}	8^b
Absorption maxima	280 and 390 nm^c
e_m at 390 nm (*C. acidi-urici*)	$30,600 \, M^{-1} \, \text{cm}^{-1}$
Reducing equivalents per mole	$2^{d,f}$
ESR spectrum (reduced form)	$g = 1.892, 1.960, \text{ and } 2.005^e$
Total amino acids	54–56
E_0	$-410 \, \text{mV}^{c,f}$
Average magnetic moment per iron (oxidized form)	$2.0–2.3 \, \mu_B{}^g$
Mössbauer spectrum	Determined^g
NMR spectrum	Determined^h
ORD spectrum	Determined^i
CD spectrum	Determined^i

[a] Lovenberg et al., 1963.
[b] Hong and Rabinowitz, 1970.
[c] Tagawa and Arnon, 1962.
[d] Evans et al., 1968.
[e] Palmer et al., 1966.
[f] Sobel and Lovenberg, 1966.
[g] Blomstrom et al., 1964.
[h] Poe et al., 1970.
[i] Gillard et al., 1965.

TABLE IV

EFFECT OF FERREDOXIN STRUCTURE ON BIOLOGICAL ACTIVITY[a]

Source of ferredoxin	Relative activity in the phosphoroclastic system
C. butyricum	100
C. cylindrosporum	94
C. pasteurianum	67
C. acidi-urici	54
C. tetanomorphum	51

[a] Lovenberg, et al., 1963.

2. Amino Acid Composition of the Various Clostridial Types of Ferredoxins

The amino acid composition of a number of ferredoxins from anaerobes has been determined, and the data are presented in Table V. It is interesting to note that all of the known amino acids except tryptophan are present in one ferredoxin or another. However, arginine is found only in the *C. acidi–urici* ferredoxin. Methionine is found only in the two heat-stable ferredoxins (*C. tartarivorum* and *C. thermosaccharolyticum*) and the *P. elsdenii* ferredoxin. It is likely that each ferredoxin of this type contains eight cysteine residues. The proteins contain a high proportion of hydrophobic residues, and there is an excess of acidic over the basic residues, thus accounting for the acidic nature of the clostridial ferredoxins.

The *D. gigas* ferredoxin, although quite similar in structure to the other anaerobic ferredoxins, will be considered separately because it is a 4 Fe–4

TABLE V

AMINO ACID COMPOSITION OF VARIOUS ANAEROBIC BACTERIAL FERREDOXINS

Amino acid	1[a]	2	3	4	5	6	7	8
Lysine	1	0	1	0	2	2	2	1
Histidine	0	0	0	0	2	2	1	0
Arginine	0	0	0	1	0	0	0	1
Aspartic acid	8	9	8	8	4	4	3	11
Threonine	1	3	0	1	4	4	5	0
Serine	5	3	5	3	1	1	4	3
Glutamic acid	4	5	4	4	7	7	6	9
Proline	3	3	5	4	2	2	2	4
Glycine	4	5	4	4	5	5	5	1
Alanine	8	7	7	9	10	10	7	6
Half cystine	8	8	8	8	8	8	8	6
Valine	6	6	4	6	4	4	5	5
Methionine	0	0	0	0	0	0	1	2
Isoleucine	5	4	6	5	5	5	4	5
Leucine	0	0	0	0	0	0	0	1
Tyrosine	1	0	2	2	1	1	1	0
Phenylalanine	1	2	0	0	0	0	0	1
Total	55	55	54	55	55	55	54	56

[a] 1–8 represent proteins from *C. pasteurianum* (Tanaka *et al.*, 1966), *C. butyricum* (Benson *et al.*, 1967), *M. aerogenes* (Tsunoda *et al.*, 1968), *C. acidi–urici* (Rall *et al.*, 1969), *C. tartarivorum* (Tanaka *et al.*, 1971b), *C. thermosaccharolyticum* (Tanaka *et al.*, 1973b), *P. elsdenii* (Azari *et al.*, 1973b), and *D. gigas* (Travis *et al.*, 1971).

S^{2-} rather than a 8 Fe–8 S^{2-} ferredoxin and its function is different from the function of anaerobic ferredoxins.

3. PRIMARY STRUCTURE OF THE FERREDOXINS FROM ANAEROBES

Ferredoxins sequenced to date are shown in Fig. 1. It should also be pointed out that the primary structure of the *C. pasteurianum* ferredoxin was determined independently by Cole's group (1964) at the University of California at Berkeley, and the proposed sequence by Tanaka *et al.* (1964) was confirmed by these workers.

In order to compare the sequences of the various ferredoxins, we have chosen to consider that there is a line of symmetry in the molecule after residue 28. In addition, we have assumed that a deletion occurred between residues 4 and 5 or that an insertion of aspartic acid occurred in position 33. The sequence data of the *P. elsdenii* ferredoxin suggest that the latter possibility may be correct since the aspartic acid is missing in position 33 (Azari *et al.*, 1970). In the case of the *M. aerogenes* ferredoxin, a gap is inserted after residues 21 and 26. In the case of all the ferredoxins except the *M. aerogenes* ferredoxin, residue 56 has been deleted. If we make the above-mentioned corrections, there is a better alignment of the various ferredoxin molecules from the various bacteria.

The various ferredoxins were analyzed in terms of the hydrophilic, hydrophobic, acidic, and basic residues, and the results are shown in Table VI. In this chapter the following residues are designated as hydrophobic residues: glycine, proline, methionine, phenylalanine, tryptophan, valine, leucine, isoleucine, and alanine. Serine, threonine, cysteine, glutamine, asparagine, and tyrosine are considered neutral, while the remainder of the amino acids are considered hydrophilic.

A comparison of the similarities in the upper halves (residues 1–28) of the various ferredoxins (Table VII) as well as of the similarities in the lower halves (residues 29–55 or 56) was made. The similarities in the sequences of various species differ when we compare the NH$_2$-terminal and the COOH-terminal halves. The values ranged from 40–54% homology in the sequence, and this evidence was used as possible evidence for two independent, active sites or gene duplication during the process of evolution of these microorganisms. However, the recent crystal X-ray diffraction studies of the ferredoxins clearly indicate that present day ferredoxin is not the simple joining together of two smaller ferredoxin precursors (Adman *et al.*, 1973). A comparison of the similarity in the complete sequences of the various ferredoxins was also determined, and the results are presented in Table VIII. There is no doubt that these ferredoxins are homologous and that they have arisen from some common ancestor.

Upper half (residues 1–26)

M. A.
Ala-Tyr-Val-Ile-Asn-Asp-Ser-Cys-Ile-Ala-Cys-Gly-Ala-Cys-Lys-Pro-Glu-Cys-Pro-Val-Asn- -Ile-Gln-Gln-Gly- -Ser-

C. B.
Ala-Phe-Val-Ile-Asn-Asp-Ser-Cys-Val-Ser-Cys-Gly-Ala-Cys-Ala-Gly-Glu-Cys-Pro-Val-Ser-Ala-Ile-Thr-Gln-Gly-Asp-Thr-

C. P.
Ala-Tyr-Lys-Ile-Ala-Asp-Ser-Cys-Val-Ser-Cys-Gly-Ala-Cys-Ala-Ser-Glu-Cys-Pro-Val-Asn-Ala-Ile-Ser-Gln-Gly-Asp-Ser-

C. A. U.
Ala-Tyr-Val-Ile-Asn-Glu-Ala-Cys-Ile-Ser-Cys-Gly-Ala-Cys-Glu-Pro-Glu-Cys-Pro-Val-Asp-Ala-Ile-Ser-Gln-Gly-Asp-Ser-

C. T.
Ala-His-Ile-Ile-Thr-Asp-Glu-Cys-Ile-Ser-Cys-Gly-Ala-Cys-Ala-Gly-Glu-Cys-Pro-Val-Glu-Ala-Ile-His-Gly-Thr-Gly-

P. E.
Met-His-Val-Ile-Ser-Asp-Glu-Cys-Val-Lys-Cys-Gly-Ala-Cys-Glu-Pro-Glu-Cys-Pro-Val-Glu-Ala-Ile-His-Glu-Gly-Gly-Thr-

C. Th.
Ala-His-Ile-Ile-Thr-Asp-Glu-Cys-Ile-Ser-Cys-Gly-Ala-Cys-Ala-Ser-Thr-Cys-Pro-Thr-Gly-Ala-Ile-His-Glu-Gly-Thr-Gly-

Lower half (residues ~27–55)

M. A.
Ile-Tyr-Ala-Ile-Ala(\Asp)-Asp-Ser-Cys-Ile-Asp-Cys-Gly-Ser-Cys-Ala-Ser-Val-Cys-Pro-Val-Gly-Ala-Pro-Asn-Pro-Glu-Asp-OH

C. B.
Gln-Phe-Val-Ile-Ala(\Asp)-Asp-Thr-Cys-Ile-Asp-Cys-Gly-Asn-Cys-Ala-Asn-Val-Cys-Pro-Val-Gly-Ala-Pro-Asn-Gln-Glu-OH

C. P.
Ile-Phe-Val-Ile-Ala(\Asp)-Asp-Thr-Cys-Ile-Asp-Cys-Gly-Asn-Cys-Ala-Asn-Val-Cys-Pro-Val-Gly-Ala-Pro-Val-Gln-Glu-OH

C. A. U.
Arg-Tyr-Val-Ile-Ala(\Asp)-Asp-Thr-Cys-Ile-Asp-Cys-Gly-Ala-Cys-Ala-Gly-Val-Cys-Pro-Val-Asp-Ala-Pro-Val-Gln-Ala-OH

C. T.
Lys-Tyr-Gln-Val-Ala(\Asp)-Asp-Thr-Cys-Ile-Asp-Cys-Gly-Ala-Cys-Gln-Ala-Val-Cys-Pro-Thr-Gly-Ala-Val-Lys-Ala-Glu-OH

P. E.
Lys-Tyr-Val-Val-Thr-Asp-Ser-Cys-Ile-Asp-Cys-Gly-Ala-Cys-Glu-Ala-Val-Cys-Pro-Thr-Gly-Ala-Ile-Ser-Ala-Glu-OH

C. Th.
Lys-Tyr-Glu-Val-Ala-Asp-Thr-Cys-Ile-Asp-Cys-Gly-Ala-Cys-Glu-Ala-Val-Cys-Pro-Thr-Gly-Ala-Val-Lys-Ala-Glu-OH

Fig. 1. Method of alignment of the various ferredoxins from anaerobes. Gaps indicate deletions. Aspartic acid in position 33 in the lower half is assumed to be due to an insertion, but it is possible that aspartate has been deleted in the upper half. The symbols M. A., C. B., C. P., C. A. U., C. T., P. E., and C. Th. stands, respectively, for *M. aerogenes, C. butyricum, C. pasteurianum, C. acidi-urici, C. tartarivorum, P. elsdenii,* and *C. thermosaccharolyticum.*

TABLE VI

Types of Residues in the Ferredoxins from Anaerobes

Bacteria	Number of residues					Total No. of residues	Net change
	Hydrophobic	Neutral	Hydrophilic	Acidic[a]	Basic[b]		
M. aerogenes	26	20	8	8	2	54	−6
C. butyricum	27	21	7	8	1	55	−7
C. pasteurianum	27	20	8	8	2	55	−6
C. acidi-urici	28	17	10	10	2	55	−8
C. tartarivorum	26	16	13	10	5	55	−5
P. elsdenii	24	18	12	10	4	54	−6
C. thermosaccharolyticum	26	14	15	12	5	55	−7

[a] Includes carboxyl group of COOH-terminal amino acids.
[b] Amino group of NH_2-terminal residues included.

TABLE VII
SIMILARITIES IN THE CARBOXYL TERMINAL HALVES
(29–55 OR 56) OF BACTERIAL FERREDOXINS[a]

	M. A.	C. B.	C. P.	C. A. U.	C. T.	P. E.	C. Th.
M. A.	—	20	20	18	16	15	16
C. B.	20	—	25	20	16	14	16
C. P.	20	25	—	21	16	14	16
C. A. U.	18	20	21	—	16	14	16
C. T.	16	16	16	16	—	20	25
P. E.	15	14	14	14	20	—	21
C. Th.	16	16	16	16	25	21	—

SIMILARITIES IN THE AMINO TERMINAL HALVES
(1–28) OF BACTERIAL FERREDOXINS[a]

	M. A.	C. B.	C. P.	C. A. U.	C. T.	P. E.	C. Th.
M. A.	—	18	19	20	15	12	15
C. B.	18	—	21	19	17	16	17
C. P.	19	21	—	20	17	15	17
C. A. U.	20	19	20	—	16	12	16
C. T.	15	17	17	16	—	16	28
P. E.	12	16	15	12	16	—	16
C. Th.	15	17	17	16	28	16	—

[a] M. A., C. B., C. P., C. A. U., C. T., P. E., and C. Th. represent *M. aerogenes*, *C. butyricum*, *C. pasteurianum*, *C. acidi-urici*, *C. tartarivorum*, *P. elsdenii*, and *C. thermosaccharolyticum*, respectively. The number refers to the number of identical residues in the sequence.

The *C. tartarivorum* and *C. thermosaccharolyticum* are thermophilic bacteria containing thermostable ferredoxins (Devanathan *et al.*, 1970). In the same report, the ferredoxins, in general, were shown to have little α-helical content, and it was concluded that the heat stability was due to a more stable chelate structure possibly due to the presence of more ionic and basic residues as compared to the ferredoxins from mesophiles. Since the *P. elsdenii* ferredoxin (Azari *et al.*, 1970) contains histidine and two lysine residues and is not heat stable, the location of certain basic residues appears to be critical for conferring heat stability.

4. CONSTANT RESIDUES OF THE BACTERIAL FERREDOXINS

Now that seven different ferredoxins of this class have been sequenced, it is interesting to compare the different ferredoxins. Figure 2 shows the constant residues when the different ferredoxins are aligned as discussed previously. There are only 23 residues which are constant. Most of the constant residues are the ones in the vicinity of the active site providing a hydrophobic environment for the iron–sulfur clusters as well as

TABLE VIII

SIMILARITIES IN THE AMINO ACID SEQUENCES OF BACTERIAL FERREDOXINS

Species	C. pasteurianum	C. butyricum	M. aerogenes	C. acidi-urici	C. tartarivorum	P. elsdenii	C. thermosaccharolyticum
C. pasteurianum	—	46	39	41	33	29	33
C. butyricum	46	—	38	39	33	30	33
M. aerogenes	39	38	—	38	31	27	31
C. acidi-urici	41	39	38	—	32	26	32
C. tartarivorum	33	33	31	32	—	36	53
P. elsdenii	29	30	27	26	36	—	37
C. thermosaccharolyticum	33	33	31	32	53	37	—

aromatic residues which are in contact with the active sites. However, there are some degrees of freedom here since instead of valine at position 20 and 49, threonine is present in some of the ferredoxins. In addition, from a structure-function standpoint, some very conservative amino acid substitutions are observed at positions 9, 30, and 32, where isoleucine replaces a valine, tyrosine replaces a phenylalanine, and valine replaces an isoleucine residue. Such comparisons are of interest since they indicate essential parts of the molecule and since they provide an insight into the structure of the precursor ferredoxins from which all the ferredoxins evolved millions of years ago.

5. DISTRIBUTION OF TYPES OF RESIDUES

X-Ray studies of the structure of proteins indicate that the majority of hydrophobic residues are present in the hydrophobic core of the protein molecules and that the majority of ionic residues are present on the surface of the molecule in contact with the solvent. Therefore, it is of interest to look at the different types of residues in a protein. The number of hydrophobic, neutral, and hydrophilic residues in the clostridial type of ferredoxin have been calculated, and the results are shown in Fig. 3 and Table VI.

6. SECONDARY STRUCTURE

From the recent crystal X-ray diffraction data (Adman et al., 1972) on the M. aerogenes ferredoxin, it is known that the ferredoxin molecule is mainly of the random chain conformation. One turn of the 3_{10} helix is evident at residues 32–35, where Ala 32 carbonyl is hydrogen-bonded to the Cys 35 amino group. Two additional regions of probable 3_{10} helix

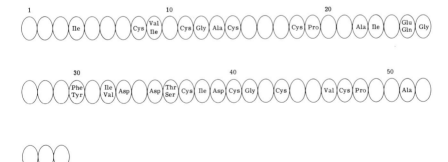

Fig. 2. The constant residues in the various anaerobic bacterial ferredoxins.

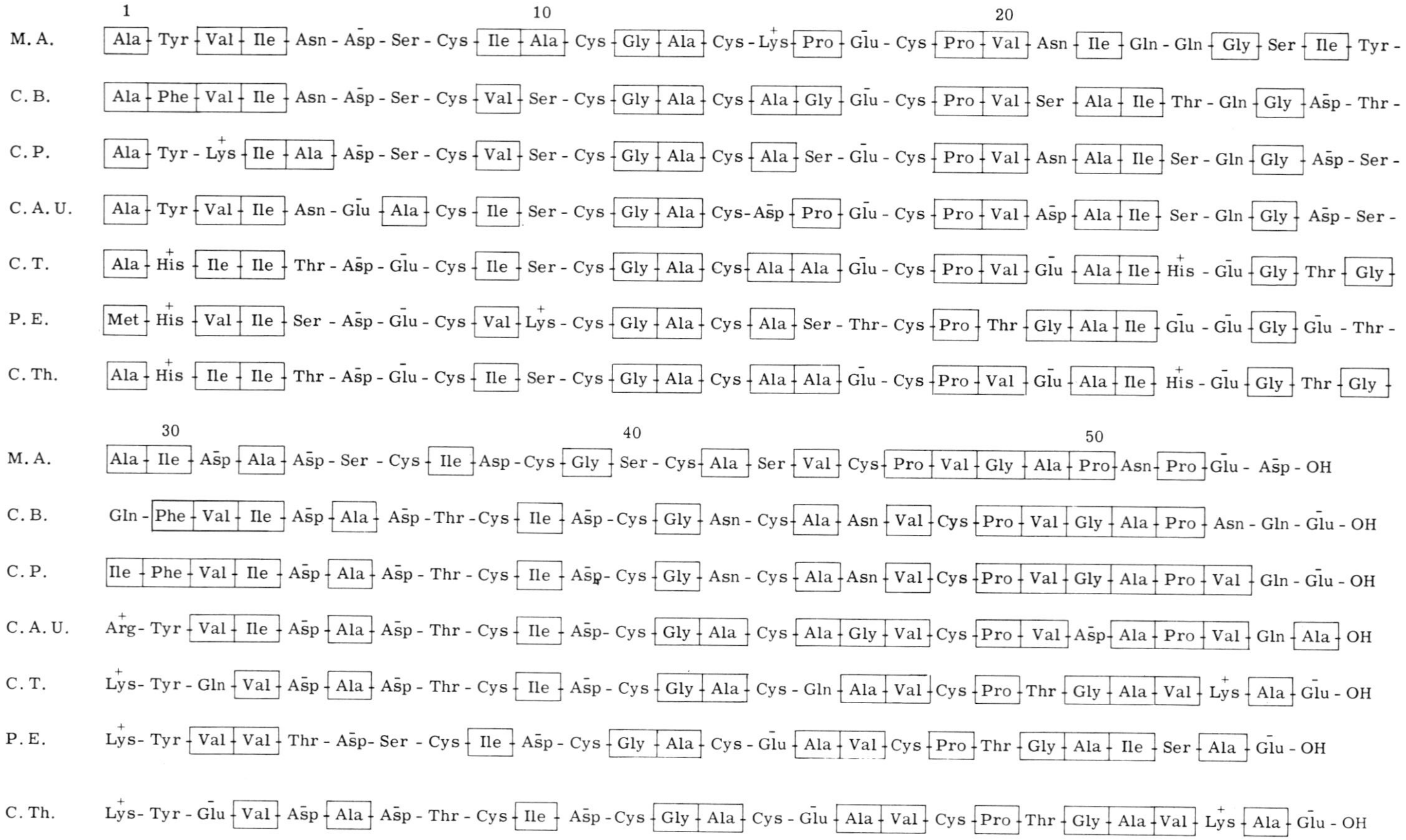

Fig. 3. Types of residues in the anaerobic ferredoxins. In the figure, the square indicates hydrophobic residues, while + and — indicate ionic residues.

Residues 1–28 (numbering marks 1, 10, 20):

M.A.: Ala–Tyr–Val–Ile–Asn–Asp–Ser–Cys–Ile–Ala–Cys–Gly–Ala–Cys–Lys⁺–Pro–Glu–Cys–Pro–Val–Asn–Ile–Gln–Gln–Gly–Ser–Ile–Tyr–

C.B.: Ala–Phe–Val–Ile–Asn–Asp–Ser–Cys–Val–Ser–Cys–Gly–Ala–Cys–Ala–Gly–Glu–Cys–Pro–Val–Ser–Ala–Ile–Thr–Gln–Gly–Asp–Thr–

C.P.: Ala–Tyr–Lys⁺–Ile–Ala–Asp–Ser–Cys–Val–Ser–Cys–Gly–Ala–Cys–Ala–Ser–Glu–Cys–Pro–Val–Asn–Ala–Ile–Ser–Gln–Gly–Asp–Ser–

C.A.U.: Ala–Tyr–Val–Ile–Asn–Glu–Ala–Cys–Ile–Ser–Cys–Gly–Ala–Cys–Asp–Pro–Glu–Cys–Pro–Val–Asp–Ala–Ile–Ser–Gln–Gly–Asp–Ser–

C.T.: Ala–His⁺–Ile–Ile–Thr–Asp–Glu–Cys–Ile–Ser–Cys–Gly–Ala–Cys–Ala–Ala–Glu–Cys–Pro–Val–Glu–Ala–Ile–His⁺–Glu–Gly–Thr–Gly

P.E.: Met–His⁺–Val–Ile–Ser–Asp–Glu–Cys–Val–Lys⁺–Cys–Gly–Ala–Cys–Ala–Ser–Thr–Cys–Pro–Thr–Gly–Ala–Ile–Glu–Glu–Gly–Glu–Thr–

C.Th.: Ala–His⁺–Ile–Ile–Thr–Asp–Glu–Cys–Ile–Ser–Cys–Gly–Ala–Cys–Ala–Glu–Cys–Pro–Val–Glu–Ala–Ile–His⁺–Glu–Gly–Thr–Gly

Residues 29–56 (numbering marks 30, 40, 50):

M.A.: Ala–Ile–Asp–Ala–Asp–Ser–Cys–Ile–Asp–Cys–Gly–Ser–Cys–Ala–Ser–Val–Cys–Pro–Val–Gly–Ala–Pro–Asn–Pro–Glu–Asp–OH

C.B.: Gln–Phe–Val–Ile–Asp–Ala–Asp–Thr–Cys–Ile–Asp–Cys–Gly–Asn–Cys–Ala–Asn–Val–Cys–Pro–Val–Gly–Ala–Pro–Asn–Gln–Glu–OH

C.P.: Ile–Phe–Val–Ile–Asp–Ala–Asp–Thr–Cys–Ile–Asp–Cys–Gly–Asn–Cys–Ala–Asn–Val–Cys–Pro–Val–Gly–Ala–Pro–Val–Gln–Glu–OH

C.A.U.: Arg⁺–Tyr–Val–Ile–Asp–Ala–Asp–Thr–Cys–Ile–Asp–Cys–Gly–Ala–Cys–Ala–Gly–Val–Cys–Pro–Val–Asp–Ala–Pro–Val–Gln–Ala–OH

C.T.: Lys⁺–Tyr–Gln–Val–Asp–Ala–Asp–Thr–Cys–Ile–Asp–Cys–Gly–Ala–Cys–Ala–Gln–Val–Cys–Pro–Thr–Gly–Ala–Val–Lys⁺–Ala–Glu–OH

P.E.: Lys⁺–Tyr–Val–Val–Thr–Asp–Ser–Cys–Ile–Asp–Cys–Gly–Ala–Cys–Ala–Val–Cys–Pro–Val–Ser–Ala–Ile–Ser–Ala–Glu–OH

C.Th.: Lys⁺–Tyr–Glu–Val–Asp–Ala–Asp–Thr–Cys–Ile–Asp–Cys–Gly–Ala–Cys–Ala–Ala–Val–Cys–Pro–Thr–Gly–Ala–Val–Lys⁺–Ala–Glu–OH

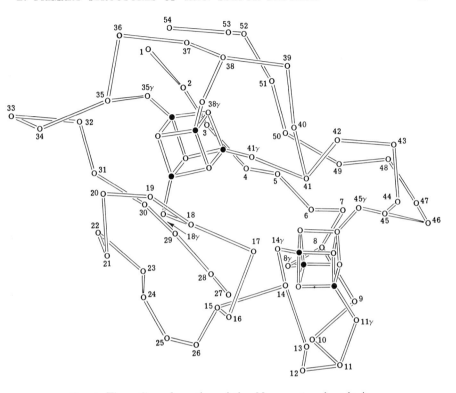

Fig. 4. The α-C configuration of the *M. aerogenes* ferredoxin.

occur in the three residue segments between the clusters, including the cysteines at each end. A 2.2_7 bend occurs at residues 6–8. The polypeptide backbone configuration of the *M. aerogenes* ferredoxin is shown in Fig. 4.

An important interaction occurring between the main chains involves the O and N atoms of residue 3 (Val) and the N and O atoms of residues 50 (Pro) and 51 (Asn), respectively. This region can be regarded as a very short section of a 3_{10} helical structure, too short to be a prominent feature but important in anchoring the two terminal sections of the chain to each other.

7. Chelate Structure of Anaerobic Type of Ferredoxins

Due to the excellent investigations of Adman *et al.* (1973), the chelate structure of the active site of the *M. aerogenes* ferredoxins is known. Although it was estimated that the iron and sulfide are present at alternate corners of a cube (Sieker *et al.*, 1972), more detailed calculations indicate that it is not exactly cuboidal but a slightly squashed cube. The sulfhydryl groups of the cysteine residues are attached to the iron. Thus, at active site 1, cysteine residues 8, 11, 14, and 45 are involved, and at active site 2, cysteine residues 35, 38, 41, and 18 are chelated to iron as shown in Fig. 4. In addition, at active site 1, tyrosine-28 (or another aromatic residue in other clostridial ferredoxins) is in contact with the iron–sulfur cluster, and at the active site 2, tyrosine-2 is in contact with the iron–sulfur cluster. Around the active site are hydrophobic amino acid residues. For example, at the active sites, there are isoleucine-9, glycine-12, proline-46, and valine-47. At the second site, there are isoleucine-36, glycine-39, proline-19, and valine-20 in the exactly similar or equivalent sites. In fact, there is a line of symmetry in the molecule although it is necessary to rotate the axis about the line of symmetry to see the two equal halves (Fig. 5). Thus, in essence, there are two nearly equivalent active sites involving 4 Fe, 4 S^{2-}, 4 cysteine residues, and tyrosine (or another aromatic residue in other ferredoxins) which are surrounded by hydrophobic amino acid residues. The active sites are buried essentially in a hydrophobic environment and communicate with the aqueous environment through the tyrosine residue. It is postulated that the tyrosine may be involved in the redox reactions. The two active sites are about 12 Å apart and are not in contact with one another. There may be a residue of water between the active sites which is in the hydrophobic core of the protein.

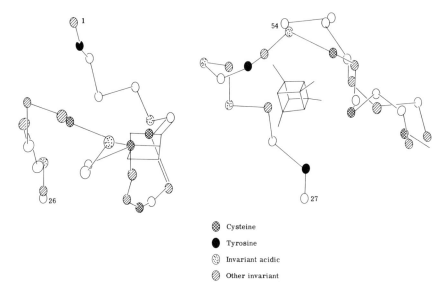

Fig. 5. Line of symmetry in the *M. aerogenes* ferredoxin molecule.

8. FURTHER DETAILS OF THE THREE-DIMENSIONAL STRUCTURE
FROM X-RAY DIFFRACTION OF CRYSTALLINE
M. aerogenes FERREDOXIN

The investigations of Adman *et al.* (1973) showed that the ferredoxin is an oblate ellipsoid with the approximate dimensions of 27 × 22 Å. The major axis is about parallel to the line joining the two iron–sulfur clusters or active sites. The active site structure has already been described, but it should be mentioned that each iron–sulfur cluster has one cysteine exposed to the solvent, although each of these is partially shielded by a nearby invariant proline residue. There are no side groups present between the active sites. The S atoms of Cys-14 and Cys-41 are approximately 7 Å apart, the distance of closest approach between the two iron–sulfur clusters. The S(Cys)-Fe, the Fe–S, Fe–Fe and the S–S distances were 2.19, 2.30, 2.85, and 3.53 Å, respectively. The two active sites are very similar in chemical structure.

Asparagine-37 appears to be linked by a hydrogen bond to the NH_2 terminus, binding it to the body of the molecule. All of the remaining invariant acidic residues either project from or lie along the surface. Three of the five are on one side of the molecule, while the remaining two are more isolated. The fact that three of the five acidic residues occur in regions which have secondary structure lends further significance to those regions: They may prove to be a part of an as yet undetermined function, such as a binding site to a partner in the redox chain. It has been shown for example that bacterial ferredoxins bind to ferredoxin:NADP reductase from spinach to form a one-to-one complex (Foust *et al.*, 1969).

For further details of the three-dimensional structure, one must consult the Kendrew model of ferredoxin which has been constructed in the laboratory of Dr. L. Jensen at the University of Washington.

9. THE EFFECT OF CHEMICAL SUBSTITUTION
ON THE ACTIVITY AND STABILITY

Hong and Rabinowitz (1970) have chemically modified the *C. acidiurici* ferredoxin with the goal of investigating structure-function relationships. The biological assay adopted in this study was the phosphoroclastic cleavage of pyruvate to acetyl CoA. The native ferredoxin cannot be acetylated and is not digested by carboxypeptidase A. However, when the apoferredoxin was acetylated, and the COOH-terminal alanine and the penultimate glutamine residues were quantitatively removed by carboxypeptidase A. Since holoferredoxin can be obtained upon the addition of iron and sulfide to the apoferredoxin, the altered residues are not required for activity. In addition, the following derivatives were also prepared: N-acetimido, N-succinyl, tetraiodo, various N-amino acyl derivatives (glycyl, phenylalanyl, lysyl, glutamyl, and methionyl), and N-t-butyloxycarbonyl. All of the modified apoferredoxins, except the N-succinyl and the tetraiodo derivatives, can be converted to the corresponding ferredoxin derivatives. These derivatives have both lower biological activities and stabilities than the native protein. Those with a positive charge at the NH_2-terminal end are more stable than those with no charge (acetyl and t-butyloxycarbonyl). Steric effects of the added amino acid derivatives were also noted. These investigators concluded that both the NH_2- and COOH-terminal amino acids are important for conferring stability to the ferredoxin molecule.

It is interesting to look at these chemical modifications in terms of the three-dimensional structure obtained by X-ray diffraction techniques. As mentioned earlier in this article, the NH_2 group of the Ala-1 is H-bonded to the carboxyl group of aspartate 37. Thus, substitution of the NH_2 group may disturb the ion pair arrangement. In addition, iodination of the apoferredoxin results in a tetraiodoferredoxin which could not be reconstituted by the addition of iron and sulfide. Hong and Rabinowitz (1970) postulated that this inactivation might be due to iodination of the tyrosine residues. The X-ray studies suggest that tyrosine-2 and -28 are in contact with the iron–sulfur clusters and evidently are possibly involved in the oxidation–reduction process which the ferredoxin undergoes in the bacteria.

B. *Desulfovibrio gigas* Type of Ferredoxin

Despite the fact that this ferredoxin is from an anaerobic, nonphotosynthetic bacterium, it is different in that it contains four molecules of Fe and sulfide per molecule of protein (Laishley *et al.*, 1969). Furthermore, it does not have a clostridial ferredoxin type of active center, which involves an aromatic amino acid residue in contact with the iron–sulfur cluster, since there is only one aromatic residue and it is not present at position 22. For these reasons, it is considered as a separate entity here rather than classified with the rest of the ferredoxins. A few of its properties have been determined and are summarized in Table IX.

1. FUNCTION OF THE *D. gigas* FERREDOXIN

The ferredoxin is required for the reduction of sulfite by molecular hydrogen. During this reaction, one molecule of ATP is produced and it is possible that ferredoxin is required for ATP production (Peck, 1966).

TABLE IX
SOME PHYSICOCHEMICAL PROPERTIES OF THE *D. gigas* TYPE OF FERREDOXIN

Property	Value
Molecular weight	6570^a
Moles Fe and S^{2-} per mole protein	4^b
Total No. amino acid residues	56
Absorption maxima	280, 305, and 390 nm

[a] Laishley et al., 1969.
[b] LeGall and Dragoni, 1966.

2. AMINO ACID COMPOSITION OF THE *D. gigas* FERREDOXIN

The amino acid composition of the ferredoxin has been reported by Laishley et al., (1969). However, the values are incorrect since it was reported to contain over 60 amino acids. The sequence has been determined (Travis et al., 1971), and the corrected values are shown in Table X. The

TABLE X
AMINO ACID COMPOSITION OF THE *D. gigas* FERREDOXIN[a,b]

Amino acid	Moles per mole protein
Lysine	1
Histidine	0
Arginine	1
Tryptophan	0
Glutamic acid	9
Threonine	0
Serine	3
Aspartic acid	11
Proline	4
Glycine	1
Alanine	6
Cysteine	6
Valine	5
Methionine	2
Isoleucine	5
Leucine	1
Phenylalanine	1
Tyrosine	0
Total amino acids	56

[a] From Travis et al., 1971.
[b] Net charge is −6.

$D.$ $gigas$ ferredoxin is quite different from the clostridial ferredoxins. It has only five cysteine residues and contains both arginine and two residues of methionine but no tryptophan. The only other ferredoxin to contain arginine is the $C.$ $acidi$-$urici$ ferredoxin. The two heat-stable ferredoxins ($C.$ $tartarivorum$ and $C.$ $thermosaccharolyticum$) and the $P.$ $elsdenii$ ferredoxin are the only ferredoxins to contain histidine. The $D.$ $gigas$ ferredoxin contains 56 amino acids as compared to 54–55 for the other bacterial-type ferredoxins. The net charge of the protein is —6, and thus, it is an acidic protein.

3. The Primary Structure of the $D.$ $gigas$ Ferredoxin

The amino acid sequence has been reported by Travis et $al.$ (1971) and is shown in Fig. 6. There is homology in the NH_2-terminal section up to residue 28. The COOH-terminal section from residue 29 differs considerably from the other type of anaerobic ferredoxins. However, the question which is of importance is whether the $D.$ $gigas$ ferredoxin is more ancient than the clostridial type of ferredoxin. Although there is no experimental proof, we favor the hypothesis that the $D.$ $gigas$ ferredoxin is indeed more ancient. The argument which we would like to advance is that a protein with two active sites is more efficient than one with one active site (Peck, 1966). Furthermore, the recent crystal X-ray diffraction results of Adman et $al.$ (1973) do not favor the gene duplication theory advanced by Fitch (1966). According to this theory, there was a precursor ferredoxin which contained 28 amino acids. Owing to gene duplication, it was postulated that a molecule roughly double this size originated. However, the X-ray diffraction studies show that cysteine residues 8, 11, 14, and 45 are coordinated in one active site, and cysteine residues 18, 35, 38, and 41 in the other. Thus, the ferredoxin molecule must have been at least 45 residues long and more likely 55 residues long from the time the ferredoxin gene evolved in the anaerobes. If there was

```
            1                              10                             20
C. P.   Ala- Tyr- Lys - Ile - Ala - Asp- Ser - Cys- Val - Ser- Cys- Cly - Ala - Cys- Ala - Ser - Glu - Cys- Pro- Val - Asn- Ala
D. G.        Pro- Ile  - Gln- Val - Asp- Asn- Cys- Met- Ala- Cys- Glu - Ala - Cys - Ile - Asn- Glu - Cys- Pro- Val - Asp- Val

                        30                             40
C. P.   Ile - Ser - Gln - Gly - Asp- Ser - Ile - Phe- Val - Ile - Asp- Ala - Asp- Thr- Cys - Ile - Asp- Cys- Gly - Asn- Cys- Ala
D. G.   Phe- Gln - Met- Asp- Glu - Gln - Gly - Asp- Lys- Ala- Val - Asn - Ile - Pro- Asn- Ser - Asn- Leu- Asp- Asp- Gln - Cys

                        50               55
C. P.   Asn- Val - Cys- Pro- Val - Gly - Ala - Pro- Val - Gln - Glu - COOH
D. G.   Val- Glu - Ala - Ile - Gln - Ser - Cys- Pro- Ala - Ala - Ile - Arg- Ser - COOH
```

Fig. 6. Comparison of the amino acid sequence of the $D.$ $gigas$ (D.G.) with the $C.$ $pasteurianum$ (C.P.) ferredoxin.

TABLE XI

SIMILARITIES IN THE PRIMARY STRUCTURES OF THE
D. gigas AND THE CLOSTRIDIAL FERREDOXINS

Ferredoxin[a]	Similarities		
	Residues 1–28	Residues 29–54	Total 1–54
D. g./M. a.	11	1	12
D. g./C. b.	9	1	10
D. g./C. p.	9	1	10
D. g./C. a. u.	9	1	10
D. g./C. t.	10	1	11
D. g./P. e.	8	1	9
D. g./C. th.	10	1	11

[a] D. g., *D. gigas;* M. a., *M. aerogenes;* C. b., *C. butyricum;* C. p., *C. pasteurianum;* C. a. u., *C. acidi-urici;* C. t., *C. tartarivorum;* P. e., *P. elsdenii;* C. th., *C. thermosaccharolyticum.*

no gene duplication then it is possible that *D. gigas* ferredoxin represents a more primitive type of ferredoxin than the clostridial type of ferredoxin. The sequence of the *C. pasteurianum* and the *D. gigas* ferredoxins are shown in Fig. 6. In order to compare them, we have decided to align the sequences so that the cysteine residues match up in the NH$_2$-terminal half of the molecule. When the two proteins are compared (Table XI), there are only ten identical residues in identical positions out of the 54 that are compared. This is about a 19% homology which normally would have marginal significance. However, if one compares the first twenty residues there is a nine out of twenty, or a 45%, homology which is indeed significant. Thus, we have adopted the theory that the two proteins are homologous and that they have arisen from the same common ancestor. However, as Peck (1966) has speculated, we believe that the *D. gigas* is a more primitive organism than the clostridial species, and, therefore, the same argument applies to the ferredoxins present in these organisms. The argument which is applied here for the above-mentioned theory is that (1) a molecule with two active sites is more active than a molecule with one active site, and (2) the metabolism of the *D. gigas*, which is geared to metabolize sulfite, a compound which probably existed on primordial earth, is possibly more primitive than the metabolism of the clostridial species. If these assumptions turn out to be correct, it will be interesting to determine the possible genetic error or mutational pressure that brought about a change from a one active site to a two active site ferredoxin.

TABLE XII

Types of Residues in the *D. gigas* Ferredoxin

Hydrophobic	Neutral	Hydrophilic	Acidic	Basic	Total
25	20	11	9	2	56

4. Distribution of Types of Residues in the *D. gigas* Ferredoxin

The types of residues of *D. gigas* ferredoxin are classified as hydrophobic, neutral, or hydrophilic as described above. The distribution of the various types of residues is similar to that observed with clostridial ferredoxins (Table XII).

5. Chelate Structure of the *D. gigas* Ferredoxin

Since this ferredoxin contains only 4 Fe and 4 S^{2-} per molecule of protein, the cysteine residues 7, 10, 13, and probably 43 are involved in the binding of iron and sulfide. However, this will have to be determined by X-ray diffraction studies on crystalline ferredoxin. Moreover, this ferredoxin lacks an aromatic residue at positions equivalent to 2 and 28 found in the *M. aerogenes* ferredoxin. The only aromatic amino acid residue present is phenylalanine in position 22. Thus, the active site of the *D. gigas* ferredoxin is different from the clostridial ferredoxins where the two aromatic residues are present in positions 2 and 28 and the cysteine residues are present at positions 8, 11, 13, and 17 in one-half of the molecule and at positions 35, 38, 41, and 45 at the other half of the molecule.

C. Ferredoxin from Photosynthetic Bacteria

Losada *et al.* (1961) first isolated a ferredoxin from the photosynthetic bacterium, *Chromatium*. It was found that the *Chromatium* ferredoxin as well as clostridial ferredoxin could replace spinach ferredoxin in the photoreduction of NADP mediated by spinach chloroplasts (Tagawa and Arnon, 1962). Bachofen and Arnon (1966) crystallized and characterized the *Chromatium* ferredoxin. The absorption spectrum of this ferredoxin resembles those of the clostridial ferredoxins, and its oxidation–reduction potential was found to be the lowest (−490 mV) of any ferredoxin isolated thus far. The molecular weight of the *Chromatium* ferredoxin is 9,500–10,000 daltons, and the molecule contains 5–6 moles of iron and the same number of moles of inorganic sulfide per mole of protein (Sasaki and Matsubara, 1967). The facultatively photosynthetic nonsulfur purple bacteria such as *Rhodospirillum rubrum* contain ferredoxin that is too unstable and therefore cannot be completely purified.

Recently, Rao *et al.* (1969) have isolated ferredoxin from the photosynthetic green bacteria, *Chloropseudomonas ethylicum* and *Chlorobium thiosulfatophilum*, and reported that the ferredoxins from these organisms are more similar to the clostridial type of ferredoxin than the *Chromatium* ferredoxin. However, since that report, it was found that the reported the *Chloropseudomonas ethylicum* was not a pure culture but a mixture of a *Chlorobium* and a sulfate reducer (M. C. W. Evans and K. K. Rao, unpublished results). Some of the physicochemical properties of this type of ferredoxin are shown in Table XIII.

1. FUNCTION OF FERREDOXIN FROM PHOTOSYNTHETIC BACTERIA

The function of ferredoxin in these bacteria are twofold (Buchanan, 1966; Hall and Evans, 1969). They are required for photosynthesis, although the roles are less clearly defined than in plants. The ferredoxin is found in subcellular particles called chromatophores. In the purple bacteria, the ferredoxin is required for cyclic photophosphorylation. However, it has not been possible to demonstrate its exact function. Noncyclic electron flow has not been demonstrated in extracts of *Chromatium*. In photosynthetic green bacteria, it has been shown that the ferredoxin is photoreduced and the reduced ferredoxin is used to reduce NADP. A ferredoxin : NADP oxidoreductase has been partially purified from *Chlorobium thiosulphatophilum*. The second role for ferredoxin is to catalyze the carboxylation of acetyl CoA and succinyl CoA to pyruvate and α-ketoglutarate, respectively (Buchanan *et al.*, 1964). The two reactions permit the reversal of two steps in the oxidation of pyruvate through the tri-

TABLE XIII

SOME PHYSICOCHEMICAL PROPERTIES OF FERREDOXIN
FROM PHOTOSYNTHETIC BACTERIA[a]

Property	Chromatium[a]	Green bacteria
Molecular weight	9500–10,000[a]	6920[b]
Moles of Fe and S^{2-}	5–6 (8)[a]	(8)
Absorption maxima	—	—
E_0	−490 mV[c]	—
Total cysteine residues	9[a]	9[b]
Total amino acids	81[a]	60[b]
Reducing equivalents	2[d]	—
ESR spectrum (reduced)	$g = 1.94$	—

[a] Sasaki and Matsubara, 1967; Matsubara *et al.*, 1970.
[b] M. Tanaka, M. Haniu, K. T. Yasunobu, R. Himes, and J. Agai (unpublished data).
[c] Bachofen and Arnon, 1966.
[d] Evans *et al.*, 1968.

carboxylic acid cycle. Aerobic organisms cannot catalyze this reaction. Thus, the reduced ferredoxin makes it possible for the photosynthetic bacteria to carry out CO_2 fixation via acetyl CoA and succinyl CoA to form pyruvate and α-ketoglutarate, respectively.

2. AMINO ACID COMPOSITION OF PHOTOSYNTHETIC BACTERIAL FERREDOXINS

The amino acid composition of the *Chromatium* ferredoxin was reported by Sasaki and Matsubara (1967). However, they reported initially that the protein contained 84 amino acids. The same investigators have determined the primary structure of this protein, and the total number has now been revised to 81 residues. Rao *et al.* (1969) have determined the amino acid composition of two photosynthetic bacteria, namely, the ferredoxins from *Chlorobium thiosulfatophilum* and *Chloropseudomonas ethylicum*. However, as mentioned earlier, the culture of the *Chloropseudomonas ethylicum* has since been shown to be impure, and the extracts appear to contain two different iron–sulfur proteins. In joint work with the University of London investigators, our laboratory is investigating the two iron–sulfur proteins after each has been purified. There appears to be one ferredoxin with 52–53 amino acids and another with about 64 amino acids. For the time being we are assuming that the protein with 64 amino acids is the ferredoxin from the photosynthetic green bacteria. The amino acid compositions of the various ferredoxins mentioned above are summarized in Table XIV. Even from the few results obtained, it is becoming obvious that the different photosynthetic bacteria contain iron–sulfur proteins of different sizes. Furthermore, the ferredoxins from photosynthetic bacteria analyzed thus far lack tryptophan and phenylalanine. Methionine is present only in the *Chromatium* ferredoxin. As in the case of all ferredoxins, the acidic residues outnumber the basic residues, accounting for the net negative charge on the protein.

3. PRIMARY STRUCTURE OF THE FERREDOXIN FROM PHOTOSYNTHETIC BACTERIA

The primary structure of the ferredoxin from *Chromatium* has been completed (Matsubara *et al.*, 1970). The sequence is shown in Fig. 7, which shows that it is a single polypeptide chain protein consisting of 81 residues. The important cysteine residues are present at positions 8, 11, 13, 17, 37, 40, 43, 47, and 52. Of these cysteine residues, not all are involved in iron chelation. Like the clostridial type of ferredoxin, the NH_2-terminal residue is alanine. In fact, the sequence shows great homology with the clostridial type of ferredoxin, although it is obviously bigger

TABLE XIV
Amino Acid Composition of Some Ferredoxins
from Photosynthetic Bacteria

	Moles per mole protein	
Amino acid	Chromatium[a]	C. thiosulfatophilum 8327[b]
Lysine	2	0
Histidine	2	0
Arginine	2	0
Tryptophan	0	0
Aspartic acid	8	3
Threonine	6	3
Serine	4	3
Glutamic acid	16	9
Proline	5	4
Glycine	5	4
Alanine	3	9
Cysteine	9	7–8
Valine	6	4
Methionine	1	0
Isoleucine	6	4
Leucine	3	2
Tyrosine	3	3
Phenylalanine	0	0
Total amino acids	81	55–56

[a] Matsubara et al., 1970.
[b] Rao et al., 1969.

and contains more amino acid residues. Thus, many of the comments made previously for the clostridial ferredoxins will apply equally well for the *Chromatium* ferredoxin.

Although the so-called *Chloropseudomonas ethylicum* has since been

1   10
Ala - Leu- Met - Ile - Thr- Asp- Gln - Cys - Ile - Asn- Cys- Asn- Val - Cys- Gln - Pro- Glu - Cys-

    20   30
Pro- Asn- Gly - Ala - Ile - Ser - Gln - Gly - Asp- Glu - Thr- Tyr- Val - Ile - Glu - Pro- Ser - Leu-

    40   50
Cys- Thr- Glu - Cys- Val - Gly - His - Tyr- Glu - Thr- Ser - Gln - Cys- Val - Asp- Cys- Val - Glu -

    60   70
Val - Cys- Pro - Ile - Lys- Asp- Pro- Ser - His - Glu - Glu - Thr- Glu - Asp- Glu - Leu- Arg- Ala -

    80
Lys- Tyr- Glu - Arg - Ile - Thr- Gly - Glu - Gly

Fig. 7. Primary structure of the *Chromatium* ferredoxin.

TABLE XV
AMINO ACID COMPOSITION OF THE FERREDOXINS FROM
THE GREEN PHOTOSYNTHETIC BACTERIA[a]

	Mole per mole protein	
Amino acid	C. ethylicum[b] protein 1	C. ethylicum[b] protein 2
Lysine	1	0
Histidine	1	0
Arginine	1	0
Tryptophan	0	0
Aspartic acid	6	6
Threonine	3	4
Serine	2	1
Glutamic acid	9	9
Proline	4	3
Glycine	2	4
Alanine	7–8	9
Cysteine	9	9
Valine	7	5
Methionine	0	0
Isoleucine	6	5
Leucine	0	2
Tyrosine	4	3
Phenylalanine	0	0
Total amino acids	62–63	60

[a] From a symbiotic mixture of a *Chlorobium* and a sulfate reducer.
[b] M. Tanaka, M. Haniu, K. T. Yasunobu, R. Himes, and J. Akai (unpublished data).

shown not to be a pure bacterial preparation but a mixture of a *Chlorobium* and a sulfate reducer, M. Tanaka, M. Haniu, K. T. Yasunobu, R. Himes, and J. Akai (unpublished data) have separated from the symbiotic bacterial culture a mixture of two ferredoxins which are thought to be from the green photosynthetic bacteria and a contaminating sulfate reducer. (See Table XV for amino acid composition data.) The carboxymethylcysteine derivative of the *Chlorobium* ferredoxin (*C. ethylicum* protein 2 in Table XV) which was purified from the mixture of bacteria has been analyzed in the Beckman protein sequencer, model 890, and the partial sequence is shown in Fig. 8.

```
1                        10                              20
Ala-Leu-Tyr- Ile - Thr- Glu-Glu -Cys-Thr-Tyr-Cys-Gly -Ala-Cys-Glu-Pro-Glu-Cys-Pro-Val-Thr-Ala- Ile -

                  30                                        58      60
Ser-Ala -Gly -Asp-Asp- Ile -Tyr-Val - Ile - Asx-Ala -Asx-   -   -   -   -   -   -   -   -Val- Gln-Gly-COO
```

Fig. 8. Partial amino acid sequence of the *Chlorobium* ferredoxin.

TABLE XVI

SIMILARITIES IN SEQUENCE OF *D. gigas, C. pasteurianum,*
AND *Chromatium* FERREDOXINS

	D. gigas	C. pasteurianum	Chromatium
D. gigas	—	10	7
C. pasteurianum	10	—	25
Chromatium	7	25	—

4. A COMPARISON OF THE CLOSTRIDIAL, *D. gigas,*
AND PHOTOSYNTHETIC FERREDOXINS

The data are tabulated in Table XVI, comparing the sequences of all these ferredoxins. The NH$_2$-terminal residues of *C. pasteurianum* and *Chromatium* ferredoxins were aligned, while the NH$_2$-terminal proline residue of the *D. gigas* ferredoxin was aligned at position 2 of the other two ferredoxins. Greater homology is observed between the *D. gigas* and *C. pasteurianum* ferredoxins than the *D. gigas–Chromatium* ferredoxin pair. Moreover, the *C. pasteurianum* ferredoxin is more like the *Chromatium* ferredoxin than the *D. gigas* ferredoxin.

Similarities in the partial sequences of the *C. pasteurianum*, "*C. ethylicum*" and *Chromatium* ferredoxins are also observed and are shown in Table XVII. The *C. pasteurianum* ferredoxin is more similar to the *Chlorobium* ferredoxin (*C. ethylicum*) than the *Chromatium* or the *D. gigas* ferredoxins. The next most similar ferredoxin to the *C. pasteurianum* protein is the ferredoxin from *Chromatium*, and the least similar one is the ferredoxin from *D. gigas*. On the other hand, the *D. gigas* ferredoxin has 10, 9, and 9 similar sequences when compared with the

TABLE XVII

SIMILARITIES IN THE PARTIAL SEQUENCES OF THE *C. pasteurianum,*
C. ethylicum, Chromatium, AND *D. gigas* FERREDOXINS[a]

	C. P.	C. E.[b]	Chr	D. G.
C. pasteurianum	—	19	25	10
C. ethylicum	19	—	19	8
Chromatium	25	19	—	7
D. gigas	10	8	7	—

[a] See Table XI.
[b] Residues 1–32. For the remainder of the proteins, the entire sequence was used in the comparison.

C. pasteurianum, Chlorobium (*C. ethylicum*), and *Chromatium* ferredoxins, respectively. Thus, the *D. gigas* ferredoxin differs considerably in structure from the clostridial and photosynthetic bacterial ferredoxins.

5. A Comparison of the Structure of the *C. pasteurianum* and *Chromatium* Ferredoxins

Matsubara *et al.* (1970) have made an interesting comparison of the primary structure of these two ferredoxins. The two ferredoxins are aligned so that the NH_2-terminal alanine and the first six cysteine residues from the NH_2-terminal end of the protein are in register. A further change in the *Chromatium* ferredoxin sequence is assumed at residues 42–50 which is proposed to have occurred through some type of genetic or DNA change. Some other type of gene change must be invoked to explain the presence of 21 additional residues in the *Chromatium* ferredoxin. According to this alignment, the two ferredoxins show a 46% homology, and this is good evidence that the two proteins have arisen from a common ancestor.

6. Types of Residues in the *Chromatium* Ferredoxin

Since this ferredoxin is the only one in its class to be sequenced, it is the only one that is considered here (Fig. 9). The *Chromatium* ferredoxin (Fig. 9) appears to be less hydrophobic than the ferredoxins considered up to now. In fact, the neutral type of residues exceeds the amount of hydrophobic residues. It also has a much more ionic structure than the other ferredoxins. There is a 4 residue sequence at the NH_2-terminal end of the molecule which contains hydrophobic residues. Residues

```
   1   2   3   4   5   6   7   8   9  10  11  12  13  14  15  16  17  18  19  20  21  22  23  24  25  26  27  28  29  3
H₂N-H  H   H   H   N   -   N   N   H   N   N   N   H   N   N   H   -   N   H   N   H   H   H   N   N   H   -   -   N   )

  31  32  33  34  35  36  37  38  39  40  41  42  43  44  45  46  47  48  49  50  51  52  53  54  55  56  57  58  59  (
   H   H   -   H   N   H   N   N   -   N   H   H   +   N   -   N   N   N   N   H   -   N   H   -   H   N   H   H   +

  61  62  63  64  65  66  67  68  69  70  71  72  73  74  75  76  77  78  79  80  81
   H   N   +   -   -   N   -   -   -   H   +   H   +   N   -   +   H   N   H   -   H-COOH
```

Types of Residues in the Chromatium Ferredoxin

	Residues					
	Hydrophobic	Neutral	Hydrophilic	Acidic	Basic	Total
Number of residues	29	29	23	-18[a]	+7[b]	81

[a] Includes COOH group of C-terminal amino acid.
[b] Includes NH_2-group of N-terminal amino acid.

Fig. 9. Distribution of various types of residues in the *Chromatium* ferredoxin. N, stands for neutral residues; H, for hydrophobic residues; +, for basic residues; and −, for acidic residues.

21–23 include a portion of the molecule which contains three hydrophobic residues in a row. There are three portions where there are two hydrophobic residues in a row (resideus 31–32, 41–42, and 57–58). Otherwise, the hydrophobic residues are scattered over the entire molecule. The section from residues 51–81 is quite ionic and is a portion which is very highly negatively charged. This section of the protein may be involved in the binding to components of the redox system of which ferredoxin is a partner. Like the clostridial ferredoxins, the *Chromatium* ferredoxin binds to NADP-ferredoxin reductase of spinach to form a one-to-one complex, and the complex is dissociated by high salt concentration (Foust *et al.*, 1969).

7. CHELATE STRUCTURE OF THE *Chromatium* AND OTHER PHOTOSYNTHETIC BACTERIAL FERREDOXINS

Although Matsubara *et al.* (1970) report that the *Chromatium* ferredoxin contains 5–6 Fe and S^{2-} per molecule of the protein, the observations that the *Chromatium* ferredoxin accepts two electrons per molecule of protein indicates that the photosynthetic ferredoxins may contain 8 Fe and S^{2-} per molecule with active sites similar to the clostridial ferredoxins. Carter *et al.* (1972) postulate that since the ferredoxins of this class have very negative oxidation–reduction potentials and give an electron paramagnetic resonance (EPR) signal of 1.94 in the reduced form, it should have an active site similar to the clostridial ferredoxins. This also implies that two aromatic residues in the *Chromatium* ferredoxin are in contact with the iron–sulfur clusters. However, the structure of one of the active sites may be similar to the one present in the clostridial ferredoxins, the other one must be different since there is no aromatic residue in position 2 of the *Chromatium* ferredoxin even though the cysteine residues may be aligned as they are in the clostridial ferredoxins.

8. SOME FURTHER PROPERTIES OF THE *Chromatium* AND PHOTOSYNTHETIC BACTERIAL FERREDOXINS

The *Chromatium* ferredoxin is different from the clostridial and plant ferredoxins in that it is not reduced directly by dithionite. All the other ferredoxins are readily reduced (Evans, 1968). Furthermore, the *Chromatium* ferredoxin is not reduced by H_2–hydrogenase mixtures as are the other types of ferredoxins. However, it is reduced by dithionite in the presence of traces of methyl viologen. Hall and Evans (1969) postulate that steric effects can account for this property.

Buchanan *et al.* (1964) and Evans (1968) report that the photosynthetic ferredoxins are more active in photosynthesis and CO_2 fixation reactions than the clostridial ferredoxins.

IV. ALGAL AND PLANT FERREDOXINS

This type of ferredoxin has been called the methemoglobin reductase factor (Davenport et al., 1952) or PPNR [photosynthetic pyridine nucleotide reductase factor (San Pietro and Lang, 1958)]. The first crystalline preparation of a plant- or chloroplast-type ferredoxin was obtained from spinach by Tagawa and Arnon (1962) and it was shown to contain iron and sulfide similar to the C. pasteurianum ferredoxin.

All of the ferredoxins to this point have been isolated from prokaryotes. Now the transition to eukaryotes occurs. The blue-green algae are a prokaryote, but the higher algae and plants are all eukaryotes. However, as discussed below, all of the algae and plants have ferredoxins of very similar structure.

Let us first consider some of the physicochemical properties of the chloroplast or the 2 Fe–2 S^{2-} ferredoxins. The properties are summarized in Table XVIII. Although most of the values are for the alfalfa ferredoxin (Keresztes-Nagy and Margoliash, 1966), the other algal and plant ferredoxins have very similar properties. They all have a molecular weight of about 12,250 and contain 96–97 amino acids.

TABLE XVIII

SOME PHYSICOCHEMICAL PROPERTIES OF THE ALGAL-PLANT TYPE OF FERREDOXINS[a]

Property	Value
Molecular weight by	
a. Sedimentation equilibrium	10,000
b. Sedimentation diffusion	12,000
c. Amino acid composition	11,200
d. Fe content	11,500
$s^0_{22,w}$	1.58×10^{13} S
$D^0_{22,w}$	10.39×10^7 cm^2 second^{-1}
Partial specific volume (calculated)	0.715 ml/gm
Mobility, pH 7.2, 0.1 ionic strength	15.6×10^{-5} cm V^{-1} second^{-1}
Absorption maxima	465, 422, 331, 277 nm
Fe and S^{2-} content per mole	
Total amino acids	96–97
ESR spectrum (reduced state)	$g = 1.94^b$
Cysteine residues	4–6
ORD	Determined[c]
Mössbauer spectrum	Determined[d]

[a] Keresztes-Nagy and Margoliash, 1966.
[b] Beinert and Sands, 1960.
[c] Garbett et al., 1967.
[d] Rao et al., 1971.

A. Function of Ferredoxin

Ferredoxin is an essential component of the photosynthetic machinery of the chloroplast. It acts as an electron carrier between the photoreduction system in the chloroplast and pyridine nucleotide as shown in Fig. 1 in Chapter 4 of Volume I of this treatise.

B. Amino Acid Composition of the Plant and Algal Ferredoxins

At the present time approximately ten different ferredoxins have been analyzed for their amino acid composition. The results are summarized in Table XIX. Some of the values are very accurate, especially the

TABLE XIX
AMINO ACID COMPOSITION OF THE CHLOROPLAST FERREDOXINS

Amino acid	Moles per mole protein										
Lysine	3	5	3	4	4	4	5	5	4	3	5
Histidine	1	1	1	1	1	2	1	1	1	1	2
Arginine	1	1	1	1	1	1	1	2	1	2	1
Tryptophan	0	0	0	0	0	0	1	1	1	1	1
Aspartic acid	13	14	15	12	8–9	14	10	10+	13	16	9
Threonine	7	6	12	10	7	6	6	4	8	4	6
Serine	6	7	7	8	8	7–8	8	7	7	6	8
Glutamic acid	13	15	11	10	15–16	9	15	16+	13	18	16
Proline	4	3	3	4	4	4–5	4	4+	4	4	3
Glycine	12	6	6	7	9	9	9	6+	6	8	7
Alanine	9	11	12	10	6	7	6	7	9	8	9
Cysteine	5	4	6	6	4	5	5	5	5	4	5
Valine	4	6	9	5	6	5	10	6+	7	8	9
Methionine	1	1	0	1	1	2	0	0	0	1	0
Isoleucine	6	5	5	3	5	6	4	4	4	4	4
Leucine	9	9	7	7	8	7	6	9+	8	6	6
Tyrosine	3	4	5	4	2	3	4	3	4	2	4
Phenylalanine	1	3	2	3	4	4	2	3	2	3	2
Total amino acids	98[a]	101[b]	105[c]	96[d]	93–95[e]	95–97[f]	97[g]	96[h]	97[i]	99[j]	97[k]

[a] *Microcystis* (blue-green alga).
[b] *Bumilleriopsis* (yellow-green alga).
[c] *A. nidulans*.
[d] *Scenedesmus* (green alga).
[e] *Equisetum* (horsetail).
[f] Fern.

[g] Taro.
[h] *Leucaena glauca*.
[i] Spinach.
[j] Cotton.
[k] Alfalfa.

ferredoxins which have been sequenced, but others are approximate since detailed studies on the destruction and slow hydrolysis of certain amino acids have not been accounted for in the analyses. As in the case of all the ferredoxins, this type of ferredoxin consists of a single polypeptide chain, usually with a NH_2-terminal alanine and containing about 96–97 amino acids (Table XIX). The proteins of this type all contain at least four cysteine residues which are involved in the active site. The acidic residues exceed the basic residues which accounts for the acidic isoelectric point of all ferredoxins. All of the naturally occurring amino acids are present when the amino acid compositions of all the different ferredoxins are considered, but some of the amino acids are absent when one ferredoxin from a particular specie is considered. Tryptophan is present mainly in the dicotyledons' ferredoxins. Methionine is lacking in a number of the ferredoxins in this class and does not appear essential for activity.

Although all the plant and algal type of ferredoxins have the same chelate structure, they do not all show equal stability. For example, the ferredoxins from taro and *Leucaena glauca* are quite stable, while the spinach ferredoxin appears to deteriorate much more rapidly. Crystals of the taro and *L. glauca* ferredoxins have been kept under a nitrogen atmosphere for a year with little decomposition! At the present time, it is not possible to say which amino acids account for the differences in stability. As in all the ferredoxins, the hydrophobic residues exceed all other types of residues.

The blue-green algae which are assumed to be the precursor to all the other types of algal and plant ferredoxins have a composition which is quite similar to the other types of ferredoxins.

C. The Sequence of the Chloroplast Ferredoxins

To date, the sequence of five different ferredoxins of this type have been determined. These include the ferredoxins from spinach (Matsubara *et al.*, 1967; Matsubara and Sasaki, 1968), alfalfa (Keresztes-Nagy and Margoliash, 1966), *Scenedesmus* (Sugeno and Matsubara, 1969), *Leucaena glauca* (Benson and Yasunobu, 1969), and taro (Rao and Matsubara, 1970). The different species include a dicotyledon, blue-green algae, a tree, and a monocotyledon. On the whole, the sequences of the various chloroplast ferredoxins look quite similar. It is interesting to note that among these ferredoxins it appears that the only organism shown to produce isozymes is *Leucaena glauca*. From the analysis of the amino acid composition of the cotton ferredoxin, it appears that a similar situation exists in cotton. It appears most likely that chloroplast DNA and not nuclear DNA is responsible for the production of isozymes.

<pre>
                    1   10   20
Taro   A. Ala -Thr-Tyr-Lys-Val -Lys-Leu-Val -Thr-Pro-Ser -Gly -Gln -Gln -Glu -Phe-Gln -Cys-Pro-Asp-
Spinach   B. Ala -Ala -Tyr-Lys-Val -Thr-Leu-Val -Thr-Pro-Thr-Gly -Asn-Val -Glu -Phe-Gln -Cys-Pro-Asp-
Alfalfa   C. Ala -Ser -Tyr-Lys-Val -Lys-Leu-Val -Thr-Pro-Glu -Gly -Thr-Gln -Glu -Phe-Glu -Cys-Pro-Asp-
L. glauca D.   Ala -Phe-Lys-Val -Lys-Leu-Leu-Thr-Pro-Asp-Gly -Pro-Lys-Glu -Phe-Glu -Cys-Pro-Asp-
Scene-   E. Ala -Thr-Tyr-Lys-Val -Thr-Leu-Lys-Thr-Pro-Ser -Gly -Asp-Gln -Thr - Ile -Glu -Cys-Pro-Asp-
desmus
</pre>

<pre>
                    21   30   40
          A. Asp-Val -Tyr - Ile -Leu-Asp-Gln -Ala -Glu -Glu -Val -Gly - Ile - Asp- Leu-Pro-Tyr-Ser -Cys-Arg-
          B. Asp-Val -Tyr - Ile -Leu-Asp-Ala -Ala -Glu -Glu -Glu -Gly - Ile - Asp-Leu-Pro-Tyr-Ser -Cys-Arg-
          C. Asp-Val -Tyr - Ile -Leu-Asp-His -Ala -Glu -Glu -Glu -Gly - Ile - Val -Leu-Pro-Tyr-Ser -Cys-Arg-
          D. Asp-Val -Tyr - Ile -Leu-Asp-Gln -Ala -Glu -Glu -Leu-Gly - Ile - Asp-Leu-Pro-Tyr-Ser -Cys-Arg-
          E. Asp-Thr-Tyr - Ile -Leu-Asp-Ala -Ala -Glu -Glu -Ala -Gly - Leu-Asp-Leu-Pro-Tyr-Ser -Cys-Arg-
</pre>

<pre>
                    41   50   60
          A. Ala -Gly -Ser -Cys-Ser -Ser -Cys-Ala -Gly -Lys-Val -Lys-Val -Gly -Asp-Val -Asp-Gln -Ser -Asp-
          B. Ala -Gly -Ser -Cys-Ser -Ser -Cys-Ala -Gly -Lys-Leu-Lys-Thr-Gly -Ser -Leu-Asn-Gln -Asp-Asp-
          C. Ala -Gly -Ser -Cys-Ser -Ser -Cys-Ala -Gly -Lys-Val -Ala -Ala -Gly -Glu -Val -Asn-Gln -Ser -Asp-
          D. Ala -Gly -Ser -Cys-Ser -Ser -Cys-Ala -Gly -Lys-Leu-Val -Glu -Gly -Asp-Leu-Asp-Gln -Ser -Asp-
          E. Ala -Gly -Ala -Cys-Ser -Ser -Cys-Ala -Gly -Lys-Val -Glu -Ala -Gly -Thr-Val -Asp-Gln -Ser -Asp-
</pre>

<pre>
                    61   70   80
          A. Gly -Ser -Phe-Leu-Asp-Asp-Glu -Gln - Ile - Gly -Glu -Gly -Trp-Val -Leu-Thr-Cys-Val -Ala -Tyr-
          B. Gln -Ser -Phe-Leu-Asp-Asp-Asp-Gln - Ile - Asp-Glu -Gly -Trp-Val -Leu-Thr-Cys-Ala -Ala -Tyr-
          C. Gly -Ser -Phe-Leu-Asp-Asp-Asp-Gln - Ile - Glu -Glu -Gly -Trp-Val -Leu-Thr-Cys-Val -Ala -Tyr-
          D. Gln -Ser -Phe-Leu-Asp-Asp-Glu -Gln - Ile - Glu -Glu -Gly -Trp-Val -Leu-Thr-Cys-Ala -Ala -Tyr-
          E. Gln -Ser -Phe-Leu-Asp-Asp-Ser -Gln -Met-Asp-Gly -Gly -Phe-Val -Leu-Thr-Cys-Val -Ala -Tyr-
</pre>

<pre>
                    81   90   97
          A. Pro-Val -Ser -Asp-Gly -Thr - Ile -Glu -Thr-His -Lys-Glu -Glu -Glu -Leu-Thr-Ala
          B. Pro-Val -Ser -Asp-Val -Thr - Ile -Glu -Thr-His -Lys-Glu -Glu -Glu -Leu-Thr-Ala
          C. Ala -Lys-Ser -Asp-Val -Thr - Ile -Glu -Thr-His -Lys-Glu -Glu -Glu -Leu-Thr-Ala
          D. Pro-Arg-Ser -Asp-Val -Val - Ile -Glu -Thr-His -Lys-Glu -Glu -Glu -Leu-Thr-Gly
          E. Pro-Thr-Ser -Asp-Cys-Thr - Ile -Ala -Thr-His -Lys-Glu -Glu -Asp-Leu-Phe
</pre>

Fig. 10. The primary structures of various plant and algal ferredoxins.

The various ferredoxins are arranged in Fig. 10 so that the cysteine residues are in register. The cysteine residues are present at positions 18, 39, 44, 47, 77, and, in the *Scenedesmus* ferredoxin, at position 85, All of the ferredoxins contain a NH₂-terminal alanine residue, although it is necessary to shift the *L. glauca* ferredoxin in one residue from the NH₂ terminus of the protein to get alignment of this ferredoxin with the other types of the algal and plant ferredoxins. Similarly, the *Scenedesmus* ferredoxin seems to have suffered a deletion of one residue at the COOH terminal or the other types of proteins have added alanine at the COOH terminus. The protein is a single polypeptide chain with about 96–97 residues. Unlike the ferredoxins discussed thus far, the chloroplast ferredoxins contain all of the amino acids usually found in proteins.

D. Similarities in the Primary Structure of the Various Chloroplast Ferredoxins

There is no doubt that the sequence of the various plant and algal type of ferredoxins show homologous sequences. The rate of change of the primary structure of these ferredoxins seem to be rather low either as a consequence of the structure-function requirements or because of

TABLE XX

INTRASPECIES SIMILARITY IN THE SEQUENCE OF THE CHLOROPLAST FERREDOXINS[a]

	Taro	Spinach	Alfalfa	L. glauca	Scenedesmus
Taro	—	79	81	77	71
Spinach	79	—	78	77	67
Alfalfa	81	78	—	74	68
L. glauca	77	77	74	—	64
Scenedesmus	71	67	68	64	—

[a] Numbers refer to the number of residues which are identical in the intraspecies comparison.

a slow mutation rate. There is fossil evidence that the blue-green algae may have existed several billion years ago, while the higher plants evolved only about 100,000,000 years ago. Yet the amino acid composition shows that the blue-green algae, higher algae, and plants are quite similar in structure.

The various ferredoxins were compared with one another, and the similarities are shown in Table XX. The percent homology varies from 67–83%.

E. Constant Residues among the Various Chloroplast Ferredoxins

Constant residues of a protein show possible essential portions of the molecule. Despite the wide range of ferredoxins investigated, the chloroplast ferredoxins show considerable homology. For example, as shown in Fig. 11, residues 1, 3, 4, 6, 9, 10, 12, 16–21, 23–26, 28–30, 32, 35–42, 44–50, 54, 58, 60, 62–66, 68, 72, 74–77, 79–80, 83–84, 87, 89–93, 95, and 97 are homologous in the five ferredoxins sequenced thus far. Thus, the five ferredoxins show a 58/97 or about a 60% homology as a group. It is obvious why the cysteine residues are constant, since they are chelated to two iron atoms. In addition, it is thought that there maybe an aromatic residue in contact with the iron–sulfur cluster or active site.

F. Types and Distribution of Residues in Chloroplast Ferredoxins

It is a reasonable assumption that the majority of hydrophobic residues are buried in the interior of the protein and the majority of ionic residues

Fig. 11. Constant and variable residues in the various plant and algal ferredoxins.

are located on the surface of the protein. Until the data on the three-dimensional structures become available, a rough idea of the distribution of the types of residues is desirable. Table XXI shows the distribution of the various types of residues.

As far as the hydrophobic residues are concerned, in the constant portions of the chloroplast ferredoxins, there is one portion where there are four hydrophobic residues adjacent to one another (residues 71–74). There are six portions in the constant portion of the molecule where there are two hydrophobic residues in a row (residues 24–25, 32–33, 35–36, 41–42, 48–49, 62–63, and 77–78). There are other portions where there are hydrophobic residues in a row, but in one or another specie a nonhydrophobic residue is found in that position. There are ionic portions of the molecule. The NH_2-terminal portion is positively charged (NH_2-terminal, residue 4 and residue 6). There are two highly negatively charged regions (residues 17, 20, 21, 26, 29, and 30 and residues 59, 64, and 65). The region from residue 83 to the COOH terminal is highly ionic owing to the presence of acidic and basic residues. There are many drastic changes observed where an ionic residue is replaced by a hydrophobic residue, e.g., residues 6, 8, 11, 13, 14, 33, 52, 53, 55, 56, 66, 69, 70, 81, and 87.

TABLE XXI

NUMBER OF HYDROPHOBIC, HYDROPHILIC, AND IONIC RESIDUES IN THE CHLOROPLAST TYPE OF FERREDOXINS

	Number of hydrophobic residues	Number of neutral residues	Number of hydrophilic residues	Number of acidic residues[a]	Number of basic residues[b]	Total residues	Net charge
Taro	42	28	27	21	8	97	−13
Spinach	41	30	26	21	7	97	−14
Alfalfa	41	27	29	22	9	97	−13
L. glauca	42	23	31	24	9	96	−15
Scenedesmus	40	32	24	19	7	96	−12

[a] Includes COOH-terminal —COOH groups.
[b] Includes NH_2-terminal NH_2 groups.

G. Homology in the Primary Structure of Bacterial, Photosynthetic Bacterial, and Chloroplast Ferredoxins

Various investigators have proposed that there is a homology in the primary structure of the various ferredoxins (Matsubara et al. 1968; Eck and Dayhoff, 1966). The method for aligning the clostridial, Chromatium, and plant type of ferredoxins according to Dayhoff (1969) is shown in Fig. 12. According to their scheme, the NH_2-terminal alanine residue of the clostridial and the Chromatium ferredoxins are aligned with residue 32 of the algal and plant ferredoxins. Gaps are introduced to provide the best match of the residues among the various ferredoxins. The Matsubara-Jukes-Cantor scheme is shown in Fig. 13, and all the different ferredoxins are aligned so that the residue 1 of each protein are in register. The important point is that all of the ferredoxins appear to be homologous proteins, and the evolution of all these proteins will be treated in detail in this chapter.

H. Chelate Structure of Plant or Algal Type of Ferredoxin

The evidence to date suggests that the active site consists of two Fe, two labile sulfide, and the sulfhydryl groups of four cysteine residues. The possible structure of the active site is described in Chapter 8 of this volume. Although the plant ferredoxins contain as many as six cysteine residues, it appears almost certain that the cysteine residues 39, 44. 47, and 77 are the cysteine residues involved in iron chelation. The evidence is based on the fact that the horsetail ferredoxin does not possess a cysteine residue at position 18 (Aggarwal et al., 1971), and the fact that Scenedesmus ferredoxin is the sole ferredoxin to have a cysteine residue at position 85, which rules out this cysteine residue as a chelator. From the recent studies with bacterial ferredoxin and adrenodoxin, a tyrosine residue or some other aromatic residue should be present at the active site. At the present time, it is not possible to state whether this aromatic residue is Tyr/Phe at position 3, Tyr-23, Tyr-37, Phe-63, Phe/Trp-73, Tyr-80, or His-90.

V. PUTIDAREDOXIN

A. Introduction

Gunsalus and co-workers at the University of Illinois have isolated from the microorganism Pseudomonas putida a camphor hydroxylating

Amino acid sequence alignment of ferredoxins (the table is printed sideways on the page). Positions are grouped in numbered sections; gaps are shown as dashes.

Top block (positions 1–38; sections 1, 2, 3)

```
                  1                   2                   3
             1 2 3 4 5 6 7 8 9 0 1 2 3 4 5 6 7 8 9 0 1 2 3 4 5 6 7 8 9 0 1 2 3 4 5 6 7 8
Cl. pasteurianum  - - - - - - - - - - - - - - - - - - - - - - - - - - - - - - - A Y K I A D S
Cl. butyricum     - - - - - - - - - - - - - - - - - - - - - - - - - - - - - - - A F V I N D S
M. aerogenes      - - - - - - - - - - - - - - - - - - - - - - - - - - - - - - - A Y V I N D S
Chromatium        - - - - - - - - - - - - - - - - - - - - - - - - - - - - - - - A L M I T D Q
Alfalfa           A S Y K V K L V T P E G T Q E F E C P D D V Y I L D H A E E E G I V L P Y S
Spinach           A A Y K V T L V T P T G N V E F Q C P D D V Y I L D A A E E E G I D L P Y S
Scenedesmus       A T Y K V T L K T P S G D Q T I E C P D D T Y I L D A A E E A G L D L P Y S
Common
alternatives      A S Y K V T L V T P E G T Q E F E C P D D V Y I L D A A E E G L D L N Y Q
                  A                                                     H
                  T     K     K
                              S
                              D
```

Bottom block (positions 39–76; sections 4, 5, 6, 7)

```
                  4                   5                   6                   7
             9 0 1 2 3 4 5 6 7 8 9 0 1 2 3 4 5 6 7 8 9 0 1 2 3 4 5 6 7 8 9 0 1 2 3 4 5 6
Cl. pasteurianum  C - - V S C G A C A S E C P V N A I S Q G D S I F V I D A D T C I D C - G N
Cl. butyricum     C - - V S C G A C A G E C P V S A I T Q G D T Q F V I D A D T C I D C - G N
M. aerogenes      C - - I A C G A C K P E C P V N - I Q Q G - S I Y A I D A D S C I D C - G S
Chromatium        C - - I N C V C Q P E C P N G A I S Q G D E T Y V I E P S L C T E C V G H
Alfalfa           C R A G S C S S C A G K V A A G E V N Q S D G S F - L D D D Q - I E E - G W
Spinach           C R A G S C S S C A G K L K T G S L N Q D D Q S F - L D D D Q - I D E - G W
Scenedesmus       C R A G A C S S C A G K V E A G T V D S D Q S F - L D D S Q - M D G - G F
Common
alternatives      C - - G S C G A C A G E C P V G A I S Q G D S G D S F V I D A D Q C I D C - N
                  R A I A         V N     K               V N             E V           F
                        V N       E N     T S         L   T D             Q I           W
                                          T D             T               G Q           H
                                          E N                             T                S
                                                                          D
```

```
                    8                   9                   10                  11
    7 8 9 0 1 2 3 4 5 6 7 8 9 0 1 2 3 4 5 6 7 8 9 0 1 2 3 4 5 6 7 8 9 0 1 2 3 4 5
```

Clostridium pasteurianum: - - - - - - - - C A N V C P V Q E -

Clostridium butyricum: - - - - - - - - C A N V C P V G A P N Q E - - - - - - - - - - - - - - - - - -

Micrococcus aerogenes: - - - - - - - - C A S V C P V G A P N P E E D - - - - - - - - - - - - - - - -

Chromatium: Y E T S Q C V D C V E V C P I K D P S H E E - T E D E L R A K Y E R I T G E G

Alfalfa: V L T - - - - - C V A Y - A K S D V T I E T H K E E E L T A - - - - - - - - -

Spinach: V L T - - - - - C A A Y - P V S D V T I E T H K E E E L T A - - - - - - - - -

Scenedesmus: V L T - - - - - C V A Y - P T S D C T I A T H K E E D L F - - - - - - - - - -

Common alternatives: - - T - - - - - C A A V C P V G D P P T I E T - - E - - L - - - - - - - - - -
                           V L - S Q C V D   V N Y - A I S A V N Q A - H K - E E - T A K Y E R I T G E G
                           Y E   E   S   E   S   K K   C S H   E   D D R
                                             S   S   T   V P   D
                                                                                               F
```

Fig. 12. Homology in the sequence of the ferredoxins from anaerobic bacteria, photosynthetic bacteria, algae and plants as described by Dayhoff (1969).

In the figure: A = Ala; F = Phe; K = Lys; Y = Tyr; S = Ser; C = Cys; G = Gly; L = Leu; P = Pro; T = Thr; D = Asp; H = His; M = Met; Q = Gln; V = Val; E = Glu; N = Asn; R = Arg; and W = Trp.
```

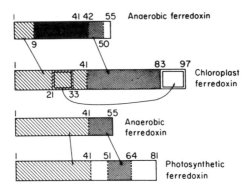

Fig. 13. Scheme for evolution of the ferredoxin gene. From Matsubara *et al.* (1968).

system (Cushman *et al.*, 1967; Katagiri *et al.*, 1968). Both this system and the adrenal steroid hydroxylating system of mammals catalyze very similar types of reactions. Like the plant ferredoxins, the putidaredoxin which has been isolated from *P. putida* is a 2 Fe–2 S²⁻ protein. Some of the general properties of the putidaredoxin are shown in Table XXII. Both this protein and adrenodoxin contain 114 amino acids and have a molecular weight of about 12,500.

TABLE XXII

Some Physicochemical Properties of Putidaredoxin

Property	Value
Molecular weight	12,500[a]
λ_{max} (oxidized form); ϵ_{mM}	280 nm; 22.5 mM^{-1} cm^{-1}[a]
	325 nm; 15.0 mM^{-1} cm^{-1}
	415 nm; 10.0 mM^{-1} cm^{-1}
	455 nm; 9.6 mM^{-1} cm^{-1}
λ_{max} (reduced form); ϵ_{mM}	545 nm; 5.0 mM^{-1} cm^{-1}[a]
Moles Fe and S²⁻ per mole protein	2, replaceable with ³³S, ⁷⁷Se, ⁸⁰Se, and ⁵⁷Fe[b]
Number of electrons accepted per mole of protein	1[a]
EPR spectra (reduced form)	$g = 1.94$[a]
Total amino acids	114[c]
Mössbauer spectra	Determined
ENDOR spectra	Determined

[a] Gunsalus *et al.*, 1971–1972.
[b] Tsibris *et al.*, 1968.
[c] Tsai *et al.*, 1971.

B. Function of Putidaredoxin

This iron–sulfur protein acts as a redox protein in a methylene hydroxylating system present in the aerobic *P. putida* (Katagiri *et al.*, 1968). It catalyzes the reaction shown in Fig. 1 in Chapter 8 of Volume I of this treatise.

C. Amino Acid Composition

A report on the amino acid composition of very highly purified putidaredoxin from *P. putida* has appeared (Tsai *et al.*, 1971). The molecules of amino acid per molecule of protein reported is shown in Table XXIII. Our laboratory has only run an analysis of a 24-hour hydrolysate which agrees fairly well with the reported results if one takes into account the residues which are hydrolyzed with difficulty. For example, six cysteine residues per mole of protein were found by both groups. If one adopts the value reported by Tsai *et al.*, there are fourteen aspartic acid residues and twelve glutamic acid residues, giving a total of 26 acidic

TABLE XXIII
AMINO ACID COMPOSITION OF PUTIDAREDOXIN

Amino acid	Residues per mole protein	
Lysine	3	3
Histidine	2	2
Arginine	5	5
Aspartic acid	14	13
Threonine	5	5
Serine	7	7
Glutamic acid	12	10
Proline	4	4
Glycine	9	8
Alanine	10	9
Cysteine	6	6
Valine	15	14
Methionine	3	3
Isoleucine	6	6
Leucine	7	6
Tyrosine	3	3
Phenylalanine	2	1
Tryptophan	1	1
Total number of amino acids	114[a]	106[b]

[a] Tsai *et al.*, 1971.
[b] From Tanaka *et al.*, 1973c.

groups. There are five arginine, three lysine, and two histidine residues yielding ten basic groups. Therefore, the net charge is -7 which accounts for the strong affinity of putidaredoxin for DEAE cellulose and for its acidic isoelectric point. Putidaredoxin contains a high content of hydrophilic amino acids, especially alanine and valine. If the analogy from the bacterial ferredoxin is applied to putidaredoxin, one of the three tyrosine residues present in the protein is involved in the electron transfer process.

D. Primary Structure of Putidaredoxin

A very preliminary sequence of putidaredoxin was published by Tsai et al. (1971). In order to complete the sequence, our laboratory together with Dr. Gunsalus's group at the University of Illinois are jointly attempting to complete the sequence of putidaredoxin. Our preliminary data which are not included here make it appear very likely that the primary structures of adrenodoxin and putidaredoxin are homologous as reported by Tsai et al. (1971). Both laboratories agree that putidaredoxin is a single polypeptide chain protein.

E. Chelate Structure of Putidaredoxin

The chelate structure of the putidaredoxin is thought to be very similar to the chelate structure of the chloroplast ferredoxins and adrenodoxin (Eaton et al., 1971). Thus, the active site proposed for the chloroplast ferredoxins would apply equally well here. A number of analogues have been prepared by replacing the sulfide with various S and Se isotopes, and replacing the iron with ^{57}Fe to yield stable derivatives. Various physicochemical studies have been made on these derivatives to aid in determining the structure of the active site of this iron–sulfur protein (Tsibris et al., 1968). Recent studies have led to the conclusion that the two iron atoms exist in nonequivalent binding sites and are present as two high-spin ferric atoms in the oxidized protein and as a high-spin ferric and high-spin ferrous atom following one electron reduction (Gunsalus et al., 1971/1972).

VI. ADRENODOXIN AND TESTERODOXIN

A. Introduction

This type of iron–sulfur protein was isolated by two groups almost simultaneously (Kimura, 1968; Omura et al., 1966). There is a review

TABLE XXIV

SOME PHYSICOCHEMICAL PROPERTIES OF BOVINE ADRENODOXIN[a]

Property	Value
Molecular weight	11,400[a]
	12,638[b]
Sedimentation coefficient	1.55 S
Diffusion coefficient	11×10^{-7} cm^2 sec^{-1}
Partial specific volume	0.70 ± 0.01 cm^3
Moles of iron per mole of protein	2
Moles of sulfide per mole of protein	2
λ_{max} (oxidized form) (in nm)	455$_{(m)}$, 414$_{(m)}$, 518$_{(s)}$, 320$_{(m)}$, 276$_{(m)}$, 265$_{(m)}$, 259$_{(m)}$, 283$_{(s)}$, and 253$_{(s)}$
Molecular extinction coefficient at 276 nm	13×10^3 cm^{-1} M^{-1}
λ_{max} (reduced form)	540 nm
ESR spectrum of reduced form	$g = 1.94$
Magnetic susceptibility	
(a) Oxidized form	Diamagnetic
(b) Reduced form	—
E_0	−60 mV (pH 7.4 and 26°C)
Moles of reducing equivalents per mole of protein	1

[a] Kimura, 1968.
[b] Tanaka et al., 1973a.

article by Kimura (1968) on the properties of adrenodoxin, but much of the data presented were preliminary in nature and have now been more accurately determined. These properties are summarized in Table XXIV. Kimura (1968) reported a molecular weight of 11,400, but this value appears to be low. The molecular weight calculated from the total amino acid residues (sequence studies show that there are 114 amino acid residues) in addition to 2 gm atoms of iron and 2 gm atoms of sulfide yield a calculated molecular weight of 12,638 daltons. It is fairly certain that the adrenodoxin like the plant ferredoxins, algal ferredoxins, and putidaredoxin contain 2 gm atoms of iron and the corresponding amount of sulfide.

It appears that the purification procedure previously reported by Kimura (1968) and by Omura et al. (1966) yielded impure adrenodoxin. In these studies, the absorbance ratio at 414/276 nm was reported to be 0.76. However, examination of the carboxymethylcysteine derivatives of adrenodoxin of this purity by disk electrophoresis has always shown as many as four components. The presence of these multiple components could be due to the presence of isozymes or to the presence of impurities. This question appears to have been resolved. Suhara et al. (1972) have recently isolated bovine adrenodoxin with a 414/276 nm ratio of 0.86, and these preparations showed a single band by disk electrophoretic analyses. In addition, our laboratory has separated some of the protein fractions and has determined the NH_2-terminal sequence. The multiple amino acid phenylthiohydantoins isolated at each step of the Edman degradation show that impurities are present. How much the impurities have interfered in the physicochemical studies of adrenodoxin cannot be said with certainty at the present time.

B. Biological Function

The function of adrenodoxin has been elaborated mainly by the studies of Kimura (1968) and by Omura et al. (1966). In general, adrenodoxin is a component of a steroid hydroxylation system which carries out the reaction shown in Fig. 10 in Chapter 7 of Volume I of this treatise. The system is known to be required for steroid 11β-hydroxylation as well as in the 22, 21, 20, 18, and 17 positions. Kimura (1968) investigated the specificity of adrenodoxin in this reaction. Although the testes and ovary iron–sulfur proteins are active, spinach ferredoxin, fatty acid desaturase from Euglena, the Pseudomonas rubredoxin and putidaredoxin are all inactive. Recently, Kimura has reported evidence that a tyrosine residue, most probably at position 82. is involved in the redox reaction of adrenodoxin (1968).

C. Amino Acid Composition of Bovine Adrenodoxin

Kimura (1968) gave a preliminary amino acid composition of bovine adrenodoxin. The amino acid composition differs slightly from the values obtained in our laboratory (Table XXV). The purified carboxymethylcysteine derivative was used in our experiments. The values are in agreement with the primary structure which was determined (Tanaka et al., 1973a). Adrenodoxin does not contain any tryptophan residues and contains only one tryosine residue which Kimura and Ting (1971) claim is essential for activity. The protein contains five cysteine residues of which four are chelated to iron. The methionine content of the protein is also in agreement with the fact that cyanogen bromide cleavage yields four peptide fragments which have been isolated in a pure form (Tanaka et al., 1973a). Adrenodoxin contains eighteen aspartic and eleven glutamic acid residues yielding twenty-nine acidic residues. However, eleven of these acidic residues are present as amides (seven asparagines and four glutamines). The protein contains twelve basic residues (five lysines, three histidines, and four arginines). The difference between the acidic

TABLE XXV

AMINO ACID COMPOSITION OF BOVINE ADRENODOXIN

Amino acid	Residues per mole protein	
	a	b
Lysine	5	5
Histidine	3	3
Arginine	3	4
NH$_3$	6	11
Aspartic acid	14	18
Threonine	7	10
Serine	6	7
Glutamic acid	10	11
Proline	1	1
Glycine	7	8
Alanine	6	7
Cysteine	4	5
Valine	5	7
Methionine	1	3
Isoleucine	7	8
Leucine	9	12
Tyrosine	1–2	1
Phenylalanine	3	4
Tryptophan	0	0
Total number of residues	∼100	114

^{a} Kimura, 1969.
^{b} Tanaka et al., 1973a.

and basic residues is 6, which accounts for the affinity of adrenodoxin for DEAE cellulose. The amino acid content of the porcine adrenodoxin has been determined and is quite similar to the bovine adrenodoxin (Cammack et al., 1971b).

D. Primary Structure

The bovine adrenodoxin is the first mammalian iron–sulfur protein whose sequence has been determined. The molecule is made up of 114 amino acids in the form of a single polypeptide chain as shown in Fig. 14. Our first reported sequence was in error, and in the original sequence, residues 78, 79, and 80 (Asx-Glx-Leu) should be deleted.* The peptides were obviously not pure and further purification has led to the corrected sequence. The five cysteine residues are present in positions 46, 52, 55,

* Asx, aspartic acid or asparagine; Glx, glutamic acid or glutamine.

92 and 95. It is not known at the present time which of the five are chelated to the iron.

E. Distribution of Types of Residues in Bovine Adrenodoxin

Without crystal X-ray data, a fair assumption is that hydrophobic residues are in the protein core while the ionic residues are mainly on the surface of the protein. Figure 15 shows the distribution of the hydrophobic residues in bovine adrenodoxin using the previously discussed classification of amino acids. Thus, there are two sections in the molecule where there are four hydrophobic residues in a row (residues 32–34 and 42–45), one section with three hydrophobic residues in a row (residues 57–59), and fourteen sections where there are two hydrophobic residues adjacent to one another (residues 11–12, 25–26, 29–30, 32–33, 50–51, 63–64 69–70, 77–78, 80–81, 83–84, 90–91, 99–100, 107–108, and 110–111). There are eleven additional hydrophobic residues scattered throughout the molecule adjacent to neutral or hydrophilic residues. The ionic amino acids in general are scattered throughout the molecule, although there are several regions where there are two charged amino acids in a row (e.g., 5–6, 14–15, 65–66, 73–74, 86–87). In addition, there is a cluster of negative charges in the NH_2-terminal end of the adrenodoxin molecule (residues 5–17, 22–31, 60–68, 86–89). This distribution is different from that observed in ferredoxins.

F. Chelate Structure of Adrenodoxin

Kimura (1968), Johnson et al. (1971), and Eaton et al. (1971) have attempted to elucidate the chelate structure of adrenodoxin. The current model is discussed in Chapter 8 of this volume. In addition, there may

1   10   20
Ser -Ser -Ser -Gln -Asp- Lys - Ile -Thr-Val-His -Phe - Ile -Asn- Arg-Asp-Gly -Glu -Thr- Leu-Thr-Thr-

                             30   40
Lys-Gly -Lys - Ile -Gly -Asp-Ser -Leu- Leu-Asp-Val -Val -Val -Gln -Asn-Asn-Leu-Asp- Ile -Asp-Gly -

                             50   60
Phe-Gly -Ala -Cys-Glu -Gly -Thr-Leu-Ala -Cys-Ser -Thr-Cys-His -Leu- Ile - Phe-Glu -Gln-His - Ile -

                             70   80
Phe-Glu -Lys-Leu-Glu -Ala - Ile - Thr-Asn-Glu -Glu -Asn-Asn-Met-Leu-Asp-Leu-Ala -Tyr-Gly-Leu-

                             90   100
Thr-Asp-Arg-Ser -Arg-Leu-Gly -Cys-Gln - Ile - Cys-Leu-Thr-Lys-Ala -Met-Asp-Asn-Met-Thr-Val-

                  110   114
Arg-Val -Pro-Asp-Ala -Val -Ser -Asp-Ala

Fig. 14. The primary structure of bovine adrenodoxin as proposed by Tanaka et al. (1973a).

Residue	1	2	3	4	5	6	7	8	9	10	11	12
	N	N	N	N	-	+	H	N	H	+	H	H

	13	14	15	16	17	18	19	20	21	22	23	24
	N	+	-	H	-	N	N	N	N	+	H	+

	25	26	27	28	29	30	31	32	33	34	35	36
	H	H	-	N	H	H	-	H	H	H	N	N

	37	38	39	40	41	42	43	44	45	46	47	48
	N	H	-	H	-	H	H	H	H	N	-	H

	49	50	51	52	53	54	55	56	57	58	59	60
	N	H	H	N	N	N	N	+	H	H	H	-

	61	62	63	64	65	66	67	68	69	70	71	72
	N	+	H	H	-	+	H	-	H	H	N	N

	73	74	75	76	77	78	79	80	81	82	83	84
	-	-	N	N	H	H	-	H	H	N	H	H

	85	86	87	88	89	90	91	92	93	94	95	96
	N	-	+	N	+	H	H	N	N	H	N	H

	97	98	99	100	101	102	103	104	105	106	107	108
	N	+	H	H	-	N	H	N	H	+	H	H

	109	110	111	112	113	114
	-	H	H	N	-	H

Fig. 15. Distribution of types in bovine adrenodoxin. N, H, −, and + stands, respectively, for neutral, hydrophobic, acidic, and basic residues.

be a tyrosine residue (residue 82) in contact with the iron–sulfur cluster according to the proposal by Kimura and Ting (1971) and by the analogy pointed out between bacterial ferredoxins and adrenodoxin by Adman et al. (1973).

VII. HIGH-POTENTIAL IRON PROTEIN (HIPIP)

A. Introduction

This iron–sulfur protein is present in some photosynthetic bacteria. Its presence has been shown in *Chromatium* D (Bartsch, 1963), *Rhodopseudomonas gelatinosa*, *Rhodospirillum spheroides*, *Rhodospirillum capulatus*, and *Rhodopseudomonas palustrus* (DeKlerk and Kamen, 1966). Of these proteins, the protein from *Chromatium* D has been investigated the most thoroughly. These proteins contain 4 Fe–4 S^{2-} per molecule of protein, and their most characteristic feature is their positive redox potential of about +350 mV (Bartsch, 1963). Some of the general

TABLE XXVI

SOME PHYSICOCHEMICAL PROPERTIES OF SOME HIGH-POTENTIAL IRON PROTEINS

Property	Value	
	Chromatium[a]	Rhodopseudomonas
Molecular weight	$10,000^a$	$10,000^b$
E^0	$+330$–350 mV[c]	$+330$ mV
Moles of Fe and S^{2-} per mole	4	4
Reducing equivalents	2	—
Absorption maxima		
(a) Oxidized form	450, 375, 325, and 283 nm	—
(b) Reduced form	388 and 283 nm	—
Molecular extinction coefficient		
at 375 nm	$20,000$ M^{-1} cm^{-1}	—
CD spectrum	Determined	—
ESR spectra		
(a) Oxidized form	$g = 2.12$, $g = 2.04^d$	—
(b) Reduced form	No signal	—
Reducing equivalents	1^d	—
Magnetic susceptibility	Determined[e]	—
Mössbauer spectra	Determined[f,g]	—
Total amino acids	92	90
Total cysteine residues	4	4

[a] Dus et. al., 1967.
[b] Flatmark and Dus, 1969.
[c] Mayhew et al., 1969.
[d] Palmer et al., 1966.
[e] Ehrenberg and Kamen, 1965; Evans et al., 1970.
[f] Bearden et al., 1965.
[g] Moss et al., 1968.

properties of the HIPIP are shown in Table XXVI. In addition, one of the unusual features of this protein is that it is isolated in the reduced form. The iron can be oxidized by ferricyanide (Mayhew et al., 1969) and reduced by dithionite.

B. Function of HIPIP

There is no known function for the high-potential protein at the present time (Bearden et al., 1965).

C. Amino Acid Composition of HIPIP

The amino acid composition of HIPIP from Chromatium D and Rhodo-spirillum gelatinosa have been determined (Table XXVII) (Dus et al.,

1967). According to the amino acid analyses, the total amino acid content of these single polypeptide chain proteins is about 90–92. As far as the iron binding sites are concerned, there are four cysteine residues. The *Chromatium* HIPIP contains all of the naturally occurring amino acids (Table XXVII) but has a very high content of alanine. The amino acid content appears to have a great effect on the oxidation–reduction potential of the iron–sulfur proteins, since the crystal X-ray data indicate that the active site of HIPIP is very similar to one of the active sites of the bacterial ferredoxin. Yet one has a redox potential of about —420 mV (ferredoxin), and the HIPIP has a redox potential of about +350 mV.

D. Primary Structure of HIPIP

Only one protein of this class has been sequenced completely. Dus *et al.* (1967) have completed the amino acid sequence of the *Chromatium* D protein (Fig. 16). The molecule is a single polypeptide chain with a

TABLE XXVII

AMINO ACID COMPOSITION OF THE HIGH-POTENTIAL IRON PROTEINS[a]

Amino acids	*Chromatium* strain D	*R. gelatinosa* strain ATCC-11169
Lysine	7	11
Histidine	1	1
Arginine	2	0
Cysteic acid	4	4
Aspartic acid	8	7
Asparagine	3	2
Methionine sulfone	1	0
Threonine	4	1
Serine	4	5
Glutamic acid	6	2
Glutamine	4	4
Proline	5	4
Glycine	6	10
Alanine	20	19
Valine	3	7
Isoleucine	2	0
Leucine	5	4
Tyrosine	2	3
Phenylalanine	2	4
Tryptophan	3	2
Total	92	90

[a] From Dus *et al.*, 1967.

　　　　　　　　KERRY T. YASUNOBU AND MASARU TANAKA

<pre>
      1   10
 ₂HN-Ser -Ala -Pro-Ala -Asn-Ala -Val -Ala -Ala -Asp-Asn-Ala -Thr-Ala - Ile - Ala -Leu-Lys-

         20   30
    Tyr-Asn-Gln -Asp-Ala -Thr-Lys-Ser -Glu -Arg-Val -Ala -Ala -Ala -Arg-Pro-Gly -Leu-

           40   50
    Pro-Pro-Glu -Glu -Gln -His -Cys-Ala -Asp-Cys-Gln -Phe-Met-Gln -Ala -Asx-Ala -Ala -

              60   70
    Gly -Ala -Thr-Asp-Glu -Trp-Lys-Gly -Cys-Gln -Leu-Phe-Pro-Gly -Lys-Leu - Ile -Asn-

                80   86
    Val -Asn-Gly -Trp (Cys, Ala) Ala -Ser -Trp-Thr-Leu-Lys-Ala -Gly -COOH
</pre>

Fig. 16. The amino acid sequence of the high-potential iron protein.

<pre>
 1   2   3   4   5   6   7   8   9 10 11 12 13 14 15 16 17 18 19 20 21 22 23
 N   H   H   H   N   H   H   H   H   -   N   H   N   H   H   H   H   +   N   N   N   -   H

24 25 26 27 28 29 30 31 32 33 34 35 36 37 38 39 40 41 42 43 44 45 46
 N   +   N   -   +   H   H   H   H   +   H   H   H   H   H   -   -   N   +   N   H   -   N

47 48 49 50 51 52 53 54 55 56 57 58 59 60 61 62 63 64 65 66 67 68 69
 N   H   H   N   H   -   H   H   H   H   N   -   -   H   +   H   N   N   H   H   H   H   +

70 71 72 73 74 75 76 77 78 79 80 81 82 83 84 85 86
 H   H   N   H   N   H   H   N   H   H   N   H   N   H   +   H   H
</pre>

Fig. 17. Distribution of the various amino acid residues in HIPIP. In the figure, N, H, — and + refer to neutral, hydrophobic, acidic, and basic residues, respectively.

NH_2-terminal serine residue and a COOH-terminal glycine residue. The important cysteine residues are situated at positions 43, 46, 61, and 70 and are chelated to iron. The distribution of the different types of residues in the HIPIP is shown in Fig. 17 and Table XXVIII. There is one portion in the molecule where there are five hydrophobic residues in a row (residues 34–38). There are two portions in the molecule where there are four hydrophobic residues adjacent to one another (residues 6–9 and 14–17). There are two places in the molecule where there are three hydrophobic

TABLE XXVIII

TOTAL NUMBER OF DIFFERENT TYPES OF RESIDUES
IN THE CHROMATIUM HIPIP

Number of residues					
Hydro-phobic	Neutral	Hydro-philic	Acidic[a]	Basic[a]	Net charge
47	22	17	−10	+9	−1

[a] The total includes the NH_2 and COOH groups of NH_2- and COOH-terminal amino acids.

residues together (residues 66–68, 77–79, and 83–85). There are five positions in the molecule where there are two residues in a row (residues 3–4, 48–49, 53–54, 62–63, and 91–92). The interior of the polypeptide chain contains numerous charges. For example, 25–28, 39–42, and 57–59 are highly charged regions. Although the primary structure of the *Rhodopseudomonas* HIPIP is not yet completed, Dus *et al.* (1967) have shown that the NH_2-terminal sequence of this HIPIP was Ala-Pro-Val-Asp-Glu-Lys-Asn-Pro-Glu-(Ala, Lys, Asp)-Ala which indicates that the NH_2-terminal serine present in the *Chromatium* HIPIP is deleted in the *P. gelatinosa* protein or that the NH_2-terminal serine has been added in the *Chromatium* protein. From a comparison of the NH_2-terminal section of the two HIPIP molecules, it appears that there will be many differences in the primary structure of these two proteins.

E. Total Number of Hydrophobic, Neutral, and Hydrophilic Residues

From the published sequence data, the total of the various types of these residues was calculated. The hydrophobic residues make up 53%, the neutral residues 25%, and the hydrophilic residues 22% of the total amino acids present in the *Chromatium* HIPIP (Table XXVIII).

F. Chelate Structure of HIPIP

The investigations of the three-dimensional structure of the *Chromatium* HIPIP have been underway in the laboratory of Kraut at the University of San Diego for a number of years (Kraut *et al.*, 1968; Strahs and Kraut, 1968). According to the latest information, the continuing studies show that the binding of the 4 Fe–4 S^{2-} and four cysteine residues is almost identical to that found for one of the active sites of the *M. aerogenes* ferredoxin. It is interesting to note that the three-dimensional structure determination of the *Chromatium* HIPIP shows that there is no aromatic residue in contact with this iron–sulfur protein as observed for the *M. aerogenes* ferredoxin by Adman *et al.* (1973). Thus, the environment around the active site appears to play an important role in the redox properties of the iron–sulfur proteins.

VIII. *Euglena* IRON–SULFUR PROTEIN

A. Introduction

Nagai and Bloch (1966) have shown that photoauxotrophic *Euglena gracilis* extracts contain an enzyme system which converts a stearyl acyl carrier protein to the corresponding monounsaturated acids. Thus the function of this sytem is as a fatty acid desaturase, and the enzyme system is present in the soluble fraction of the *Euglena*. It is important to point out that *Euglena* grown heterotrophically in the dark desaturates the fatty acid CoA derivatives by the same mechanism that is widely distributed in nonphotosynthetic organisms (Nagai and Bloch, 1966). There are very few details on the properties of the iron–sulfur protein which is a component of the fatty acid acyl carrier protein desaturase system.

B. Function of the Fatty Acid Desaturase System

Nagai and Bloch (1966) were able to separate three components of the fatty acid desaturase system. The components were a NADP oxidase, a desaturase, and an iron–sulfur protein which were capable of photoreducing NADP in the presence of light and a chloroplast, like the plant ferredoxins. However, spinach ferredoxin shows a very low activity as compared to the *Euglena* iron–sulfur protein. Furthermore, the fatty acid desaturase system is quite specific for the stearyl acyl carrier protein, although it slowly turns over the palmityl acyl carrier protein.

C. Other Properties of the Iron–Sulfur Protein from the
Euglena Fatty Acid Desaturase System

It appears that the amino acid composition of the iron–sulfur protein from the fatty acid desaturase system has not been determined. Kimura has examined the iron–sulfur protein from *Euglena* as a substitute for adrenodoxin but no activity was found (Kimura, 1968). Nagai and Bloch have also demonstrated that spinach extracts also contain the fatty acid desaturase system and therefore probably contain the *Euglena*-type iron–sulfur protein as well as ferredoxin.

IX. *Azotobacter* IRON–SULFUR PROTEINS I, II, AND III

A. Introduction

The presence of iron–sulfur proteins I and II was demonstrated both by Shethna *et al.* (1964, 1966, 1968) and by Bulen and LeComte (1966). Iron–sulfur protein III was isolated by Shethna (1970), and the same protein or one very similar to it was isolated by Yoch *et al.* (1969), al-

TABLE XXIX
SOME OF THE PHYSICOCHEMICAL PROPERTIES OF THE *Azotobacter*
IRON–SULFUR PROTEIN III

Property	Value[a]
Molecular weight	$13,000 \mp 1000$
Partial specific volume	0.684 cm^3
Iron and S^{2-}/mole	6–7
Absorptivity at 400 nm	
(a) Oxidized	4500 M^{-1} cm^{-1}
(b) Reduced	4000 M^{-1} cm^{-1}
EPR parameters	
(a) Oxidized	$s_m = 2.01; g_m = 2.00; s_m = 1.975$
(b) Reduced	$s_m = 2.03; g_m = 2.01; s_m = 2.00$

[a] Shethna, 1970.

though there was a disagreement concerning the molecular weight for iron–sulfur protein III. Some of the properties of the various iron–sulfur proteins from *Azotobacter vinelandii* are summarized in Table XXIX.

B. Function of the Azotobacter Iron–Sulfur Proteins I–III

Azotobacter vinelandii is a nitrogen-fixing organism, and it is possible that some of the iron–sulfur proteins are involved in nitrogen fixation. Bulen and LeComte (1966) call iron–sulfur proteins I and II, nitrogenase fractions I and II. However, Dervartanian *et al.* (1969) reported that the functions of iron–sulfur proteins I and II are unknown. Yoch *et al.* (1970) have shown that the third iron–sulfur protein has many ferredoxin-like properties, including the ability to photoreduce NADP in the presence of chloroplasts and the ability to transfer electrons to the *Azotobacter* nitrogenase.

C. Amino Acid Composition

Yoch *et al.* (1969) have determined the amino acid composition of the *Azotobacter* ferredoxin (iron–sulfur protein III). In addition, Shethna (1970) has determined the amino acid composition of the iron–sulfur protein I. The reported values of these two iron–sulfur proteins are shown in Table XXX. These proteins are not like some of the other iron–sulfur proteins which lack certain amino acids found naturally.

TABLE XXX

AMINO ACID COMPOSITION OF *Azotobacter* IRON–SULFUR PROTEINS I AND III

Amino acid	Iron–sulfur protein I (moles/mole)[a]	Iron–sulfur protein III	
		Moles/20,000 gm[b]	Protein moles/ 13,000 gm protein[c]
Lysine	8	8	6
Histidine	4	3	2
Arginine	7	2	1
Tryptophan	3	1	1
Aspartic acid	15	19	13
Threonine	8	9	6
Serine	6	6	4
Glutamic acid	24	43	28
Proline	12	8	5
Glycine	16	6	4
Alanine	24	14	9
Cysteine	5–6	6	4
Valine	12	14	9
Methionine	3	2	1
Isoleucine	9	10	6
Leucine	15	11	7
Tyrosine	6	3	2
Phenylalanine	4	6	4
Total residues	181–182	171	112

[a] Dervartanian *et al.*, 1969.
[b] Yoch *et al.*, 1969.
[c] Shethna, 1970.

X. IRON–SULFUR PROTEIN FROM COMPLEX III OF MITOCHONDRIA

A. Introduction

Owing to the pioneering efforts of Green (1956) and Beinert (1965), it was realized that the mitochondria contained greater amounts of non-heme iron than heme iron. Utilizing chiefly EPR measurements, Rieske *et al.* (1964a,b) showed that complex III from bovine heart mitochondria contained an iron–sulfur protein with a g value of 1.90. The possible site of action of the iron–sulfur protein was probed by the use of inhibitors. Detailed chemical analyses have not been performed on this mitochondrial iron–sulfur protein.

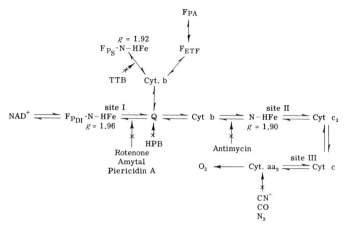

Fig. 18. The proposed function of the iron-sulfur protein in complex III in mitochondria.

B. Function

The general outline for the scheme of electron transport in the mitochondria and the oxidative phosphorylation sites is shown in Fig. 18 (Lardy and Ferguson, 1969). In the scheme, the role of the iron–sulfur protein under discussion is shown to be between cytochrome b and cytochrome c_1. However, Yamashita and Racker (1968), using purified succinic dehydrogenase, cytochrome b, cytochrome c_1, and cytochrome oxidase, showed that oxidation of succinate proceeded at a normal rate in the absence of the iron–sulfur protein. From their studies, these investigators suggested that the iron–sulfur protein present in complex III may be required not for the oxidation of succinate but for the formation of ATP from ADP and P_i. However, since their reconstituted system did not carry out phosphorylation concomitantly with oxidation, the exact role of the iron–sulfur protein is still in doubt.

XI. *Clostridium pasteurianum* NITROGENASE

A. Introduction

Mortenson (1966) and co-workers (Jeng *et al.*, 1969) have purified the nitrogenase present in *C. pasteurianum*. Two protein components were separated and purified which Mortenson calls azoferredoxin and molybdoferredoxin. Mortenson and co-workers have obtained in pure form both components of nitrogenase. Hardy *et al.* (1965) have also isolated an iron–sulfur protein from nitrogen-fixing *C. pasteurianum* and brought it to a homogeneous state.

B. Function

The function of nitrogenase is covered in a detailed review article by Hardy and Burns (1968). In general, the enzyme converts N_2 to ammonia through a complex series of reactions. In addition, it shows a reduced donor, ATP, metal and electron acceptor requirement and produces oxidized donor, $ADP + P_i = H^+$, H_2, and reduced substrates. The exact mechanism of action of nitrogenase is not understood at the present time, but a theoretical mechanism is given in Fig. 1 in Chapter 3 by Hardy and Burns in Volume I of this treatise.

XII. *Bacillus polymyxa* FERREDOXIN AND THE BACTEROID IRON–SULFUR PROTEIN

Introduction

Two similar iron–sulfur proteins have been isolated from the *Bacillus polymyxa* strain Hino (Shethna, 1970) and from a bacteroid which was originally *Rhizobium japonicum* (Koch *et al.*, 1970). The former is a facultative organism capable of fixing nitrogen under anaerobic conditions. The latter grows symbiotically with the soy bean. The molecular weight of the *Bacillus polymyxa* ferredoxin is reported to be (Table XXXI) about 8100 (Shethna, 1970), while the bacteroid iron–sulfur protein is reported to be 8300 (Koch *et al.*, 1970). Both proteins are reported to contain three molecules of Fe and sulfide per molecule of protein. The *Bacillus polymyxa* ferredoxin shows an optical spectrum (maximum at 372 nm) and a temperature sensitive EPR signal with a g value of 1.94. The protein is reduced by hydrogen and hydrogenase from *C. pasteurianum*. The bacteroid iron–sulfur protein is reported to be inac-

TABLE XXXI

SOME PHYSICOCHEMICAL PROPERTIES OF THE *Bacillus polymyxa* FERREDOXIN

Property	Values[a]
Molecular weight	8,800
Moles Fe and S^{2-} per mole of protein	4
Oxidation–reduction potential	−390 mV
Absorption maxima	280 and 390 nm
Reducing equivalents	1

[a] Yoch and Valentine, 1972.

TABLE XXXII

AMINO ACID COMPOSITION OF *Bacillus polymyxa* FERREDOXIN[a]

Amino acid	Amino acid residues per molecule	
	From analysis	Nearest integer
Lysine	3.25	3
Histidine	0	0
Arginine	1.25	1
Tryptophan	—	—
Aspartic acid	16.00	16
Threonine	5.74	6
Serine	3.10	3
Glutamic acid	8.00	8
Proline	4.12	4
Glycine	6.60	7
Alanine	10.90	11
Half-cystine	4.10	4
Valine	1.95	2
Methionine	0	0
Isoleucine	7.19	7
Leucine	3.48	3–4
Tyrosine	0.57	0–1
Phenylalanine	2.09	2
Total residues		77–79
Nonheme iron		4
Acid-labile sulfide		4

[a] From Yoch and Valentine, 1972.

tive in the phosphoroclastic cleavage of pyruvate and in the light-dependent reduction of NADP. However, this protein is required for nitrogen fixation by partially purified extracts of the bacteroid. Obviously, further studies are needed to define the properties, especially of the bacteroid iron–sulfur protein. The amino acid composition of the *B. polymyxa* ferredoxin is shown in Table XXXII.

XIII. CLASS II IRON–SULFUR PROTEINS, FLAVODOXIN, IMMUNOCHEMISTRY, AND SYNTHESIS OF IRON–SULFUR PROTEINS

A. Rubredoxin

1. INTRODUCTION

Two types of rubredoxin have been shown to exist in nature. One type is called the clostridial or anaerobic type of rubredoxin. This type is

TABLE XXXIII

Physicochemical Properties of Rubredoxin

	Rubredoxin	
Property	Aerobic type[a]	Anaerobic type[b]
Molecular weight	20,000	6000
Mole Fe/mole protein	1-2	1
Absorption maxima		
(a) Oxidized state	497, 380, and 280 nm	490, 380, 280, 560 (s), 350 (s)
(b) Reduced state	—	330, 310, 275 nm
Oxidation–reduction potential	—	−0.06 mV
ESR spectrum	$g = 4.3, 9.0$	$g = 4.3$ and 9.4
NMR spectrum	—	Determined
Magnetic susceptibility		
(a) Oxidized form	—	High-spin iron[c]
(b) Reduced form	—	High-spin iron[c]
Mössbauer	—	High-spin iron[c]
Ligand field spectrum	—	6250 cm^{-1}(m)
ORD and CD spectrum	—	Determined

[a] Lode and Coon, 1971.
[b] McCarthy, 1972.
[c] Phillips et al., 1970.

present in many of the anaerobes which contain ferredoxin. Section XVI summarizes some of the microorganisms which have been shown to contain anaerobic rubredoxin. The other type is found in the aerobic bacterium, Pseudomonas oleovorans. Some of the characteristic physicochemical properties of the rubredoxins are summarized in Table XXXIII.

Rubredoxin was first observed in C. pasteurianum by Buchanan et al. (1963) and by Mortenson (1964). In 1965, Lovenberg and Sobel purified and crystallized the C. pasteurianum rubredoxin and determined the basic properties of the molecule. Since that time, numerous investigators have isolated rubredoxin from different species of bacteria (see the Appendix).

Recently, Peterson et al. (1966) have isolated another type of iron–sulfur protein from the aerobic bacterium, Pseudomonas oleovorans, which has characteristics similar to rubredoxins isolated from anaerobic bacteria. It is a single polypeptide chain which chelates iron, contains no sulfide, and exhibits a visible and ultraviolet absorption spectrum similar to rubredoxin from anaerobic bacteria. However, it has a molecular weight which is three times that of the rubredoxins from anaerobic bacteria, and it has the potential of chelating two molecules of Fe per molecule (Lode and Coon, 1971).

2. FUNCTION OF RUBREDOXIN

There is no known role for the rubredoxin present in anaerobic bacteria. However, rubredoxin can substitute for ferredoxins in a variety of electron transfer reactions (Lovenberg and Sobel, 1965; Mayhew and Peel, 1966) but at a much lower activity, since most ferredoxin reactions are low-potential reactions considerably below the redox potential of rubredoxin (Lovenberg and Sobel, 1965). Rubredoxin can be chemically reduced by agents such as sodium hydrosulfite or can be coupled to biological reducing systems such as the hydrogen-hydrogenase system or the ferredoxin:NADP oxidoreductase reaction system of spinach (Lovenberg and Sobel, 1965; Mayhew and Peel, 1966; Lovenberg, 1972).

On the other hand, the role of rubredoxin in *Pseudomonas oleovorans* is well documented. It has been shown that rubredoxin is a component of a redox system which is required for the ω-hydroxylation of fatty acids and hydrocarbons (Peterson *et al.*, 1966, 1967; Kusunose *et al.*, 1964a,b; Baptist *et al.*, 1963; Gholson *et al.*, 1963; Lode and Coon, 1971). Figure 1 in Chapter 6 of Volume I illustrates the reaction pathway and the role of rubredoxin in the ω-hydroxylation system.

3. AMINO ACID COMPOSITION OF THE VARIOUS RUBREDOXINS

The amino acid composition of several rubredoxins has been determined, and the values are summarized in Table XXXIV. The reported values for the *M. aerogenes, P. elsdenii,* and *C. pasteurianum* are in agreement with the total residues proposed from the amino acid sequence data, while the values for the other species must be considered as approximations because of the presence of impurities or the lack of time course studies.

The most characteristic feature of the amino acid composition is the presence of four cysteine residues in the anaerobic type and ten cysteine residues in the aerobic type of rubredoxin. Another characteristic trait is the presence of one tryptophan residue in the anaerobic type of rubredoxin. In keeping with the observed acid isoelectric point of rubredoxin, there is an excess of aspartic and glutamic acids over the total residues of lysine (Table XXXIV). The anaerobic type of rubredoxin contains no histidine and no arginine residues. It is interesting to note the presence of three tyrosine residues in all the anaerobic rubredoxins thus far analyzed. All the rubredoxins of the anaerobic type contain 6–7 aromatic amino acids.

The aerobic type of rubredoxin contains all of the known amino acids and has a high content of hydrophobic amino acids as does the anaerobic type.

TABLE XXXIV

COMPARISONS OF AMINO ACID COMPOSITIONS OF RUBREDOXINS FROM
DIFFERENT BACTERIA

Type of amino acid	P. o.[a] an-aerobe	C. p.[b] an-aerobe	P. e.[c] an-aerobe	M. a.[d] an-aerobe	M. l.[e] an-aerobe	D. g.[f] an-aerobe	D. d.[g] an-aerobe
Asp	19	11	10	8	5	8	7
Thr	12	3	2	2	1	2	2
Ser	12	0	1	1	1	4	2
Glu	18	6	3	8	7	5	8
Pro	13	5	2	4	3	5	6–7
Gly	15	6	5	5	5	6	6
Ala	12	0	7	3	2	5	6
Cys	10	4	4	4	4	4	4
Val	10	5	3	4	8	4	5
Met	1	1	2	1	2	1	1
Ile	6	2	2	1	1	3	2
Leu	11	1	1	3	1	2	0
Tyr	8	3	3	3	3	3	3
Phe	4	2	2	3	2	3	3
Lys	10	4	4	2	4	5	4
His	4	0	0	0	0	0	0
Arg	3	0	0	0	0	0	0
Trp	6	1	1	1	2	1	1
Total	174	54	52	53	51	61	60–61

[a] Benson et al., 1971.
[b] McCarthy and Lovenberg, 1972.
[c] Bachmayer et al., 1968b.
[d] Bachmayer et al., 1967.
[e] Lovenberg, 1966.
[f] Laishley et al., 1969.
[g] Newman and Postgate, 1968.

4. PRIMARY STRUCTURES

The amino acid sequence of the *M. aerogenes, P. elsdenii*, and the *C. pasteurianum* rubredoxins has been determined. The primary structure of the *P. oleovorans* rubredoxin is nearly completed. The sequences of the anaerobic type of rubredoxin are summarized in Fig. 19. The partial amino acid sequence of the *P. oleovorans* rubredoxin is shown in Fig. 20.

A consideration of the primary structure of the anaerobic type of rubredoxin discloses a number of constant features. For this comparison, the active site, cysteine residues, and the five buried aromatic residues are aligned. The matching of residues in this manner causes or necessi-

<pre>
                         5   10   15
C. P.   f-Met-Lys-Lys-Tyr-Thr-Cys-Thr-Val -Cys-Gly -Tyr - Ile -Tyr-Asp-Pro-Glu -Asp-
P. E.   Met-Asp-Lys-Tyr-Glu-Cys- Ser - Ile - Cys-Gly -Tyr - Ile -Tyr-Asp-Glu -Ala -Glu -
M. A.   Met-Gln -Lys-Phe-Glu -Cys-Thr-Leu-Cys-Gly -Tyr - Ile -Tyr-Asp-Pro-Ala -Leu-

            20   25   30
Gly -Asp-Pro-Asp-Asp-Gly -Val -Asn-Pro-Gly -Thr-Asp-Phe-Lys-Asp - Ile -Pro-
Gly -Asp----- Asp-Gly -Asn-Val -Ala -Ala -Gly -Thr-Lys-Phe-Ala -Asp-Leu-Pro-
Val -Gly -Pro-Asp-Thr-Pro-Asp-Gln -Asp-Gly------Ala-Phe-Glu -Asp-Val -Ser -

   35   40   45   50
Asp-Asp-Trp-Val -Cys-Pro-Leu-Cys-Gly -Val -Gly -Lys-Asp-Glu -Phe-Glu -Glu -
Ala -Asp-Trp-Val -Cys-Pro-Thr-Cys-Gly -Ala -Asp-Lys-Asp-Ala -Phe-Val -Lys-
Glu -Asn-Trp-Val -Cys-Pro-Leu-Cys-Gly -Ala -Gly -Lys-Glu -Asp-Phe-Glu -Val -

       54
Val -Glu -Glu -COOH
Met-Asp-COOH
Tyr-Glu -Asp-COOH
</pre>

Fig. 19. The primary structures of the rubredoxin present in anaerobic bacteria. In the figure, f stands for formyl.

tates the insertion of deletions in certain rubredoxins, but this is a common practice among structural evolutionists.

McCarthy and Lovenberg (1970) noted that the NH_2-terminal group of NH_2-terminal methionine residue of the *C. pasteurianum* rubredoxin was formylated. However, examination of the NH_2-terminal peptide of the

<pre>
   1   10   20
H₂N-Ala -Ser -Tyr-Lys-Cys-Pro-Asp-Cys-Asn-Tyr-Val -Tyr-Asp-Glu -Ser -Ala -Gly -Asn-Val -His -
                         30   40
Glu -Gly -Phe-Ser -Pro-Gly -Thr-Pro-Trp-His - Leu - Ile -Pro-Glu -Asp-Trp-Asp-Cys-Pro-Cys-
                         50   60
Cys-Ala -Val -Arg-Asp-Lys-Leu-Asp-Phe-Met-Leu - Ile -Glu -Ser -Gly -Val -Gly -Glu -Lys-Gly-
                         70   80
Val -Thr-Ser -Thr-His -Thr-Ser -Pro-Asn-Leu-Ser -Glu -Val -Ser -Gly -Thr-Ser -Leu-Thr-Ala -
                         90   100
Glu -Ala -Val -Val -Ala -Pro-Thr-Ser -Leu-Glu -Lys-Leu-Pro-Ser -Ala -Asp-Val -Lys-Gly -Gln -
                         110   120
Asp-Leu-Tyr-Lys-Thr-Glu -Pro-Pro-Arg-Ser -Asp-Ala -Glu -Gly -Gly -Lys-Ala -Tyr-Leu-Lys-
                         130   140
Trp - Ile -Cys - Ile -Thr-Cys-Gly -His - Ile -Tyr -Asp-Trp-Glu -Ala -Leu-Gly -Asp-Glu -Ala -Glu -
                         150   160
Gly -Phe-Thr-Pro-Gly -Thr-Arg-Phe-Glu -Asp- Ile - Pro-Asp-Trp-Asp-Cys-Cys-Trp-Cys (Asx,
                         170   174
Pro) Gly -Ala - Thr-Lys-Glu -Asn-Tyr-Val -Leu-Tyr-Glu -Glu -Lys-COOH
</pre>

Fig. 20. The primary structure of the rubredoxin from *P. oleovorans*.

tryptic peptide, Met-Gln-Lys, from *M. aerogenes* by the same techniques used in the work with the *C. pasteurianum* ferredoxin disclosed that the NH$_2$-terminal residue of this protein was not formylated. Since the formyl group is not essential for function, further discussion on this topic is not warranted here.

5. Types of Residues in the Various Rubredoxins

The rubredoxins are all single polypeptide chain molecules. All of the anaerobic rubredoxins contain either a formylmethionine or methionine as the NH$_2$-terminal amino acid. The rubredoxin from *P. oleovorans* contains an NH$_2$-terminal alanine residue. The anaerobic type of rubredoxin contains 52–54 amino acids, while the *P. oleovorans* rubredoxin contains 174 amino acid residues. The anaerobic type of rubredoxin contains 42–48% hydrophobic residues, 19–25% neutral residues, and 28–37% hydrophilic residues. The similar values for the *P. oleovorans* rubredoxin are 45, 27, and 28%, respectively (Table XXXV). All of the rubredoxin molecules contain an excess of negatively charged amino acids with a net charge varying from −11 to −15 (Table XXXV).

6. Constant Residues

From a comparison of a protein from various species, the residues that remain constant may aid in determining the essential parts of the molecule. With this goal in mind, the constant residues in the three bacterial rubredoxins which have been sequenced thus far were compared. The Met-1 remains constant, although it is not clear yet whether the rubredoxins from the three species all contain formylated methionine. However, the formyl group appears to play no important role. Lysine-3 is constant although it is unknown what the role of the lysine is in the tertiary structure. Cysteine-6, -9, -39, and -42 remain constant because they are involved in the chelation of the iron. It is not known why the protein portion from residue 10–15 is constant. However, Tyr-11 is the only tyrosine residue which is on the surface of the rubredoxin molecule. All of the remaining aromatic residues are buried in the hydrophobic core of the protein. The reason why aspartic acidic residues 15 and 21 are constant is unknown. Phenylalanine-30 may be constant because it forms a π-bond with the aromatic residues in position 4 (Tyr or Phe). Aspartic acid-32 and Trp-37 are also constant for unknown reasons. The Trp-37 is buried in the center of the protein obviously not forming any type of bond with any of the other amino acid residues. The portion of the molecule with the sequence Val-Cys-Pro (residues 38–40) is also found in the ferredoxins isolated from anaerobes, and in the case of the ferre-

TABLE XXXV

DISTRIBUTION OF DIFFERENT TYPES OF RESIDUES IN THE RUBREDOXIN MOLECULES

Rubredoxin	Residues					Net charge	Total
	Hydrophobic	Neutral	Hydrophilic	Acidic	Basic		
C. pasteurianum	23 (43%)[a]	11 (20%)	20 (37%)	17[b]	5[c]	−12	54
P. elsdenii	25 (48%)	11 (21%)	16 (31%)	13	5	−8	52
M. aerogenes	25 (47%)	13 (25%)	15 (28%)	14	3	−11	53
P. oleovorans	78 (45%)	47 ~ 48 (27%)	48 ~ 49 (28%)	32 ~ 33	18	−14 ~ −15	174

[a] Percent of a particular type of residue in the total protein.
[b] Includes the —COOH group of the COOH-terminal amino acid.
[c] Includes the —NH_2 group of the NH_2-terminal amino acid.

doxins, its function is to provide a hydrophobic environment for the active site and a similar function may be cited for residues 38–40 in the rubredoxin molecules. The sequence Cys-Gly-Ala-Val (residues 42–45) is also present in the anaerobic ferredoxins. In both the ferredoxins and rubredoxins, they provide a hydrophobic active site while the glycine is necessary to get the proper bend of the polypeptide chain. Phenylalanine-49 is constant for some unknown reason and is buried in the interior of the molecule. Further insight into the constant residue can be obtained by further viewing of the three-dimensional structure of rubredoxin from the set of coordinates obtained from Jensen and computerized for visual display by Richard Feldman with the help of Lovenberg and Eaton at the National Institutes of Health. The constant regions among the three clostridial types of rubredoxin seem to occur more toward the NH$_2$-terminal portion (residues 1–15) and from residue 30–43.

There are additional constant regions if one considers the type of residue under consideration. For example, at position 4, either tyrosine or phenylalanine is present, indicating the necessity for an aromatic residue. At positions 8 and 33, either Val, Ile, or Leu are present, fulfilling the need for a hydrophobic branched chain amino acid. Similar reasoning can be used to explain either Val or Ala in position 44. At position 47, either Asp or Glu is present and it may be that an acidic amino acid is required. The constant regions then extend from residues 1–15 and from residue 30–49 although some drastic changes occur in portions of the above-mentioned regions such as change of a charged or a basic amino acid to a noncharged amino acid.

7. Sequence Homology of the Clostridial and P. oleovorans Rubredoxins

The clostridial type of rubredoxin is found in anaerobic bacteria. The *P. oleovorans* rubredoxin is present in an aerobic microorganism. Thus, no sequence homology was expected. However, when the sequences of the two rubredoxins were compared, a very interesting homology was observed. Residues 1–54 and 119–174 of the *P. oleovorans* rubredoxin showed sequences which were homologous with the anaerobic type of rubredoxin (Fig. 21). This of course meant that within the *P. oleovorans* rubredoxin itself, there were two homologous sections. Such internal duplication is thought to occur by a process of gene duplication.

In Table XXXVI the number of residues are given which are identical when the various rubredoxins are compared with one another. In the comparisons, the alignment discussed previously was used where the aromatic and cysteine residues are in identical positions. This alignment necessi-

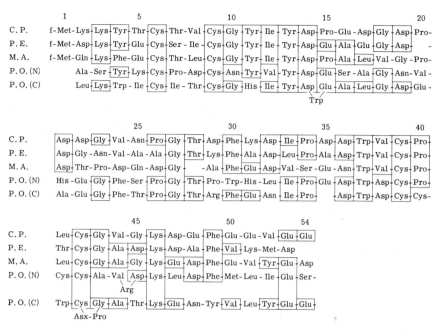

Fig. 21. The homology in the primary structures of the anaerobic, and aerobic rubredoxin molecules. In the figure, P. E., M. A., P. O. (N), and P. O. (C) stand for *P. elsdenii, M. aerogenes,* residues 1–59 in the *P. oleovorans* rubredoxin molecule, and residues 119–174 in the *P. oleovorans* rubredoxin molecule, respectively.

tated the insertion of gaps in the *M. aerogenes* and the *P. elsdenii* rubredoxins and the incorporation of gaps and insertions in the *P. oleovorans* rubredoxin.

TABLE XXXVI

COMPARISON OF THE NUMBER OF INVARIANT RESIDUES IN DIFFERENT RUBREDOXINS[a,b]

	C. P.	P. E.	M. A.	P. O. (N)	P. O. (C)
C. P.	—	29	28	22	24
P. E.	—	—	24	19	23
M. A.	—	—	—	15	21
P. O. (N)	—	—	—	—	22
P. O. (C)	—	—	—	—	—

[a] From McCarthy, 1972.

[b] The symbols are C. P., *C. pasteurianum;* P. E., *P. elsdenii;* M. A., *M. aerogenes;* N, the amino-terminal half; and C, the carboxyl-terminal half of *P. oleovorans* rubredoxin.

8. X-Ray Crystallographic Studies of Rubredoxin

Herriott *et al.*, 1970, have solved the three-dimensional structure of the *C. pasteurianum* rubredoxin. The rubredoxin molecule is a single polypeptide chain consisting of 54 amino acid residues. In the unit cell, nine molecules are packed together in a hexagonal array. Each molecule of rubredoxin is spherical with a diameter of about 20 Å.

Like the other proteins whose structure has been resolved by X-ray diffraction techniques, the residues located on the surface are mainly ionic and those in the interior of the molecule are hydrophobic. The active site which consists of iron attached to the four cysteinyl residues has a roughly tetrahedral structure and is located near the surface of the molecule (see Chapter 4 of this volume). This situation is quite different in the ferredoxin molecule where the active site is buried in the interior of the molecule. The peptide backbone structure of the *C. pasteurianum* rubredoxin is shown in Fig. 16 in Chapter 4 of this volume. The NH_2- and COOH-terminal portions of the protein in the figure are shown at the bottom right portion of the molecule. The two chains proceed upward toward the active site. The polypeptide chain then curves to the left to form a loop. The chain then curves back toward the active site and then downward toward the portion of the molecule containing the NH_2-terminal end of the molecule. No α-helix is present in the rubredoxin molecule. However, there are two sections which exist as antiparallel-chain pleated sheet structures. One section involves a part of the molecule where the NH_2 terminal, COOH terminal, and a portion of the polypeptide chain immediately NH_2 terminal of the active site are adjacent to one another. The other portion of the molecule where the antiparallel-chain pleated is present in the far end of the loop itself.

An interesting feature of the rubredoxin molecule is the fact that five of the six aromatic residues are buried in the hydrophobic core of the protein. The only aromatic residue which is situated on the outside of the protein is tyrosine-11. The sole tryptophan is located in position 40 and is buried in the hydrophobic core of the rubredoxin molecule. There is no evidence that it is interacting in any way with other amino acid side chains. In all of the rubredoxins, there is a tyrosine or phenylalanine in position 4 from the NH_2-terminal end of the polypeptide chain. In the core of the protein, this aromatic residue is π-bonded to the phenylalanine present in position 30 since the X-ray diffraction studies indicate that the two benzene rings of the two aromatic residues are parallel to one another and in close proximity.

Other interesting features of the rubredoxin molecule which emerge from the X-ray diffraction studies include possible hydrogen bonding of threonine-28 with tyrosine at position 13. Also lysine-46 appears to form an internal salt bond with the aspartic acid present in position 36. Many other interesting structural details can be observed in the rubredoxin structure which is computerized at the National Institutes of Health by Feldman *et al.* (1972). The structure may be viewed on a television screen and the information can be transferred to a tape which will then print out the structure of the rubredoxin molecule.

B. Flavodoxin

1. INTRODUCTION

Although the flavodoxins are not iron–sulfur proteins, they are found in the same anaerobic bacteria which contain ferredoxin and rubredoxin. Thus, for evolutionary studies, flavodoxin is the third protein which can be sequenced and studied. A comparison of the sequences of the ferredoxin, rubredoxin, and flaxodoxin from the same bacteria will allow an evaluation of the evolutionary and genetic data obtained from any single protein.

Flavodoxin, a FMN protein, was initially isolated in crystalline form from *Clostridium pasteurianum* (Knight *et al.*, 1966; Knight and Hardy, 1966). These investigators demonstrated that flavodoxin was produced by *C. pasteurianum* when the iron content in the growth medium was low. Furthermore, it was shown that flavodoxin could replace ferredoxin in certain reactions normally involving ferredoxin. Since the original isolation of flavodoxin from *C. pasteurianum*, the protein has been isolated in pure form from *Desulfovibrio gigas* (Dubourdieu and LeGall, 1970), *Peptostreptococcus elsdenii* (Mayhew *et al.*, 1969), *Desulfovibrio vulgaris* (Dubourdieu and LeGall, 1970), and *Clostridium* MP (Mayhew, 1971).

2. PRIMARY STRUCTURE

The amino acid composition of the flavodoxins from various sources have been determined, and the data are summarized in Table XXXVII. All of the flavodoxins are single polypeptide chain proteins with 137–151–152 amino acids. Other than the histidine residue which is lacking in all but the *D. vulgaris* protein and the lack of cysteine residues at least in the *C. pasteurianum* and *P. elsdenii* flavodoxins, they contain all of the amino acids which are normally found in proteins. However, they are acidic proteins like the rubredoxins and ferredoxins.

TABLE XXXVII
AMINO ACID COMPOSITION OF VARIOUS FLAVODOXINS

Amino acid	Residues per mole of protein				
	C. P.[a]	C. MP.[b]	P. E.[c]	D. G.[d]	D. V.[e]
Lysine	10	10	9	8	4
Arginine	2	2	2	3	6
Histidine	0	0	0	0	1
Aspartic acid	18	17	15	17	20
Threonine	4	5	8	9	6
Serine	14	8	7	8	7
Glutamic acid	19	21	17	18	17
Proline	4	4	5	6	4
Glycine	17	14	14	14–15	19
Alanine	14	6	18	15	18
Cysteine	1	3	2	5	5
Valine	15	10	13	16	10
Methionine	4	5	5	2	0
Leucine	12	8	7	14	13
Isoleucine	5	15	5	5	9
Phenylalanine	3	5	4	3	6
Tyrosine	2	3	2	5	5
Tryptophan	4	4	4	1	1–2
Total amino acids	148	140	137	149–150	151–152

[a] Knight and Hardy, 1967.
[b] Mayhew and Massey, 1969.
[c] Tanaka et al., 1971a.
[d] Dubourdieu and LeGall, 1970.
[e] Dubourdieu and LeGall, 1970.

3. SEQUENCE STUDIES ON THE FLAVODOXIN MOLECULES
   FROM VARIOUS SOURCES

The primary structure of the *P. elsdenii* flavodoxin has been completed (Tanaka *et al.*, 1973d). The primary structure of the *C. pasteurianum* flavodoxin is nearing completion (Fox and Brown, 1971; Tanaka *et al.*, 1971c). Sequence studies are in progress in our laboratory on the *Clostridium* MP flavodoxin (Tanaka *et al.*, 1972b). The partial sequences of the various flavodoxin molecules are shown in Fig. 22. It is obvious that many more flavodoxins will have to be sequenced to obtain evolutionary and genetic data about these microorganisms.

P. E.   Met-   -Val -Glu - Ile - Val -Tyr-Trp-Ser -Gly -Thr-Gly -Asn-Thr-Glu -Ala -Met-Ala -
C. P.   Met-Lys-Val -Asn- Ile - Ile - Tyr-Trp-Ser -Gly -Thr-Gly -Asn-Thr-Glu -Ala -Met-Ala -
C. MP.   Met-Lys-   -   - Ile -Val -Tyr-Trp-Ser -Gly -Thr-Gly -Asn-Thr-Glu -Lys-Met-Ala -

P. E.   Asn-Glu - Ile   Glu -Ala -Ala -Val -Lys-Ala -Ala -Gly -Ala -Asp-Val -Glu -Ser -Val -Arg-
C. P.   Lys-Leu- Ile - Ala -Glu -Gly -Ala -Gln -Glu -Lys-Gly -Ala -Glu -Val -Lys-Leu-Leu-Asn-
C. MP.   Glu -Leu-Ile -Ala - Lys -Gly - Ile - Ile-Glu- Ser -Gly -Lys-Asp-Val -Asn-Thr- Ile -Asn-

P. E.   Phe-Glu -Asp-Thr-Asn-Val -Asp-Asp-Val -Ala -Ser - Lys-Asp-Val - Ile - Leu-Leu-Gly -
C. P.   Val -Ser (Asp, Ala)Lys-Glu -Asp-Asp-Val - Lys-Glu -Ala -Asp-Val -Val- Ala -Phe-Gly -
C. MP.   Val- Ser -Asp-Val-Asn- Ile -Asp-Glu -Leu-Leu-Asn-Glu -Asp- Ile -Leu- Ile -Leu-Gly -

P. E.   Cys-Pro-Ala -Met-Gly -Ser -Glu -Glu -Leu-Glu -Asp-Ser -Val -Val -Glu -Pro-Phe-Phe-
C. P.   Ser -Pro-Ser -Met-Gly -Ser -Glu -Val (Ser, Gln, Glu, Glu, Pro, Met)Phe-Leu-Asp-Val -

P. E.   Thr-Asp-Leu-Ala - Pro-Lys-Gly - Lys-Lys-Leu-Lys-Val -Gly - Leu-Phe-Gly -Ser -Tyr-
C. P.   Val -Ser -Ser - Ile - Val -Thr-Gly - Lys-Lys-   -   -   -   -   -   -   -   -   -

P. E.   Gly -Trp-Gly -Ser -Gly -Glu -Trp-Met-Asp-Ala -Trp-Lys-Gln -Arg-Thr-Glu -Asp-Thr-

P. E.   Gly -Ala -Thr-Val - Ile - Gly -Thr-Ala - Ile - Val -Asn-Glu -Met-Pro-Asp-Asn-Ala -Pro-

P. E.   Glu -Cys-Lys-Glu -Leu-Gly -Glu -Ala -Ala -Ala -Lys-Ala -COOH

Fig. 22. The partial structures of flavodoxin isolated from anaerobic bacteria. In the figure, P. E., C. P., and C. MP. stand for *P. elsdenii, C. pasteurianum,* and *Clostridium* MP, respectively.

4. X-Ray Studies of Flavodoxin

Two groups have made considerable progress on the three-dimensional structure of the flavodoxin. Jensen's group at the University of Washington has obtained the data on the *D. vulgaris* flavodoxin and Ludwig's group at the University of Michigan is in the midst of solving the three-dimensional structure of the *Clostridium* MP flavodoxin. Once the X-ray data become resolved at a high level, it will be possible to investigate structure-function relationships.

C. Chemical Synthesis of Iron–Sulfur Proteins

1. Ferredoxins

Bayer and Hagenmaier (1968) reported on the synthesis of the *C. pasteurianum* ferredoxin by the Merrifield (1969) solid phase synthesis procedure. However, the chemically synthesized product showed little if any biological activity after addition of iron and sulfide to the apoprotein.

2. RUBREDOXIN

Yasunobu and Hagemaier (1972) synthesized the *M. aerogenes* and *C. pasteurianum* rubredoxin molecules by the Merrifield procedure (1969). The iron reconstituted aporubredoxins showed about 5–7% of the activity of the natural proteins in the NADP:ferredoxin reductase–cytochrome c assay. However, the control experiments of the effect of HF on the *C. pasteurianum* aporubredoxin showed that very little of the natural analogue could be reactivated with iron. Thus, the observed activity of 5–7% will be much higher if corrections are made for the inactivation of the aporubredoxin by HF.

D. Immunochemistry of the Iron–Sulfur Proteins

1. FERREDOXIN

Hong and Rabinowitz (1970) obtained antibodies to both the *C. acidi-urici* native and apoproteins. The investigators studied the cross reactivity of the *C. acidi-urici* antiferredoxin with the *C. pasteurianum* ferredoxin and could find no cross reaction. The reactions were studied by both the quantitative precipitin and complement fixation tests.

2. RUBREDOXIN

Yasunobu and Lovenberg (1973) injected the *C. pasteurianum* rubredoxin into goats and obtained antisera to rubredoxin. It was estimated that about 5 mg of anti-rubredoxin antisera was produced per ml of serum by the quantitative precipitin test. The reaction of the *C. pasteurianum* antirubredoxin with the *P. elsdenii, C. pasteurianum, M. aerogenes,* and *P. oleovorans* rubredoxin molecules were investigated by the quantitative precipitin test. The only protein producing a precipitate was the *C. pasteurianum* rubredoxin and aporubredoxin. The anti-rubredoxin was purified by affinity chromatography on columns of *C. pasteurianum* rubredoxin-sepharose. The purified antibody was coupled to sepharose, and it was shown that soluble antigen–antibody complexes are formed with all of the other rubredoxin molecules. Further evidence for the formation of soluble complexes was obtained by the fact that the antibody inhibited the activity of the various rubredoxin molecules in the NADPH:ferredoxin reductase–cytochrome c assay.

XIV. EVOLUTION

The topic of "protein evolution" has been a subject of a number of books and review articles. The reader is referred to the texts on this topic by Anfinsen (1959), Dayhoff (1969), Feeney and Allison (1969), Bryson and Vogel (1965), Florkin (1964), Watson (1965), and Woese (1967). Excellent reviews include articles by Zukerkandl and Pauling (1962) on the hemoglobins and myoglobins, Dixon (1966), Margoliash and Smith (1965) on cytochrome c, and Lennox and Cohen (1967) on the immunoglobulins.

A. Methods for the Determination of the Gene for the Iron–Sulfur Proteins

There are numerous approaches to the problem. One approach would include the isolation of the gene and the messenger RNA and a sequence study of the nucleic acids. However, this approach is not possible at the present time owing to experimental difficulties.

A second approach would involve the isolation of the DNA from the bacteria under consideration followed by annealing experiments. This involves the specific hydrogen bonding or "complementariness" of bases over larger or smaller lengths of DNA. One determines how readily the DNA's from organisms occupying different positions in the taxonomic scale form double helices, and by determining the melting point, one can determine the relatedness of the organisms. Although this method is rapid, it is not as quantitative as other methods described here.

Another possible approach is to isolate the work out the structure of the messenger RNA which has a complimentary structure to the DNA. Again, this is not a good approach at the present time because of the low steady-state concentration of the RNA and the difficulties in purifying it.

The mechanism of protein synthesis was first postulated by Crick (1958), where the control of protein synthesis occurs from the DNA via mRNA to the protein. This theory was subsequently verified by the studies on tryptophan synthetase locus of *E. coli* (Yanofsky *et al.*, 1964), and at the head protein locus in the T4 bacteriophages (Sarabhai *et al.*, 1964). In addition, the colinearity of the genetic elements and the amino acid sequences have been demonstrated by the use of polynucleotides of defined sequence as templates in cell-free systems (Nishimura *et al.*, 1965). Advantage is taken of the fact that proteins are considered the primary products of the genetic process and that at present it is possible to predict the nucleotide sequence of the gene from the knowledge of the protein sequence. The possible sources of difficulty include such things as degeneracy of the codons (Crick, 1963) and reading errors. Nevertheless, since there is no way at the present time to obtain samples of the predecessors of the living species which existed millions or billions of years ago, protein evolutionists treat the protein sequence and the gene as though they are synonymous.

B. Mechanism of Protein Evolution

In the studies to be discussed, it should be kept in mind that the two fundamental interacting processes in evolution are mutation and natural selection as espoused by Darwin (1859). The effect of mutation is an alteration in the DNA base sequence of the gene which results in proteins of altered sequence and can lead to different genotypes. Natural selection then allows for the survival of an organism with a phenotype which is best able to adapt to the environment. For further details, one should consult for example, the text by Eaton (1970) on the effects of natural selection.

C. Types of DNA Mutations

The types of mutation and the resulting changes in protein have been summarized by Dixon (1966) and are (1) point mutation involving a single base replacement and a substitution of one amino acid for another in the protein, (2) addition of a single base resulting in a frame shift mutation and an alteration in the amino acid sequence, (3) deletion of single base resulting in frame shift mutant, again with an alteration in the amino acid sequence, (4) inversion of a base sequence within a portion of gene resulting in an altered sequence, (5) duplication of a base sequence which is intracistronic and which can be recognized by a repeating amino acid sequence, and (6) gene duplication where the entire sequence of a smaller protein is repeated in a single protein molecule. During the examination of the primary structures of the iron–sulfur proteins, we have attempted to detect the mutations which are listed above.

D. Rates of Mutation

Since there is no method of studying extinct organisms which existed millions to 1 billion years ago, even rough qualitative figures concerning the rates of mutation are of value in estimating the times of divergence of one species from another. Studies by Zuckerkandl and Pauling (1962) based on the difference between horse and human α-chains of hemoglobin yielded a value of 14.5×10^6 years as the average mutation rate. A similar study by Margoliash and Smith (1965) on the cytochrome c molecule have yielded a value of 22.6×10^6 years as the average period required for a single residue difference to occur in two diverging evolutionary lines. However, these numbers are useful only as rough guides, as pointed out by others, since there may have been back mutations once mutants were formed; since nothing is known about the mutational pressures which existed during various periods of evolution; and since mutations which were lethal have resulted in the obliteration of a particular species. Furthermore, it is the belief of evolutionists that single-celled organisms were the first to be evolved on the earth and that anaerobic bacteria were the next higher form of life to evolve. This was followed by the origin of photosynthetic bacteria. The point is that the bacteria are thought to have evolved very early as far as the geological time of the earth is concerned. Therefore, it was anticipated that many interesting genetic changes might occur in bacteria which would be reflected in the sequence of proteins from different bacterial species.

E. Convergent versus Divergent Evolution

When one is concerned with protein evolution, it is important to keep in mind that a similarity in two different proteins might have arisen from two different types of evolutionary mechanisms. The two possible types of evolutionary mechanisms are shown in Fig. 23. Convergent evolution results in the production of analogous proteins, while divergent evolution results in the production of homologous proteins.

F. Methods of Creating Phylogenetic Trees from Sequence Data

Two detailed efforts have been reported to create phylogenetic trees from protein sequence data of a particular protein. Fitch and Margoliash (1967) have converted the sequence into the corresponding sequence of nucleotide codons (Fig. 24) and have thus obtained the minimal base difference per codon (MBDC). Corrections are made if the protein from different species have different numbers of amino acids. A rough phylogenetic tree is created by comparing the MBDC differences between the various proteins isolated from different organisms and by selecting pairs

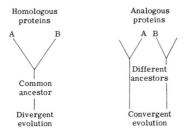

Fig. 23. Possible mechanisms for evolution.

	Asp	Cys	Thr	Phe	Glu	His	Lys	Ala	Met	Asn	Tyr	Pro	Gln	Arg	Ser	Try	Leu	Val	Ile	Gly
	A	C	E	F	G	H	I	L	M	N	O	P	Q	R	S	T	U	V	W	Y
Aspartic acid	0	2	2	2	1	1	2	1	3	1	1	2	2	2	2	3	2	1	2	1
Cysteine	2	0	2	1	3	2	3	2	3	2	1	2	3	1	1	1	2	2	2	1
Threonine	2	2	0	2	2	2	1	1	1	1	2	1	2	1	1	2	2	2	1	2
Phenylalanine	2	1	2	0	3	2	3	2	2	2	1	2	3	2	1	2	1	1	1	2
Glutamic acid	1	3	2	3	0	2	1	1	2	2	2	2	1	2	2	2	2	1	3	1
Histidine	1	2	2	2	2	0	2	2	3	1	1	1	1	1	2	3	1	2	2	2
Lysine	2	3	1	3	1	2	0	2	1	1	2	1	1	2	2	2	2	2	2	1
Alanine	1	2	1	2	1	2	2	0	2	2	2	1	2	2	1	2	2	1	2	1
Methionine	3	3	1	2	2	3	1	2	0	2	3	2	2	1	2	2	1	1	1	2
Asparagine	1	2	1	2	2	1	1	2	2	0	1	2	2	2	1	3	2	2	1	2
Tyrosine	1	1	2	1	2	1	2	2	3	1	0	2	2	2	1	2	2	2	2	2
Proline	2	2	1	2	2	1	2	1	2	2	2	0	1	1	1	2	1	2	2	2
Glutamine	2	3	2	3	1	1	1	2	2	2	2	1	0	1	2	2	1	2	3	2
Arginine	2	1	1	2	2	1	1	2	1	2	2	1	1	0	1	1	1	2	2	1
Serine	2	1	1	1	2	2	2	1	2	1	1	2	1	1	0	1	1	2	1	1
Tryptophan	3	1	2	2	2	3	2	2	2	3	2	2	1	1	1	0	1	2	3	1
Leucine	2	2	2	1	2	1	2	2	1	2	2	1	1	1	1	1	0	1	1	2
Valine	1	2	2	1	1	2	2	1	1	2	2	2	2	2	2	2	1	0	1	1
Isoleucine	2	2	1	1	3	2	2	2	1	1	2	2	3	2	1	3	1	1	0	2
Glycine	1	1	2	2	1	2	2	1	2	2	2	2	2	1	1	1	2	1	2	0

Fig. 24. The amino acid codon assignments utilized in the calculation of minimal base difference per codon.

with the lowest mutation distances. Alternative trees are tested and the tree with the lowest percent deviation is selected.

Dayhoff (1969) has used a similar method but has considered the amino acid differences instead of the codons when comparing homologous proteins from different species. The second step is similar to that used by Fitch and Margoliash (1967) and involves the use of a computer to create phylogenetic trees. The one with the lowest standard deviation is selected. In addition, Dayhoff has created an ancestral sequence after a number of sequences of a particular protein have been determined. In order to create a phylogenetic tree by this method, the sequence of a particular protein is compared with the ancestral sequence. Other methods resulting in a statistical improvement for creating phylogenetic trees are described by Dayhoff (1969). A further method for obtaining phylogenetic trees from sequence data has been published by Gibbs and McIntyre (1970). This method will be discussed in further detail later.

G. Evolutionary Time Scale

Figure 25 briefly outlines the origin and evolution of life on earth with respect to the geological time scale. According to evolutionists, it is hypothesized that the earth was created about 5 billion years ago. At the start, the earth's atmosphere was anaerobic. Gradually the earth cooled, and sometime during the first billion years, the earth's crust cooled sufficiently and a period of chemical evolution occurred. During this time period, nature was experimenting with different compounds to determine which would be used as foodstuff and for building blocks of cells. Out of this process evolved the first primordial cell, the primitive precursor to all cells present on the earth today. It is thought that the first organisms to evolve from the primordial cells were the anaerobic bacteria since the earth's atmosphere was anaerobic. Peck (1966) postulates that chemoautolithotrophs such as the sulfate reducers are among the oldest organisms present on the earth. His reasoning is based on the metabolic pattern and the $^{32}S/^{34}S$ ratio of sulfur present on the earth. Arguments are also advanced which favor the theory that the green and purple sulfur bacteria were the next to evolve and that the clostridial species evolved after the primitive photosynthetic bacteria. After this, it is postulated that the blue-green algae evolved (Cammack *et al.*, 1971a). The blue-green algae have cells which are more primitive than those of the higher algae and more like the bacteria. Craig (1971) postulates that the blue-green algae lived symbiotically with plant cells and eventually evolved into the chloroplast. There is fossil evidence that blue-green algae existed on the earth 2 billion years ago. Two important developments occurred when

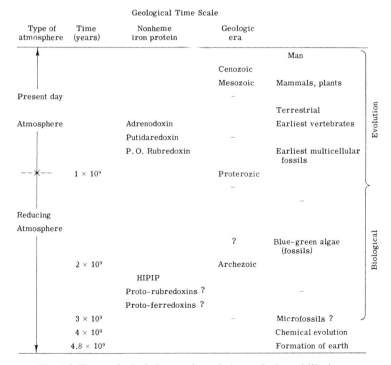

Fig. 25. The geological time scale and the evolution of life forms.

the photosynthetic machinery was developed. First of all, the solar energy was used to carry out the photolysis of water which led to evolution of the important component, oxygen. Second, carbon dioxide and water were converted to carbohydrate. Thus, two important biochemical compounds resulted from the development of the photosynthetic machinery in algae. As oxygen accumulated in the atmosphere, aerobic organisms could now evolve and utilize the carbohydrate for energy and building blocks by the well-known biochemical pathways. The precursors of the fungi and animals now evolved in this new milieu and utilized oxygen and carbohydrate. The fossils which existed at a time between 500–600 million years ago, in the Cambrian period, indicate there was a sudden development of animals with hard materials. The molluscs, brachiopods, bryozoans, corals, echinoderms, and arthropods are, therefore, known to exist at this time. The further evolution of life in the post-Cambrian periods have been well documented in numerous texts (e.g., Eaton, 1970) and need not be discussed here.

H. Evolution of Organisms Containing Iron–Sulfur Proteins

As shown in Section XVI, organisms from procaryotes to eucaryotes have been shown to contain iron–sulfur proteins. As mentioned previously, there are very few methods for obtaining evolutionary data other than that of comparing the sequence of a specific protein from numerous species. If the arguments of Eck and Dayhoff (1966) and Cammack et al. (1971a) that the ferredoxins are living fossils are correct, then the sequence studies of the ferredoxins should provide us with evolutionary data of living organisms which may have existed as far back as 3 billion years ago. Such a study would complement nicely the evolutionary data obtained from sequence comparisons of the cytochrome c (Fitch and Margoliash, 1967), the hemoglobin–myoglobin (Zuckerkandl and Pauling, 1962), and the immunoglobins (Lennox and Cohen, 1967) from diverse species.

I. General Aspects of the Evolution of Ferredoxin-Containing Anaerobic Microbes

A number of scientists have claimed that ferredoxin may be ancient protein. One of the first to make this claim was Eck and Dayhoff (1966). Based on the presence and lack of certain amino acids in ferredoxin, they postulated that ferredoxin was one of the first proteins to emerge from the primeval "soup" several billion years ago. They also postulated that there may have been a tetrapeptide precursor which somehow polymerized to give rise to ferredoxin containing about 28 amino acids. Gene duplication was proposed to give rise to a molecule double the size of the 28 amino acid intermediate. Jukes (1966) proposed a different tetra-peptide precursor with a different amino acid composition. Fitch (1966) suggested that the present day ferredoxin of about 54–56 amino acid residues arose from gene duplication. Cammack *et al.* (1971a) reconsidered the problem and outlined additional reasons for their belief that ferredoxins are indeed ancient proteins. The arguments advanced were the following. (1) Ferredoxin biosynthesis is relatively simple. Once the protein is synthesized, iron and sulfur readily fall into place in the molecule. (2) The examination of the amino acid composition of some of ferredoxins show that they contain only fourteen different amino acids, nine of which are common to all four organisms. The same nine amino acids are identical with those that are readily made in laboratory experiments that simulate conditions on primeval earth. In addition, they cite that the Murchison meteorite that fell in Australia in 1969 contained six of the nine amino acids found in the four ferredoxins mentioned above. In general, it is very difficult to appraise these proposals, but the tetrapeptide precursor hypothesis has not been accepted on the grounds that there is no sound evidence of a repeating tetrapeptide precursor when the sequences of the various ferredoxins are examined. It is also interesting to note that the *C. tartarivorum* and *C. thermosaccharolyticum* are heat-stable or thermophilic bacteria. Likewise, the ferredoxins from these microbes are largely heat resistant for 1 hour at 70°C. The question may be raised whether these heat-stable organisms are more primitive than the meso-philic bacteria of this group or vice versa. The argument might be advanced that these bacteria originated on the earth while the earth was still relatively hot and anaerobic. However, we favor the hypothesis that the heat stability is an acquired property. The bacteria, in order to survive in environments such as hot springs, mutated from the mesophilic microorganisms. This is based on the fact that the thermo-philes contain such residues as histidine and methionine which are not found in the other "anaerobic" type of ferredoxins. However, it would be desirable to obtain experimental proof for this hypothesis. In addition, the recent report by Adman *et al.* (1973) on the three-dimensional structure of the *M. aerogenes* ferredoxin by X-ray diffraction methods provides no additional evidence for the gene duplication hypothesis advanced by numerous biochemists.

J. Extraction of Specific Evolutionary Data of Anaerobic Bacteria

In the first place, a visual comparison of the amino acid sequences of the eight ferredoxins from different anaerobic bacteria (Fig. 2) shows that the sequences are homologous. Whatever differences that occur between them can be attributed to deletions, insertions, and point mutations during the evolution of the bacteria. Second, calculations of the minimum base difference per codon (MBDC) yield values which show that the sequences are homologous (Table XXXVIII). Third, the runs index obtained by the method of Gibbs and McIntyre (1970) also indicates this fact. This method is dependent upon a statistical analysis of a two-dimensional matrix which is generated by the direct comparison of two amino acid sequences. One sequence is plotted along the Y axis and the other sequence along the X axis. Whenever a column and a row contain the same amino acid, an intersect mark is made. Therefore, if two stretches of a sequence are similar, one will see a line running through the main diagonal. If a deletion or addition of an amino acid residue occurs, the line will be shifted parallel to the main diagonal. The number of contiguous matches on a diagonal is then recorded. Similarly, the number of contiguous matches expected by chance is computed and also recorded. The runs index is the log ratio of the sum of the observed lengths of run squared to the sum of the expected lengths of run squared, i.e.,

$$\log_{10} X_1 f_i \text{ (observed)}/X_1 f_i^1 \text{ (expected)}$$

where X_1 is the length of run; f_i, the frequency of this length of run; and f_i^1, the corresponding expected frequency. Comparison of the *C. pasteurianum* and *M. aerogenes* yielded a runs index of 0.673. A comparison of the *C. pasteurianum* and *P. elsdenii* ferredoxins yielded a runs index of 0.599. The comparison of the *P. elsdenii* and *M. aerogenes* ferredoxins yielded a runs index of 0.593. Further comparisons are underway at the

TABLE XXXVIII

AVERAGE MBDC VALUES OBTAINED FROM THE INTRASPECIES COMPARISON OF ANAEROBIC FERREDOXINS[a]

	C. p.	C. b.	M. a.	C. a.	C. t.	P. e.	C. Th.	D. g.
C. pasteurianum	—	0.30	0.36	0.39	0.65	0.65	0.62	1.33
C. butyricum	0.30	—	0.34	0.39	0.64	0.64	0.60	1.41
M. aerogenes	0.36	0.34	—	0.34	0.48	0.60	0.44	1.32
C. acidi-urici	0.39	0.39	0.34	—	0.54	0.68	0.51	1.32
C. tartarivorum	0.65	0.64	0.48	0.54	—	0.48	0.036	1.30
P. elsdenii	0.65	0.64	0.60	0.68	0.48	—	0.46	1.34
C. thermosaccharolyticum	0.62	0.60	0.44	0.51	0.036	0.46	—	1.30
D. gigas	1.33	1.41	1.32	1.31	1.30	1.34	1.30	—
D gigas NH_2-half (1–28)	1.00	1.07	0.92	1.07	1.00	1.11	1.00	
D. gigas COOH-half (28–55)	1.67	1.74	1.68	1.56	1.59	1.58	1.59	

[a] Average MBDC values. MBDC values from 0–0.8 usually are indicative of a common ancestor for a pair of proteins. However, other factors such as the biological activity of the proteins must be taken into consideration.

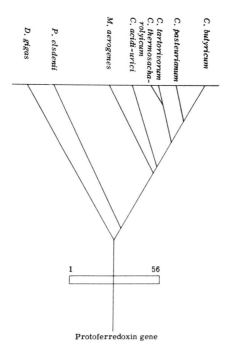

Fig. 26. The phylogenetic tree of anaerobic bacteria as deduced from the primary structures of the ferredoxins.

present so that a statistically significant phylogenetic tree can be calculated. A rough tree is shown in Fig. 26.

Gibbs and McIntyre (1970) have compared the *C. pasteurianum* sequence against itself, and the runs index obtained showed that indeed there is internal symmetry in the ferredoxin molecule, which is not surprising since visual inspection of the *C. pasteurianum* sequence also will lead one to the same conclusion. However, their cautionary note that internal symmetry does not necessarily mean that gene duplication has occurred is important. Indeed, the X-ray diffraction results show that the active site cysteine residues are distributed in such a way that it is highly unlikely that gene duplication has occurred in the ferredoxin genome.

K. Evolution of the *Desulfovibrio gigas*

This sulfate reducer was shown to be quite different from the clostridial type of ferredoxin by Travis *et al.* (1971). In contrast to the clostridial type of ferredoxin which contains eight cysteine residues, the *D. gigas* contains five cysteine residues. Four of the five cysteine residues are in analogous positions, namely, positions 8, 11, 14, and 18 and the fifth is in position 44 (provided that one counts the NH_2-terminal proline as residue 2 in order to get alignment of all the ferredoxins). In the clostridial ferredoxins, the residue equivalent to the cysteine in position 44 is in position 43. Moreover, all the "anaerobic" type of ferredoxins have aromatic residues in positions 2 and 30 (when they are aligned as shown in Fig. 1) which are in contact with the iron–sulfur cluster. However, the *D. gigas* ferredoxin contains proline and aspartic acid in these positions. Thus, at the present time, it is exceedingly difficult to say whether or not the primary structures of the *D. gigas* and clostridial type of ferredoxin are homologous and whether these bacteria have evolved from the same ancestor or whether they have undergone convergent evolution.

The comparison of the *D. gigas* ferredoxin with the other seven bacterial ferredoxins whose sequence have been determined in terms of the MBDC values is summarized in Table XXXVIII. The MBDC value obtained varied from 1.30–1.41 which does not indicate any homology, but when the NH_2-terminal halves are compared (residues 1–28) when aligned as shown in Fig. 3, the MBDC values ranged from 0.92–1.11. These values suggest that the NH_2-terminal portion of the various ferredoxin molecules have most probably arisen from the same common ancestor and that this portion of the various ferredoxin molecules are homologous. Some very interesting questions can be raised at this point. First of all, is the *D. gigas* ferredoxin more primitive than the clostridial type of ferredoxin? Second, if it is more primitive, what type of mutational pressure brought about such a drastic change in the primary structure of the clostridial ferredoxins? Third, are the active sites of the *D. gigas* and the clostridal ferredoxins identical?

L. Evolution of the Photosynthetic Bacteria

Sequence data for obtaining evolutionary information about this type of bacteria are very limited at the present time. However, from the evident homology of the *Chromatium* ferredoxin to the clostridal type of ferredoxin, Matsubara *et al.* (1968) have postulated a possible genetic mechanism which would account for the differences observed between the clostridial and *Chromatium* types of ferredoxin (Fig. 13). However, since the first proposal, Matsubara *et al.* (1970) have another proposal, one in which a genetic error has caused two changes. One of the alterations include the insertion of a nona-peptide portion (residues 42–50) and the other is a lengthening of the molecule (residues 65–81) (Fig. 27). The sequence of the *Chromatium* ferredoxin is also homologous with ferredoxin found in plants and algae *vida infra*.

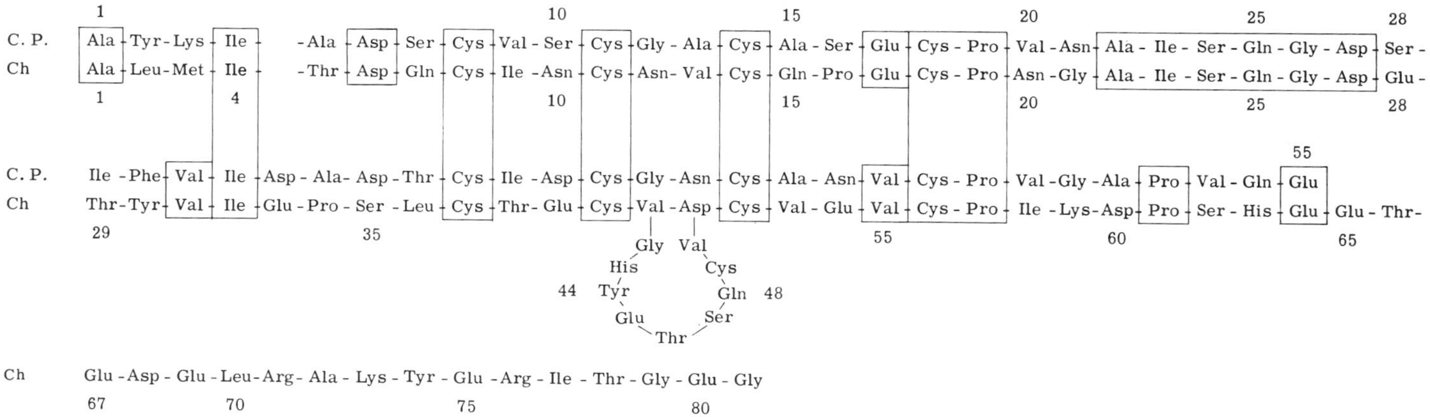

C. P.

```
           1
         ┌─────────────┐
   Ala - │ Tyr - Lys - Ile │ - Ala - ┌─────┐ ┌─ Ser - Cys ┬ Val - Ser ┬ Cys ┬ Gly - Ala ┬ Cys ┬ Ala - Ser ┬ Glu ┬ Cys - Pro ┬ Val - Asn ┬ Ala - Ile - Ser - Gln - Gly - Asp ┬ Ser -
                                      │ Asp │                                                                                                                              
```

C. P. / **Ch** ferredoxin sequence alignment

Row C.P. (positions 1–28):
1 Ala - Tyr - Lys - Ile - Ala - Asp - Ser - Cys - Val - Ser - Cys - Gly - Ala - Cys - Ala - Ser - Glu - Cys - Pro - Val - Asn - Ala - Ile - Ser - Gln - Gly - Asp - Ser - 28
(markers at 15, 20, 25, 28)

Row Ch (positions 1–28):
Ala - Leu - Met - Thr - Asp - Gln - Cys - Ile - Asn - Cys - Asn - Val - Cys - Gln - Pro - Glu - Cys - Pro - Asn - Gly - Ala - Ile - Ser - Gln - Gly - Asp - Glu - 28
(markers at 1, 4, 10, 15, 20, 25, 28)

Row C.P. (positions 29–):
Ile - Phe - Val - Ile - Asp - Ala - Asp - Thr - Cys - Ile - Asp - Cys - Gly - Asn - Cys - Ala - Asn - Val - Cys - Pro - Val - Gly - Ala - Pro - Val - Gln - Glu
(markers at 35, 55)

Row Ch (positions 29–65):
29 Thr - Tyr - Val - Ile - Glu - Pro - Ser - Leu - Cys - Thr - Glu - Cys - Val - Asp - Cys - Val - Glu - Val - Cys - Pro - Ile - Lys - Asp - Pro - Ser - His - Glu - Glu - Thr- 65
(markers at 55, 60, 65)

Circular segment (positions 44–48):
44 His - Tyr ⟋ Gly - Val ⟍ Cys
   Glu ⟋ Thr ⟍ Ser ⟍ Gln 48

Row Ch (positions 67–80):
67 Glu - Asp - Glu - Leu - Arg - Ala - Lys - Tyr - Glu - Arg - Ile - Thr - Gly - Glu - Gly 80
(markers at 70, 75, 80)

Fig. 27. The mechanism of evolution of the *Chromatium* (Ch) genome from the *C. pasteurianum* (C.P.) ferredoxin genome.

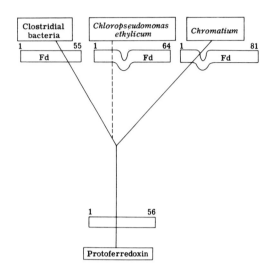

Fig. 28. The phylogenetic tree of the anaerobic and photosynthetic bacteria as deduced from the ferredoxin sequences.

Cammack *et al.* (1971a) have isolated a ferredoxin from an unidentified photosynthetic green bacteria. However, the investigations have been clouded by the fact that the culture was not pure. It appears that the photosynthetic bacteria is producing a ferredoxin which is 64 residues long. The ferredoxin appears to be an intermediate between the anaerobic or clostridial type and the photosynthetic purple bacteria (*Chromatium*). Thus, a rough evolutionary tree can be drawn up showing that a protoferredoxin was the precursor to the clostridial type of ferredoxin and to the green photosynthetic and the purple photosynthetic bacterial ferredoxins (Fig. 28).

M. Higher Algae and Plants

Thus far, five ferredoxins of this type have been sequenced. These include *Scenedesmus* (a green alga), taro (a monocot), alfalfa (a dicot), spinach (a dicot), and *Leucaena glauca* (a dicot and a tree). Rao and Matsubara (1970) and Cammack *et al.* (1971a) claim that the phylogenetic tree obtained by computerizing the sequence data resembles the tree obtained by the botanists from morphological data (Fig. 29). Thus, as in the case of cytochrome c (Fitch and Margoliash, 1967), the sequence data do indeed provide information on the evolutionary processes that have occurred since life was created on earth.

Furthermore, in the case of the ferredoxin-containing organisms, there was a primitive gene which from the start coded for a protein with about 54–56 amino acids. The gene has undergone mutations and other chromosomal-type abberations, and it has differentiated into the genes now found in the anaerobic bacteria, photosynthetic bacteria, algae, and plants (procaryotes to eucaryotes). However, the rough outlines of the genetic changes that have occurred in the ferredoxin gene during the process of evolution are evident. Numerous theories have been postulated on how the gene has changed, e.g., gene duplication, frame shift mutants, tetrapeptide precursor hypothesis, etc., which have been shown to be untenable in the light of recent research. Thus, caution should be exercised and perhaps more time should be devoted to obtaining primary structure data. Cammack *et al.* (1971a) point out that a possible explanation for the similarity in the ferredoxins might be given as follows. Namely, the blue-green algae, a procaryote, was the precursor of the chloroplast in the higher algae and plants, thus accounting for great similarity in the sequence of various algal and plant ferredoxins. No blue-green algae has been sequenced thus far, but the amino acid composition of the *Microcystis* ferredoxin has been determined, and it contains about the same number of amino acids as the green algae and the higher plants. Thus, the experimental findings are in agreement with the proposal of Craig (1971) that many millions of years ago, the blue-green algae precursor was incorporated into cells of higher algae and plants where they lived symbiotically and eventually evolved into the chloroplast.

Let us now look at the clostridial, photosynthetic, and plant (algal) evolution by comparing the ferredoxin sequences. Matsubara *et al.* (1968) claimed that all the ferredoxins have portions of the molecule which are homologous, indicating that they have all arisen from the same common ancestor (Fig. 30). The anaerobic type of ferredoxin and the photosynthetic ferredoxin were claimed to have homologous sequences

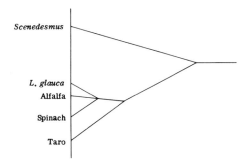

Fig. 29. The phylogenetic tree of the algae and plants as calculated from the primary structures of the ferredoxin molecules.

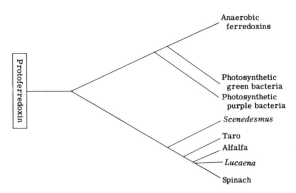

Fig. 30. The phylogenetic tree of the anaerobic bacteria, photosynthetic bacteria, plants, and algae showing the common origin from the precursor protoferredoxin.

from residues 1–41. Furthermore, residues 51–64 were considered to be homologous. There is an insertion of a decapeptide section (residues 41–51) and the lengthening of the photosynthetic ferredoxin sequence (residues 64–81) due to genetic errors and mutations. In the case of the chloroplast ferredoxin, it was proposed that residues 1–41 in the anaerobic and chloroplast ferredoxins are homologous, although residues 1–9 in the anaerobic ferredoxin somehow gave rise to residues 21–33 in the chloroplast ferredoxin. Furthermore, it is postulated that a portion of the gene coding for residues 9–50 gave rise to the portion of the gene now coding for residues 41–83, although further mutations in this section have now caused residues 41–83 in the chloroplast ferredoxin to change. Finally, they propose that the portion of the gene coding for residues 83–97 in the chloroplast ferredoxin has arisen from the portion of the gene which originally coded for residues 1–9 in the protoferredoxin gene. Eck and Dayhoff (1966) have proposed a simpler scheme which is shown in Fig. 12. In this scheme, the chloroplast ferredoxin is shown to be lengthened by 31 triplets over the gene coding for the photosynthetic (*Chromatium*) ferredoxin and the anaerobic type of ferredoxin.

Finally, Keresztes-Nagy *et al.* (1969) have proposed a 26 residue precursor of plant ferredoxin which has an Ala-Ala sequence at the NH_2-terminal position. Furthermore, these investigators have proposed that there is homology in a portion of the *C. pasteurianum* and alfalfa ferredoxins. Specifically, the comparison includes residues 9–36 of the *C. pasteurianum* ferredoxin and residues 42–69 of the alfalfa ferredoxin. All of the possible 25 residue fragments of the alfalfa and *C. pasteurianum* were compared by plotting the cumulative frequency of mutations required versus the mutations required. The plot deviated from a straight-line relationship which demonstrates that the degree of similarity of the two ferredoxins is clearly greater than would be expected on the basis of random occurrences. However, these authors were careful to point out that this observation does not necessarily mean that the plant and clostridial ferredoxins are ancestrally homologous.

N. Evolutionary Data from the HIPIP

The only protein of this type to be sequenced was the HIPIP from *Chromatium* (Dus *et al.*, 1971). HIPIP is not homologous with any of the iron–sulfur proteins isolated to date. Thus, it must be concluded that the HIPIP gene has evolved separately or, less likely, it has undergone such drastic changes that the homology is no longer evident.

O. Evolutionary Data from Putidaredoxin and Adrenodoxin

Recently, Tsai *et al.* (1971) proposed that the sequence of these two proteins were homologous. However, our laboratory and the University of Illinois group have combined forces to complete the sequence of the putidaredoxin. From the work in progress, it appears that the sequence proposed by Tsai *et al.* (1971) needs considerable revision but the sequences of putidaredoxin and adrenodoxin are homologous as pointed out by these investigators. Moreover, their biological functions are quite similar, i.e., both are components of the hydroxylating system consisting of pyridine nucleotide, a flavoprotein, an iron–sulfur protein, and a cytochrome P-450.

P. Evolutionary Aspects of the Organisms Containing Rubredoxins

The primary structures of the *M. aerogenes*, *P. elsdenii*, *C. pasteurianum*, and the *P. oleovorans* rubredoxins are nearly completed. A visual inspection of the four rubredoxins suggests that the primary structures are homologous and that all of the rubredoxins have arisen from a common ancestor (Fig. 31). In addition, McCarthy (1972) has calculated the MBDC values obtained by comparing the different rubredoxins two at a time, and the results are summarized in Table XXXIX. The MBDC values show that, indeed, the various rubredoxins are homologous. (Values below a MBDC of one usually are indicative of a lack in homology.)

McCarthy has also used another method to compare the similarity of the various rubredoxins. The sequences were compared by the procedure of Gibbs and McIntyre (1970). The runs indexes obtained for the various

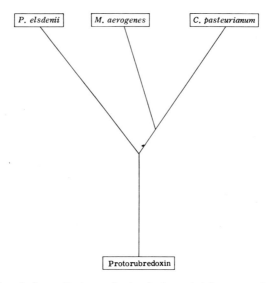

Fig. 31. The phylogenetic tree of rubredoxin-containing anaerobic microbes.

rubredoxins from different sources were between 0.462 and 0.653 as shown in Table XL. These values clearly indicate a common ancestral gene for the *C. pasteurianum, P. elsdenii,* and *M. aerogenes.* However, when the NH₂-terminal section (residues 1–54) and COOH-terminal section (residues 119–174) of the *P. oleovorans* rubredoxin are included in the comparison, and the MBDC values calculated, the results shown in Table XXXIX are obtained. These values are indicative of the fact that the portions of the various rubredoxin molecules being compared have all arisen from the same ancestral gene and that gene duplication with

TABLE XXXIX[a,b]

AVERAGE MBDC VALUES OBTAINED FROM COMPARISON OF RUBREDOXIN
AND FERREDOXIN SEQUENCES

	C. P.	P. E.	M. A.	P.O.(N)	P.O.(C)
C. P.	—	0.60 (0.65)	0.60 (0.36)	0.87	0.77
P. E.	—	—	0.67 (0.60)	0.88	0.76
M. A.	—	—	— —	1.06	0.86
P. O. (N)	—	—	— —	—	0.92
P. O. (C)	—	—	— —	—	—

[a] From K. McCarthy (1972). Ph.D. thesis. George Washington University.
[b] Ferredoxin MBDC values are in parentheses.

TABLE XL

LENGTH OF UNBROKEN RUNS OF MATCHED AMINO ACIDS AND RUNS INDEXES
OBTAINED WHEN FERREDOXINS AND RUBREDOXINS FROM *C. pasteurianum*,
P. elsdenii, AND *M. aerogenes* ARE COMPARED[a]

Comparison		0	1	2	3	4	5	6	7	Runs index
(a) Ferredoxins										
C. P./M. A.	Observed	189	14	3	3	2	0	1	0	0.673
	Random[b]	232	19.8	2.04	0.145					
C. P./P. E.	Observed	188	18	3	1	1	1	1	0	0.599
	Random	206	15.3	1.17	0.094					
P. E./M. A.	Observed	173	18	2	3	0	0	1	0	0.593
	Random	208	16.5	1.30	0.11					
(b) Rubredoxins										
C. P./M. A.	Observed	141	19	1	0	0	0	2	0	0.653
	Random	193	15	1.2	0.097					
C. P./P. E.	Observed	168	11	1	0	1	1	0	0	0.456
	Random	190	14.3	1.1	0.089					
P. E./M. A.	Observed	169	9	1	1	0	1	0	0	0.462
	Random	176	12.3	0.86	0.061					

[a] From McCarthy, 1972.

[b] The runs expected by chance when two random sequences are compared.

unequal crossing over has occurred in the *P. oleovorans*. However, runs indexes have not yet been calculated. Nevertheless, from a visual comparison of the sequences, from the MBDC values and the runs indexes, one would conclude that the data are sufficiently significant to indicate homology in the primary structures of all of the rubredoxins sequenced. At present, there is no line of symmetry apparent in rubredoxin as observed for ferredoxin.

From the phylogenetic standpoint, the MBDC and runs indexes can be used to create phylogenetic trees. An approximate phylogenetic tree is shown in Fig. 32.

Weinstein (1969) pointed out that residues 13–36 in the *M. aerogenes* rubredoxin are homologous with residues 13–36 in the spinach ferredoxin and the *Scenedesmus* ferredoxin (Fig. 33). After sequencing the *Pseudomonas oleovorans* rubredoxin in our laboratory, it came to our attention that the first four residues from the NH₂-terminal end of this protein and the first four residues of the alfalfa ferredoxin are both Ala-Ser-Tyr-Lys. We have combined our findings with observations of Weinstein. The results of our mental exercise are shown in Fig. 34 and indicate that it is possible to show some type of homology in the

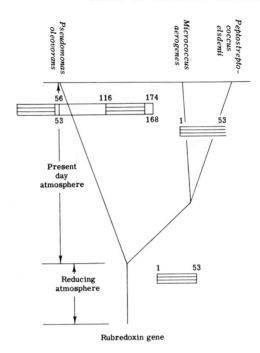

Fig. 32. The phylogenetic tree of the rubredoxin-containing organisms showing the relationship of the aerobic and anaerobic bacteria and the common origin of the various types of rubredoxin molecules.

Spinach ferredoxin (13–36) and *M. Aerogenes* rubredoxin (1–23)

Asn Val Glu *Phe* Gln *Cys* Pro Asp Asp Val *Tyr* *Ile* Leu *Asp* Ala *Ala* Glu Glu Glu *Gly* Ile *Asp* Leu *Pro*

Met Gln Lys *Phe* Glu *Cys* Thr Leu Cys Gly *Tyr* *Ile* Tyr *Asp* Pro *Ala* Leu Val   *Gly* Pro *Asp* Thr *Pro*

Base differences
 2   2   1   0   1   0   1   2   2   1   0   0   2   0   1   0   2   1   0   2   0   2   0

Minimum base differences per codon: 0.96

Scenedesmus ferredoxin (13–36) and *M. Aerogenes* rubredoxin (1–23)

Asp *Gln* Thr Ile *Glu* *Cys* Pro Asp Asp Thr *Tyr* *Ile* Leu *Asp* Ala *Ala* Glu Glu Ala *Gly* Leu *Asp* Leu *Pro*

Met *Gln* Lys Phe *Glu* *Cys* Thr Leu Cys Gly *Tyr* *Ile* Tyr *Asp* Pro *Ala* Leu Val   *Gly* Pro *Asp* Thr *Pro*

Base differences
 3   0   1   1   0   0   1   2   2   2   0   0   2   0   1   0   2   1   0   1   0   2   0

Minimum base differences per codon: 0.91

Similarities between spinach and *Scenedesmus* ferredoxins with *Micrococcus aerogenes* rubredoxin. Identical positional residues are *italic* within each peptide.

Fig. 33. Sequence homology in the *M. aerogenes* rubredoxin and the plant ferredoxins (from Weinstein, 1969).

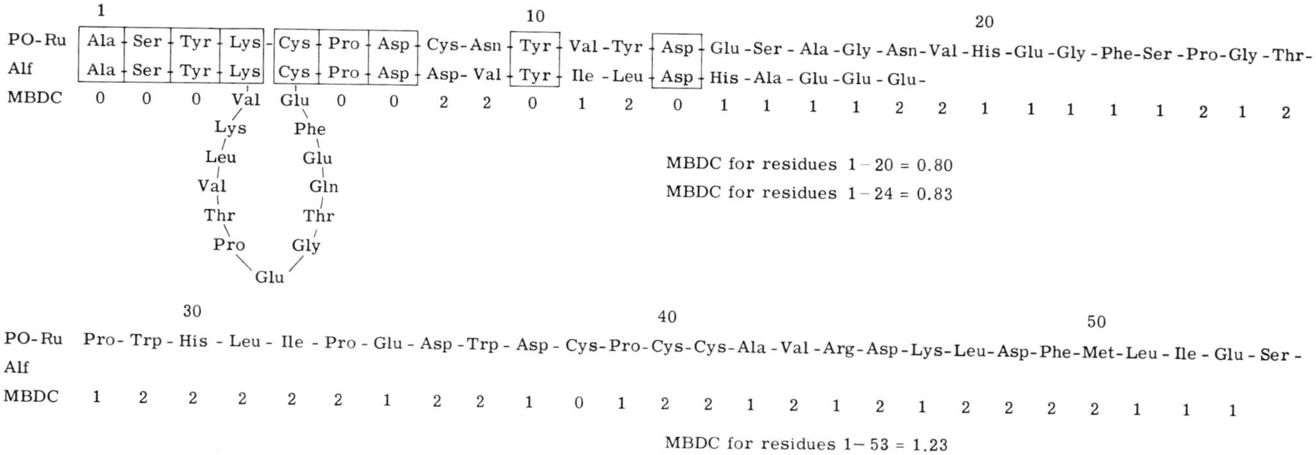

```
                    1                                              10                              20
PO-Ru   Ala–Ser–Tyr–Lys–Cys–Pro–Asp–Cys–Asn–Tyr–Val–Tyr–Asp–Glu–Ser–Ala–Gly–Asn–Val–His–Glu–Gly–Phe–Ser–Pro–Gly–Thr–
Alf     Ala–Ser–Tyr–Lys–Cys–Pro–Asp–Asp–Val–Tyr–Ile–Leu–Asp–His–Ala–Glu–Glu–Glu–
MBDC     0   0   0   0   0   0   2   2   0   1   2   0   1   1   1   1   2   1   1   1   1   1   1   2
```

MBDC for residues 1–20 = 0.80
MBDC for residues 1–24 = 0.83

(branch sequences near residue 30: Val–Lys–Leu–Val–Thr–Pro–Glu / Glu–Phe–Glu–Gln–Thr–Gly–Glu)

```
                30                               40                               50
PO-Ru   Pro–Trp–His–Leu–Ile–Pro–Glu–Asp–Trp–Asp–Cys–Pro–Cys–Cys–Ala–Val–Arg–Asp–Lys–Leu–Asp–Phe–Met–Leu–Ile–Glu–Ser–
Alf
MBDC     1   2   2   2   2   1   2   2   1   0   1   2   1   2   1   2   2   2   2   1   1   1   1
```

MBDC for residues 1–53 = 1.23

Fig. 34. Sequence homology between the *P. oleovorans* rubredoxin and plant ferredoxins.

sequences of the two proteins when residues 1–24 are compared. However, in order to obtain good homology, it is necessary to assume that in the alfalfa ferredoxin a thirteen residue section has been inserted between residues 4 and 18 or a similar section has been deleted from the *P. oleovorans* rubredoxin. With this type of juggling of the first 24 residues, an MBDC value of 0.83 is obtained. This is slightly high but is statistically significant. We earlier reported on the homology between the *P. oleovorans* rubredoxin and the clostridial type of rubredoxin (Benson *et al.*, 1971). Thus, there are inklings of homology between the ferredoxins and rubredoxins, but the homology requires manipulations and is limited to a small portion of the molecules under consideration. At this point, one cannot state whether the homology is due to convergent or divergent evolution. Perhaps the best approach to the problem is to examine the sequence of other iron–sulfur proteins which may provide additional proof of whether the proteins are truly homologous or are similar because of structure-function requirements. In addition, the sequences of the various iron–sulfur proteins must be further examined to see if genetic errors such as frame shifts can explain the lack of homology in the nonhomologous regions of the proteins being examined.

Q. Flavodoxins

All previous studies on the extraction of evolutionary and genetic data from sequence evidence have involved only one specific protein. In the case of iron–sulfur protein-containing microbes, it is possible to extract this type of data from the ferredoxins, the rubredoxins, and the flavodoxins. Thus far, the flavodoxin has been isolated from *Peptostreptococcus elsdenii*, *Clostridium pasteurianum*, *Clostridium MP*, *Desufovibrio gigas*, and *Desulfovibrio desulfuricans*. The sequence of the *P. elsdenii* flavodoxin is completed (Tanaka *et al.*, 1973b), and the primary structure of the *Clostridium pasteurianum* and *Clostridium MP* are partially known. Thus, it will soon be possible to compare the phylogenetic data from the sequence data of three different proteins which are found in the same organisms. Phylogenetic data will come from three genes present in the bacterial DNA instead of one gene and will represent the most comprehensive study of its kind.

XV. SUMMARY

The distribution of organisms containing iron–sulfur proteins in nature is given. A brief description of the structure-function relationships established for each of the iron–sulfur proteins is presented. The primary structural data and wherever possible the secondary and tertiary structural data of the various iron–sulfur proteins are presented. Section XIV is concerned with the extraction of evolutionary and genetic data of the iron–sulfur-containing organisms from the sequence data. As far as the sequence data are concerned, the ferredoxin sequences show that a protoferredoxin, the most primitive form of ferredoxin which existed billions of years ago, was the precursor to the ferredoxin present in anaerobic bacteria, photosynthetic bacteria, algae, and plants. The sequence data have been used to create a phylogenetic tree and to obtain genetic data. Rubredoxin sequences can also be used to obtain phylogenetic, evolutionary and genetic data. The interesting point established was that the rubredoxins from aerobic and anaerobic bacteria have arisen from the same common ancestor. Rubredoxin, ferredoxin, high-potential iron protein, and adrenodoxin show no homologous primary structures, and it was postulated that it is most likely that each has evolved from a separate gene. Finally, the sequence data on the flavodoxins are presented since the flavodoxins are present in the same microorganisms which contain ferredoxin and rubredoxin, and these data will eventually allow one to look indirectly at three genomes present in the bacterial DNA which will allow a better statistical treatment of the evolutionary and genetic aspects of the iron–sulfur-containing organisms. The studies to date demonstrate that this approach will provide interesting and unique evolutionary and genetic information of these organisms which range from prokaryotes to eukaryotes.

XVI. APPENDIX: DISTRIBUTION AND SOME PROPERTIES OF NONHEME IRON PROTEINS

1. FERREDOXINS

a. ANAEROBIC BACTERIA. *C. pasteurianum* (Tagawa and Arnon, 1962; Mortenson, 1964; Lovenberg *et al.*, 1963; Sieker and Jensen, 1965; Palmer *et al.*, 1966; Malkin and Rabinowitz, 1966; Sobel and Lovenberg, 1966; Gillard *et al.*, 1965; Blomstrom *et al.*, 1964; Mortenson *et al.*, 1964). *C. butyricum* (Lovenberg *et al.*, 1963). *C. acidi-urici* (Lovenberg *et al.*, 1963; Gillard *et al.*, 1965). *C. kluyveri* (Valentine, 1964; Andrew and Morris, 1965; Stern, 1965). *C. tetanomorphum* (Lovenberg *et al.*, 1963). *C. cylindrosporum* (Lovenberg *et al.*, 1963). *C. thermosaccharo-lyticum* (Wilder *et al.*, 1963). *C. nigrificans* (Akagi, 1965). *C. lactoaceto-philum* (Valentine and Wolfe, 1963). *C. stricklandii* (Stadtman, 1966). *Methanobacter omelianskii* (Buchanan and Rabinowitz, 1964). *C. botu-*

linum (Dryer and Anderson, 1968). *C. acetobutylicum* (Gay, 1970). *D. gigas* (LeGall and Dragoni, 1966). *D. desulfuricans* (Suh and Akagi, 1966). *M. lactolyticus* (Valentine et al., 1962a; Valentine and Wolfe, 1963). *M. aerogenes* (Tsunoda *et al.*, 1968). *P. elsdenii* (Gillard *et al.*, 1965). *Diplococcus glycinophilus* (Valentine, 1964). *Peptococcus glycinophilus* (Valentine *et al.*, 1963). *Butybacterium rettgeri* (Valentine and Wolfe, 1963).

b. PHOTOSYNTHETIC BACTERIA. *Rhodospirillum rubrum* (Bachofen and Arnon, 1966). *Chromatium D* (Bachofen and Arnon, 1966; Sasaki and Matsubara, 1967). *Rhodopseudomonas palustrus* (Yamanaka and Kamen, 1965). *Chlorobium thiosulfatophilum* (Buchanan *et al.*, 1965). *Chloropseudomonas ethylicum* (Rao et al., 1969).

c. PLANTS, ALGAE, PROTOZOA. Spinach (Tagawa and Arnon, 1962; Arnon, 1965; San Pietro and Black, 1965; Whatley *et al.*, 1963; Fry and San Pietro, 1963; Palmer *et al.*, 1966; Brintzinger *et al.*, 1966; Hall *et al.*, 1966; Gibson *et al.*, 1966; Thornley *et al.*, 1966). Maize (Jay and Hageman, 1966). Parsley (Bendall *et al.*, 1963). *Brassica campestris* (Fry and San Pietro, 1962). Peas (Davenport, 1960). *Laminum album* (Davenport, 1960). *Chemopodium bonus* (Davenport, 1960). *Aethusa cynapium* (Davenport, 1960). *Stelluria media* (Davenport and Hill, 1960). *Chlorella* (Geiwitz and Vollker, 1962). *Dutura* (Hill and Bendall, 1960). *Prophyratenera* (San Pietro and Black, 1965). *Euglena gracillus* (Nagai and Block, 1966). *Anacystis nidulans* (Smillie, 1965). *Chlamydomonas* (Smillie, 1965). *Navicula pelliculosa* (Black *et al.*, 1963). *Nostoc muscorum* (Arnon, 1965). *Anabaena variabilis* (Black *et al.*, 1963). *Tolypothrix tenuis* (Black *et al.*, 1963). Cotton (Newman *et al.*, 1969). Taro (Rao *et al.*, 1969). *L. glauca* (Benson and Yasunobu, 1969). *Scenedesmus* (Sugeno and Matsubara, 1969). Alfalfa (Keresztes-Nagy and Margoliash, 1966). *Microcystis* (Hall *et al.*, 1971). *Bumilleriopsis* or yellow-green algae (Hall *et al.*, 1971). *Equisetum* or horsetail (Aggarwal *et al.*, 1971). Fern or *Polystichum munitum* (Hall *et al.*, 1971). *Amararthus* (Schürmann et al., 1970).

2. RUBREDOXINS

a. ANAEROBIC BACTERIA. *C. pasteurianum* (Lovenberg and Sobel, 1965). *C. butyricum* (Benson *et al.*, 1966). *M. aerogenes* (Bachmayer *et al.*, 1968a). *Peptococcus glycinophilus* (Boginsky and Huennekins, 1966). *Peptostreptococcus elsdenii* (Mayhew and Peel, 1966). *Clostridium stricklandii* (Stadtman, 1965). *Desulfovibrio gigas* (LeGall and Dragoni, 1966). *Desulfovibrio desulfuricans* (Newman and Postgate, 1968).

b. AEROBIC BACTERIA. *Pseudomonas oleovorans* (Peterson *et al.*, 1966; Peterson and Coon, 1968).

3. HIGH-POTENTIAL IRON PROTEIN

Chromatium D (Bartsch, 1963; Dus *et al.*, 1967). *Rhodopseudomonas gelatinosa* (DeKlerk and Kamen, 1966) and probably present in *Rhodospirillum spheroides* (DeKlerk and Kamen, 1966). *Rhodosopirillum capulatus* (DeKlerk and Kamen, 1966). *Rhodospseudomonas palustrus* (DeKlerk and Kamen, 1966).

4. ADRENODOXIN AND TESTERODOXIN

Beef adrenals (Omura *et al.*, 1965a,b). Pig adrenals (Watari and Kimura, 1966; Kimura and Suzuki, 1965). Pig testes (Ohno *et al.*, 1967; Kimura and Ohno, 1968).

5. *Euglena* FERREDOXIN (NAGAI AND BLOCH, 1966)

6. PUTIDAREDOXIN (CUSHMAN *et al.*, 1967)

7. *Polymyxa* FERREDOXIN (YOCH AND VALENTINE, 1972)

8. NITROGENASE FROM *C. pasteurianum* (MORTENSON, 1965a,b)

9. *C. pasteurianum* IRON–SULFUR PROTEIN (HARDY *et al.*, 1965)

10. *Azotobacter* IRON–SULFUR PROTEINS I AND II (SHETHNA *et al.*, 1964, 1966)

11. *Azotobacter* FERREDOXIN (YOCH *et al.*, 1969)

12. NONHEME IRON PROTEIN FROM COMPLEX III OF ELECTRON TRANSPORT SYSTEM (RIESKE *et al.*, 1964a,b,c)

ACKNOWLEDGMENTS

The authors wish to acknowledge the devoted research efforts of Dr. A. M. Benson and numerous other postdoctorates who determined the primary structures of the nonheme iron proteins in our laboratory. We gratefully acknowledge the research support from the National Science Foundation Grant No. GM 18739 and the National Institutes of Health Grants GM 16228 and GM 16784.

REFERENCES

Adman, E. T., Sieker, L. C., and Jensen, L. H. (1973). *J. Biol. Chem.* **248**, 3987.
Aggarwal, S. J., Rao, K. K., and Matsubara, H. (1971). *J. Biochem. (Japan)* **69**, 601.
Akagi, J. M. (1965). *Biochem. Biophys. Res. Commun.* **21**, 72.

Andrew, I. G., and Morris, J. G. (1965). *Biochim. Biophys. Acta* **97**, 176.

Anfinsen, C. B. (1959). "The Molecular Basis of Evolution." Wiley, New York.

Arnon, D. I. (1965). *Science* **149**, 1460.

Azari, P., Tsunoda, J., Glantz, M., Mayhew, S., and Yasunobu, K. T. (1970). Unpublished data.

Bachmayer, H., Yasunobu, K. T., and Whiteley, H. R. (1967a). *Biochem. Biophys. Res. Commun.* **26**, 435.

Bachmayer, H., Piette, L. H., Yasunobu, K. T., and Whiteley, H. R. (1967b). *Proc. Nat. Acad. Sci. U.S.* **57**, 122.

Bachmayer, H., Benson, A. M., Garrard, W. T., Yasunobu, K. T., and Whiteley, H. R. (1968a). *Biochemistry* **7**, 986.

Bachmayer, H., Mayhew, S., Peel, J., and Yasunobu, K. T. (1968b). *J. Biol. Chem.* **243**, 1022.

Bachofen, R., and Arnon, D. I. (1966). *Biochim. Biophys. Acta* **120**, 259.

Baptist, J. N., Gholson, R. K., and Coon, M. J. (1963). *Biochim. Biophys. Acta* **69**, 40.

Bartsch, R. G. (1963). In "Bacterial Photosynthesis" (H. Gest, A. San Pietro, and L. P. Vernon, eds.), p. 315. Antioch Press, Yellow Springs, Ohio.

Bayer, H., and Hagenmaier, H. (1968). *Tetrahedron* **24**, 4853.

Bearden, A. J., Moss, T. H., Bartsch, R. G., and Cusanovitch, M. A. (1965). "Non-Heme Iron Proteins: Role in Energy Conversion" (A. San Pietro, ed.), p. 87. Antioch Press, Yellow Springs, Ohio.

Beinert, H. (1965). In "Non-Heme Iron Proteins: Role in Energy Conversion" (A. San Pietro, ed.), p. 23. Antioch Press, Yellow Springs, Ohio.

Beinert, H., and Sands, R. H. (1960). *Biochem. Biophys. Res. Communs.* **3**, 41.

Bendall, D. S., Gregory, R. P. F., and Hill, R. (1963). *Biochem. J.* **88**, 29P.

Benson, A. M., and Yasunobu, K. T. (1969). *J. Biol. Chem.* **244**, 955.

Benson, A. M., Mower, H. F., and Yasunobu, K. T. (1966). *Proc. Nat. Acad. Sci. U.S.* **55**, 1532.

Benson, A. M., Mower, H. F., and Yasunobu, K. T. (1967). *Arch Biochim. Biophys.* **121**, 563.

Benson, A. M., Tomoda, K., Chang, J., Matsueda, G., Lode, E. T., Coon, M. J., and Yasunobu, K. T. (1971). *Biochem. Biophys. Res. Commun.* **42**, 640.

Black, C. C., Fewson, C. A., and Gibbs, M. (1963). *Nature (London)* **198**, 88.

Blomstrom, D. C., Knight, Jr., E., Phillips, W. D., and Weiher, J. F. (1964). *Proc. Nat. Acad. Sci. U.S.* **51**, 1085.

Boginsky, M. L., and Huennekins, F. M. (1966). *Biochem. Biophys. Res. Commun.* **23**, 600.

Brintzinger, H., Palmer, G., and Sands, R. H. (1966). *Proc. Nat. Acad. Sci. U.S.* **55**, 397.

Bryson, V., and Vogel, H. J. (1965). "Evolving Genes and Proteins." Academic Press, New York.

Buchanan, B. B. (1966). *Structure Bonding* **1**, 109.

Buchanan, B. B., and Rabinowitz, J. C. (1964). *J. Bacteriol.* **88**, 806.

Buchanan, B. B., Lovenberg, W., and Rabinowitz, J. C. (1963). *Proc. Nat. Acad. Sci. U.S.* **49**, 345.

Buchanan, B. B., Bachofen, R., and Arnon, D. I. (1964). *Proc. Nat. Acad. Sci. U.S.* **52**, 839.

Buchanan, B. B., Matsubara, H., and Evans, M. C. W. (1969). *Biochim. Biophys. Acta* **189**, 46.

Bulen, W. A., and LeComte, J. R. (1966). *Proc. Nat. Acad. Sci. U.S.* **56**, 979.

Cammack, R., Hall, D., and Rao, K. (1971a). *New Sci. J.* **23**, 696.

Cammack, R., Rao, K. K., Hall, D. O., and Johnson, C. E. (1971b). *Biochem. J.* **125**, 849.

Carter, C. W., Jr., Kraut, J., Freer, S. T., Alden, R. A., Sieker, L. C., Adman, E., Jensen, L. H. (1972). *Proc. Nat. Acad. Sci. U.S.* **69**, 3526.

Cole, R. D. (1964). Univ. of California, Berkeley, private communication.

Craig, I. (1971). *New Sci. Sci. J.* **51**, 313.

Crestfield, A. M., Moore, S., and Stein, W. H. (1963). *J. Biol. Chem.* **238**, 622.

Crick, F. H. C. (1958). *Symp. Soc. Exp. Biol.* **12**, 138.

Crick, F. H. C. (1963). *Progr. Nucleic Acid Res.* **1**, 164.

Cushman, D. W., Tsai, R. L., and Gunsalus, I. C. (1967). *Biochem. Biophys. Res. Commun.* **26**, 577.

Darwin, C. (1859). "The Origin of Species." Murray, London.

Davenport, H. E. (1960). *Biochem. J.* **77**, 471.

Davenport, H. E., and Hill, R. (1960). *Biochem. J.* **74**, 493.

Davenport, H. E., Hill, R., and Whatley, F. R. (1952). *Proc. Roy. Soc. B* **139**, 346.

Dayhoff, M. (1969). "Atlas of Protein Sequence Structure," Vol. 4. National Biomedical Res. Found., Silver Springs, Maryland.

DeKlerk, H., and Kamen, M. D. (1966). *Biochim. Biophys. Acta.* **112**, 175.

Dervartanian, D. V., Shethna, Y. I., and Beinert, H. (1969). *Biochim. Biophys. Acta* **194**, 548.

Devanathan, T., Akagi, J. M., Hersh, R. T., and Himes, R. (1970). *J. Biol. Chem.* **244**, 2846.

Dixon, G. H. (1966). *In* "Essays in Biochemistry" (P. N. Campbell and G. O. Greville, eds.), p. 147. Academic Press, Inc., New York.

Dryer, J. K., and Anderson, A. W. (1968). *Appl. Microbiol.* **16**, 207.

Dubourdieu, M., and LeGall, J. (1970). *Biochem. Biophys. Res. Commun.* **38**, 965.

Dus, K., DeKlerk, H., Sletten, K., and Bartsch, R. G. (1967). *Biochim. Biophys. Acta* **140**, 291.

Dus, K., Tedro, S., Bartsch, R. G., and Kamen, M. D. (1971). *Biochem. Biophys. Res. Commun.* **43**, 1239.

Eaton, T. H. (1970). "Evolution." Norton, New York.

Eaton, W. A., Palmer, G., Fee, J. A., Kimura, T., and Lovenberg, W. (1971). *Proc. Nat. Acad. Sci. U.S.* **68**, 3015.

Eck, R. V., and Dayhoff, M. O. (1966). *Science* **152**, 363.

Ehrenberg, A., and Kamen, M. D. (1965). *Biochim. Biophys. Acta* **102**, 333.

Evans, M. C. W. (1968). *Biochem. Biophys. Res. Commun.* **33**, 146.

Evans, M. C. W., and Buchanan, B. B. (1965). *Proc. Nat. Acad. Sci. U.S.* **53**, 1420.

Evans, M. C. W., Hall, D. O., Bothe, H., and Whatley, F. R. (1968). *Biochem. J.* **110**, 485.

Evans, M. C. W., Hall, D. O., and Johnson, C. E. (1970). *Biochem. J.* **119**, 289.

Feeney, R. E., and Allison, R. G. (1969). "Evolutionary Biochemistry of Proteins." Wiley (Interscience), New York.

Feldman, H. A., Eaton, W. A., and Lovenberg, W. (1972). Private communication.

Fitch, W. M. (1966). *J. Mol. Biol.* **16**, 17.

Fitch, W. M., and Margoliash, E. (1967). *Science* **155**, 279.

Flatmark, T., and Dus, K. (1969). *Biochim. Biophys. Acta* **180**, 377.

Florkin, M. (1964). *Taxonomic Biochemistry and Serology* (C. A. Leone, ed.), p. 51. Research Press, New York.

Foust, G. P., Mayhew, S. G., and Massey, V. (1969). *J. Biol. Chem.* **244**, 964.

Fox, J. L., and Brown, J. R. (1971). *Fed. Proc.* **30**, 1242.

Fry, K. T., and San Pietro, A. (1962). *Biochem. Biophys. Res. Commun.* **9**, 218.

Fry, K. T., and San Pietro, A. (1963). "Photosynthesis Mechanisms of Green Plants," Vol. 252. Nat. Acad. Sci.—Nat. Res. Council, Publ. 1145, Washington, D.C.

Garbett, K., Gillard, R. D., Knowles, P. F., and Stangroom, J. E. (1967). *Nature (London)* **215**, 82.

Gay, R. (1970). Private communication.

Geiwitz, H. S., and Vollker, W. (1962). *Z. Physiol. Chem.* **330**, 124.

Gholson, R. K., Baptist, J. N., and Coon, M. J. (1963). *Biochemistry* **2**, 1155.

Gibbs, A. J., and McIntyre, G. A. (1970). *Eur. J. Biochem.* **16**, 1.

Gibson, J. F., Hall, D. O., Thornley, J. H. M., and Whatley, F. R. (1966). *Proc. Nat. Acad. Sci. U.S.* **56**, 987.

Gillard, R. D., McKenzie, E. D., Mason, R., Mayhew, S. G., Peel, J. L., and Stangroom, J. E. (1965). *Nature (London)* **208**, 769.

Green, D. (1965). *In* "Enzymes: Units of Biological Structures and Function," Henry Ford Hosp. Int. Symp. (O. H. Goebler, ed.). Academic Press, New York.

Gunsalus, I. C., Tyson, C. A., Tsai, R., and Lipscomb, J. D. (1971/1972). *Chem. Biol. Interactions* **4**, 75.

Hall, D. O., and Evans, M. C. W. (1969). *Nature (London)* **223**, 1342.

Hall, D. O., Gibson, J. F., and Whatley, F. R. (1966). *Biochem. Biophys. Res. Commun.* **23**, 81.

Hall, D. O., Cammack, R., and Rao, K. K. (1971). *Nature (London)* **233**, 136.

Hardy, R. W. F., and Burns, R. C. (1968). *Ann. Rev. Biochem.* **37**, 331.

Hardy, R. W. F., Knight, E., Jr., McDonald, C. C., and D'Eustachi, A. J. (1965). *In* "Non-Heme Iron Proteins: Role in Energy Conversion" (A. San Pietro, ed.), p. 275. Antioch Press, Yellow Springs, Ohio.

Herriott, J. R., Sieker, L. C., Jensen, L. H., and Lovenberg, W. (1970). *J. Mol. Biol.* **50**, 391.

Hill, R., and Bendall, F. (1960). *Biochem. J.* **76**, 478.

Hong, J. S., and Rabinowitz, J. C. (1967). *Biochem. Biophys. Res. Commun.* **29**, 246.

Hong, J. S., and Rabinowitz, J. C. (1970). *J. Biol. Chem.* **245**, 4982.

Jeng, D. Y., Morris, J. A., Bui, P. T., and Mortenson, L. E. (1969). *Fed. Proc.* **28**, 667.

Johnson, C. E., Cammack, R., Rao, K. K., and Hall, D. O. (1971). *Biochem. Biophys. Res. Commun.* **43**, 564.

Joy, K. W., and Hageman, R. H. (1966). *Biochem. J.* **100**, 263.

Jukes, T. H. (1966). Private communication.

Katagiri, M., Ganguli, B. N., and Gunsalus, I. C. (1968). *J. Biol. Chem.* **243**, 3543.

Keresztes-Nagy, S., and Margoliash, E. (1966). *J. Biol. Chem.* **241**, 5955.

Keresztes-Nagy, S., Perini, F., and Margoliash, E. (1969). *J. Biol. Chem.* **244**, 981.

Kimura, T. (1968). *Structure Bonding* **5**, 1.

Kimura, T., and Ohno, H. (1968). *J. Biochem. (Japan)* **63**, 716.

Kimura, T., and Suzuki, K. (1965). *Biochem. Biophys. Res. Commun.* **20**, 373.

Kimura, T., and Ting, J. (1971). *Biochem. Biophys. Res. Commun.* **45**, 1227.

Knight, E., Jr., and Hardy, R. W. F. (1966). *J. Biol. Chem.* **241**, 2752.

Knight, E., Jr., D'Eustachi, A. J., and Hardy, R. W. F. (1966). *Biochim. Biophys. Acta* **113**, 626.

Knight, E., Jr., and Hardy, R. W. F. (1967). *J. Biol. Chem.* **242**, 1370.

Koch, B., Wong, P., Russel, S., Evans, H. J., and Howard, R. (1970). *Biochem. J.* **118**, 782.

Kraut, J., Strahs, G., and Freer, S. T. (1968). *In* "Structural Chemistry and Molecular Biology" (A. Rich and N. Davidson, eds.), p. 55. Freeman, San Francisco, California.

Kusunose, M., Kusunose, E., and Coon, M. J. (1964a). *J. Biol. Chem.* **239**, 1374.

Kusunose, M., Kusunose, E., and Coon, M. J. (1964b). *J. Biol. Chem.* **239**, 2135.

Laishley, E. J., Travis, J., and Peck, H. D., Jr., (1969). *J. Bacteriol.* **98**, 302.

Lardy, H. A., and Ferguson, S. M. (1969). *Ann. Rev. Biochem.* **38**, 991.

LeGall, J., and Dragoni, N. (1966). *Biochem. Biophys. Res. Commun.* **23**, 145.

Lennox, E. S., and Cohen, M. (1967). *Ann. Rev. Biochem.* **36**, 365.

Lode, E., and Coon, M. J. (1971). *J. Biol. Chem.* **246**, 791.

Losada, M., Whatley, F. R., and Arnon, D. I. (1961). *Nature (London)* **190**, 606.

Lovenberg, W. (1966). *Int. Conf. Protides Biolog. Fluids, 14th, Brugge* (H. Peters, ed.). Elsevier, Amsterdam.

Lovenberg, W. (1972). Private communication.

Lovenberg, W., and Sobel, B. E. (1965). *Proc. Nat. Acad. Sci. U.S.* **54**, 193.

Lovenberg, W., and Williams, W. M. (1969). *Biochemistry* **6**, 3880.

Lovenberg, W., Buchanan, B. B., and Rabinowitz, J. C. (1963). *J. Biol. Chem.* **238**, 3899.

Malkin, R., and Rabinowitz, J. C. (1966). *Biochem. Biophys. Res. Commun.* **23**, 822.

Malkin, R., and Rabinowitz, J. C. (1967). *Ann. Rev. Biochem.* **36**, 113.

Margoliash, E., and Smith, E. (1965). *In* "Evolving Genes and Proteins" (V. Bryson and H. J. Vogel, eds.), p. 241. Academic Press, New York.

Matsubara, H., and Sasaki, R. M. (1968). *J. Biol. Chem.* **243**, 1732.

Matsubara, H., Sasaki, R. M., and Chain, R. K. (1967). *Proc. Nat. Acad. Sci.* **57**, 439.

Matsubara, H., Jukes, T. H., and Cantor, C. R. (1968). *Brookhaven Symp. Biol.* **21**, 201.

Matsubara, H., Sasaki, R. M., Tsuchiya, D. K., and Evans, M. C. W. (1970). *J. Biol. Chem.* **245**, 2121.

Mayhew, S. G. (1971). *Biochim. Biophys. Acta* **235**, 276.

Mayhew, S. G., and Massey, V. (1969). *J. Biol. Chem.* **244**, 794.

Mayhew, S. G., and Peel, J. L. (1966). *Proc. Biochem. Soc.* 80 p.

Mayhew, S. G., Petering, D., Palmer, G., and Foust, G. P. (1969). *J. Biol. Chem.* **244**, 2830.

McCarthy, K. F. (1972). Ph.D. thesis, George Washington Univ.

McCarthy, K. F., and Lovenberg, W. (1970). *Biochem. Biophys. Res. Commun.* **40**, 1053.

McCarthy, K. F., and Lovenberg, W. (1973). In press.

Merrifield, R. B. (1969). *Advan. Enzymol.* **32**, 221.

Mortenson, L. E. (1964). *Biochim. Biophys. Acta* **81**, 473.

Mortenson, L. E. (1965a). *Fed. Proc.* **24**, 233.

Mortenson, L. E. (1965b). *In* "Non-Heme Iron Proteins: Role in Energy Conversion" (A. San Pietro, ed.), p. 241. Antioch Press, Yellow Springs, Ohio.

Mortenson, L. E. (1966). *Biochim. Biophys. Acta* **127**, 18.

Mortenson, L. E., Aronson, A. E., and Nepokroeff, B. (1964). Abstract of paper, *148 Meeting Amer. Chem. Soc.,* September, Chicago, Illinois.

Mortenson, L. E., Valentin, R. C., and Carnahan, J. E. (1962). *Biochem. Biophys. Res. Commun.* **7**, 448.

Moss, T. H., Bearden, A. J., Bartsch, R. G., Cusanovitch, M. A., and San Pietro, A. (1968). *Biochemistry* **7**, 1591.

Nagai, J., and Bloch, K. (1966). *J. Biol. Chem.* **241**, 1925.

Newman, D. J., and Postgate, J. R. (1968). *Eur. J. Biochem.* **7**, 45.

Newman, D. J., Ihle, J. N., and Dure, L., III (1969). *Biochem. Biophys. Res. Commun.* **36**, 947.

Nishimura, S., Jones, D. S., Wells, R. D., Jacob, T. M., and Khorana, H. G. (1965). *Fed. Proc. Fed. Amer. Soc. Exp. Biol.* **24**, 409.

Ohno, H., Suzuki, K., and Kimura, T. (1967). *Biochem. Biophys. Res. Commun.* **26**, 651.

Omura, T., Sato, R., Cooper, D. Y., Rosenthal, O., and Estabrook, R. W. (1965a). *Fed. Proc.* **24**, 1181.

Omura, T., Sanders, E., Cooper, D. Y., Rosenthal, O., and Estabrook, R. W. (1965b). "Non-Heme Iron Proteins: Their Role in Energy Conversion" (A. San Pietro, ed.), p. 104. Antioch Press, Yellow Springs, Ohio.

Omura, T., Sanders, E., Cooper, D. Y., Rosenthal, O., and Estabrook, R. W. (1966). *Methods Enzymol.* **10**, 362.

Palmer, G., Sands, R. H., and Mortenson, L. E. (1966). *Biochem. Biophys. Res. Commun.* **23**, 357.

Peck, H. D., Jr. (1966). Lecture presented at the Univ. of Maryland on December 1, 1966.

Peterson, J. A., and Coon, M. J. (1968). *J. Biol. Chem.* **243**, 329.

Peterson, J. A., Basu, D., and Coon, M. J. (1966). *J. Biol. Chem.* **241**, 5162.

Peterson, J. A., Kusunose, M., Kusunose, E., and Coon, M. J. (1967). *J. Biol. Chem.* **242**, 4334.

Phillips, W. D., Poe, M., Weiher, J. F., McDonald, C. C., and Lovenberg, W. (1970). *Nature (London)* **227**, 574.

Poe, M., Phillips, W. D., McDonald, C. C., and Lovenberg, W. (1970). *Proc. Nat. Acad. Sci. U.S.* **65**, 797.

Raftery, M. A., and Cole, R. D. (1963). *Biochem. Biophys. Res. Commun.* **10**, 467.

Rall, S. C., Bolinger, R. E., and Cole, R. D. (1969). *Biochemistry* **8**, 2486.

Rao, K. K., and Matsubara, H. (1970). *Biochem. Biophys. Res. Commun.* **38**, 500.

Rao, K. K., Matsubara, H., Buchanan, B. B., and Evans, M. C. W. (1969). *J. Bacteriol.* **100**, 1411.

Rao, K. K., Cammack, R., Hall, D. O., and Johnson, C. E. (1971). *Biochem. J.* **122**, 257.

Rieske, J. S., MacLennan, D. H., and Coleman, R. (1964a). *Biochem. Biophys. Res. Commun.* **15**, 338.

Rieske, J. S., Hansen, R. E., and Zaugg, W. S. (1964b). *J. Biol. Chem.* **239**, 3017.

Rieske, J. S., Zaugg, W. S., and Hansen, R. E. (1964c). *J. Biol. Chem.* **239**, 3023.

Rothen, A. (1944). *J. Biol. Chem.* **152**, 679.

San Pietro, A. (1965). "Non-Heme Iron Proteins: Role in Energy Conversion." Antioch Press, Yellow Springs, Ohio.

San Pietro, A., and Black, C. C. (1965). *Annu. Rev. Plant. Physiol.* **16,** 155.

San Pietro, A., and Lang, H. M. (1958). *J. Biol. Chem.* **231,** 211.

Sarabhai, A. S., Strectton, A. O. W., Brenner, S., and Bolle, A. (1964). *Nature (London)* **201,** 13.

Sasaki, R. M., and Matsubara, H. (1967). *Biochem. Biophys. Res. Commun.* **28,** 467.

Schurmann, P., Buchanan, B. B., and Matsubara, H. (1970). *Biochim. Biophys. Acta* **223,** 450.

Shethna, Y. I., Wilson, P. W., Hansen, R. E., and Beinert, H. (1964). *Proc. Nat. Acad. Sci. U.S.* **52,** 1263.

Shethna, Y. I., Wilson, P. W., and Beinert, H. (1966). *Biochim. Biophys. Acta* **113,** 225.

Shethna, Y. I., DerVartanian, D. V., and Beinert, H. (1968). *Biochem. Biophys. Res. Commun.,* **31,** 862.

Shethna, Y. I. (1970). *Biochim. Biophys. Acta* **205,** 58.

Sieker, L. C., and Jensen, L. H. (1965). *Biochem. Biophys. Res. Commun.* **20,** 33.

Sieker, L. C., Adman, E., and Jensen, L. H. (1972). *Nature (London)* **235,** 40.

Smillie, R. M. (1965). *Biochem. Biophys. Res. Commun.* **20,** 621.

Sobel, B. E., and Lovenberg, W. (1966). *Biochemistry* **5,** 6.

Stadtman, T. C. (1965). *In* "Non-Heme Iron Proteins: Role in Energy Conversion" (A. San Pietro, ed.), p. 439. Antioch Press, Yellow Springs, Ohio.

Stadtman, T. C. (1966). *Arch. Biochem. Biophys.* **113,** 9.

Stern, J. R. (1965). *In* "Non-Heme Iron Proteins: Their Role in Energy Conversion" (A. San Pietro, ed.). p. 199. Antioch Press, Yellow Springs, Ohio.

Strahs, G., and Kraut, J. (1968). *J. Mol. Biol.* **35,** 503.

Sugeno, K., and Matsubara, H. (1968). *Biochem. Biophys. Res. Commun.* **32,** 951.

Sugeno, K., and Matsubara, H. (1969). *J. Biol. Chem.* **244,** 2979.

Suh, B., and Akagi, J. M. (1966). *J. Bacteriol.* **91,** 2281.

Suhara, K., Takemori, S., and Katagiri, M. (1972). *Biochim. Biophys. Acta* **263,** 272.

Tagawa, K., and Arnon, D. I. (1962). *Nature (London)* **195,** 537.

Tanaka, M., Nakashima, T., Benson, A. M., Mower, H., and Yasunobu, K. T. (1964). *Biochem. Biophys. Res. Commun.* **16,** 422.

Tanaka, M., Nakashima, T., Benson, A. M., Mower, H., and Yasunobu, K. T. (1966). *Biochemistry* **5,** 1666.

Tanaka, M., Haniu, M., and Yasunobu, K. T. (1970). *Biochem. Biophys. Res. Commun.* **39,** 1182.

Tanaka, M., Haniu, M., Yasunobu, K. T., Mayhew, S., and Massey, V. (1971a). *Biochem. Biophys. Res. Commun.* **44,** 886.

Tanaka, M., Haniu, M., Matsueda, G., Yasunobu, K. T., Himes, R. H., Akagi, J. M., Barnes, E. M., and Devanathan, T. (1971b). *J. Biol. Chem.* **246,** 3953.

Tanaka, M., Haniu, M., Matsueda, G., Yasunobu, K. T., Mayhew, S., and Massey, V. (1971c). *Biochemistry* **10,** 3041.

Tanaka, M., Haniu, M., Yasunobu, K. T., and Kimura, T. (1973a). *J. Biol. Chem.* **248,** 1141.

Tanaka, M., Haniu, M., Yasunobu, K. T., Himes, R., and Akagi, J. (1973b). *J. Biol. Chem.* (in press).

Tanaka, M., Haniu, M., Yasunobu, K. T., Dus, K., and Gunsalus, I. M. (1973c). *J. Biol. Chem.* submitted.

Tanaka, M., Haniu, M., Yasunobu, K. T., Mayhew, S., and Massey, V. (1973d). *J. Biol. Chem.* **248**, 4354.

Thornley, J. H. M., Gibson, J. F., Whatley, F. R., and Hall, D. O. (1966). *Biochem. Biophys. Res. Commun.* **24**, 877.

Travis, J., Newman, D. J., LeGall, J., and Peck, H. D., Jr. (1971). *Biochem. Biophys. Res. Commun.* **45**, 452.

Tsai, R. L., Gunsalus, I. C., and Dus, K. (1971). *Biochem. Biophys. Res. Commun.* **45**, 1300.

Tsibris, J. C. M., Tsai, R. L., Gunsalus, I. C., Orme-Johnson, W. H., Hansen, R. E., and Beinert, H. (1968). *Proc. Nat. Acad. Sci. U.S.* **59**, 959.

Tsunoda, J. N., Yasunobu, K. T., and Whiteley, H. R. (1968). *J. Biol. Chem.* **243**, 6262.

Valentine, R. C. (1964). *Bacteriol. Rev.* **28**, 497.

Valentine, R. C., and Wolfe, R. S. (1963). *J. Bacteriol.* **85**, 1114.

Valentine, R. C., Jackson, R. L., and Wolfe, R. S. (1962a). *Biochem. Biophys. Res. Commun.* **7**, 453.

Valentine, R. C., Brill, W. J., and Wolfe, R. S. (1962b). *Proc. Nat. Acad. Sci. U.S.* **48**, 1856.

Valentine, R. C., Brill, W. J., and Sagers, R. D. (1963). *Biochem. Biophys. Res. Commun.* **12**, 315.

Watari, H., and Kimura, T. (1966). *Biochem. Biophys. Res. Commun.* **24**, 106.

Watson, J. D. (1965). "The Molecular Biology of the Gene." Benjamin, New York.

Weinstein, B. (1969). *Biochem. Biophys. Res. Commun.* **35**, 109.

Whatley, F. R., Tagawa, K., and Arnon, D. I. (1963). *Proc. Nat. Acad. Sci. U.S.* **49**, 266.

Wilder, M., Valentine, R. C., and Akagi, J. M. (1963). *J. Bacteriol.* **86**, 861.

Woese, C. R. (1967). The Genetic Code." The Molecular Basis for Genetic Expression." Harper, New York.

Wolfe, R. S., Wolin, M. J., and Wolin, E. A. (1963). *Fed. Proc.* **22**, 355.

Yamanaka, T., and Kamen, M. D. (1965). *Biochem. Biophys. Res. Commun.* **18**, 611.

Yamashita, S., and Racker, E. (1968). *J. Biol. Chem.* **243**, 2446.

Yasunobu, K. T., and Hagenmaier, H. (1972). Unpublished results.

Yasunobu, K. T., and Lovenberg, W. (1972). Unpublished results.

Yasunobu, K. T., and Lovenberg, W. (1973). *Arch. Biochem. Biophys.* In press.

Yanofsky, C., Carlton, B. C., Guest, J. R., Helinski, D. R., and Henning, U. (1964). *Proc. Nat. Acad. Sci.* **51**, 266.

Yoch, D. C., and Valentine, R. C. (1972). *J. Bacteriol.* **110**, 1211.

Yoch, D. C., Benemann, J. R., Valentine, R. C., and Arnon, D. I. (1969). *Proc. Nat. Acad. Sci. U.S.* **64**, 1404.

Zuckerkandl, E., and Pauling, L. (1962). *In* "Horizons in Biochemistry" (M. Kasha and B. Pullman, eds.), p. 189. Academic Press, New York.

CHAPTER 3

The Iron–Sulfur Complex in Rubredoxin

WILLIAM A. EATON and WALTER LOVENBERG

I. INTRODUCTION

The rubredoxins are a group of small iron–sulfur proteins that have been isolated from aerobic and anaerobic bacteria. They are classified together because of their distinct optical absorption spectra and because they generally contain only one iron atom per molecule. The chemical feature that has historically set rubredoxins apart from other iron–sulfur proteins is the lack of so-called acid-labile sulfide (see Beinert, Chapter 1 of Volume I). Our knowledge of these proteins is in an unusual state. Whereas the three-dimensional structure of the rubredoxin from the bacterium, *Clostridium pasteurianum*, is known to a resolution of 1.5 Å from the very elegant X-ray diffraction studies of Jensen and co-workers (Herriott *et al.*, 1970; Watenpaugh *et al.*, 1971; Jensen, Chapter 4 of this volume), there is no known biochemical function for this protein or for rubredoxins from any other anaerobic organism.

The name rubredoxin was first applied to an iron–sulfur protein isolated from *C. pasteurianum*. The protein was first detected by Buchanan *et al.* (1963) and Mortenson (1964) as a red-colored fraction during the isolation of ferredoxin, which is dark brown. In 1965, Lovenberg and Sobel concentrated and purified the red material and were able to obtain

131

large, high-quality crystals by ammonium sulfate fractionation. It was soon apparent that the protein could undergo reversible reduction and oxidation and that it could function as an electron carrier in certain ferredoxin-requiring reactions. However, no unique requirement for rubredoxin was apparent for any of the known clostridial enzyme systems. Subsequently proteins were found in other anaerobes that had very similar properties, particularly the characteristic optical absorption spectrum (Stadtman, 1965; Mayhew and Peel, 1966; LeGall and Dragoni, 1966; Lovenberg, 1966; Bachmayer *et al.*, 1967; Newman and Postgate, 1968). It was of considerable interest when Peterson *et al.* (1966) isolated a rubredoxin from *Pseudomonas oleovorans*, which is one of the three proteins in the ω-hydroxylase system of this aerobic bacterium. In this set of reactions, rubredoxin is reduced by NADH and a specific reductase, and the reduced protein serves as the reducing component in the mixed function oxidase system for the hydroxylation of hydrocarbons (Lode and Coon, Chapter 7 of Volume I). Although in this organism rubredoxin has a very specific function, it provides no clue as to the role of rubredoxin in the metabolism of anaerobic bacteria.

Because of its chromophoric and magnetic properties, most of the chemical and physical investigations have focused on the iron–sulfur complex. A large variety of spectroscopic properties have been examined, which include Mössbauer, electron spin resonance, polarized single crystal absorption, natural and magnetic circular dichroism, and resonance Raman spectroscopies. The results of these investigations are potentially amenable to detailed interpretation in light of the X-ray results. Consequently, studies on rubredoxin have served as a useful guide for the interpretation of many of the results on the more complex iron–sulfur proteins, and rubredoxin is, therefore, an important "model compound" in iron–sulfur protein chemistry (see Palmer, Chapter 8 of this volume).

In this chapter we shall be mainly concerned with the chemical and physical properties of the iron–sulfur complex of rubredoxin, particularly in the way in which they relate to the structure determined by X-ray diffraction. We shall see that most of the basic properties can be readily rationalized in terms of the X-ray structure, but that several unresolved problems remain concerning more detailed correlations of the X-ray and spectroscopic results, which are important for current theories of catalysis by metalloenzymes.

II. CHEMICAL PROPERTIES

Rubredoxins from anaerobic organisms appear to share several properties with the ferredoxin isolated from these organisms. Both types of proteins are soluble in 50% aqueous acetone, both are acidic, and both can be chromatographed directly on DEAE cellulose from 50% acetone solutions (Lovenberg, 1972). This suggests that these proteins are similar in size and charge. Ultracentrifugal studies indicated an approximate molecular weight of about 6000 daltons for *C. pasteurianum* rubredoxin (Lovenberg and Sobel, 1965). Subsequent amino acid analyses and sequence studies showed that this protein was a single polypeptide chain consisting of 54 amino acids and a single iron atom (Lovenberg and Williams, 1969) with an absolute molecular weight of 6127.

Each of the rubredoxins from other anaerobic organisms also consist of a single polypeptide chain of 50 to 60 amino acids and one atom of iron. *Pseudomonas oleovorans* rubredoxin, however, has 183 amino acids and can be isolated as either a one- or two-iron protein (Lode and Coon, 1971). The acid-labile sulfur which is present in all other classes of iron–sulfur proteins has not been detected in any of the rubredoxins studied to date. The amino acid compositions and in some cases the complete amino acid sequences are known for a number of rubredoxins (Bachmayer *et al.*, 1968a,b; Benson *et al.*, 1970). Figure 1 shows the amino acid sequence of *C. pasteurianum* rubredoxin, and Table XXXV of Chapter 2 of this volume gives the amino acid content of several bacterial rubredoxins. All of the anaerobic proteins examined have methionine as the N-terminal amino acid and in the case of *C. pasteurianum* rubredoxin this appears to be blocked by an *N*-formyl group (McCarthy and Lovenberg, 1970). Some evidence has been obtained (K. T. Yasunobu, personal communication) that other rubredoxins have the N-terminal methionines blocked. These seem to be the only proteins known thus far that have retained the *N*-formylmethionine which is thought to

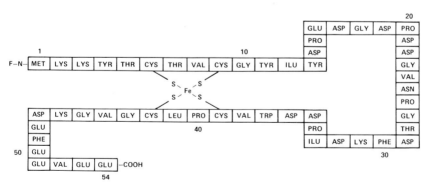

Fig. 1. The amino acid sequence of rubredoxin from *C. pasteurianum* (from McCarthy, 1972).

be the initiator amino acid in bacterial polypeptide synthesis. Most other proteins appear to have undergone complete deformylation or further proteolysis from the N-terminal end.

In general, these proteins are acidic with the preponderance of aspartate and glutamate residues. Also of interest is the observation that none of the rubredoxins contain either arginine or histidine, while all contain three tyrosines and probably one tryptophan. Recent studies on the sequence of *C. pasteurianum* rubredoxin (McCarthy, 1972) indicate that this molecule contains only one tryptophan residue rather than the two previously reported (Lovenberg and Williams, 1969). Since the visible and ultraviolet absorption spectra of *M. lactilyticus* rubredoxin were identical to that of *C. pasteurianum* (Lovenberg, 1966), it is likely that this rubredoxin also contains one tryptophan. Although of no obvious significance, it is noteworthy that *C. pasteurianum* rubredoxin lacks both serine and alanine. These amino acids are generally prevalent in proteins, and, in fact, the ferredoxin from this organism is quite rich in these two amino acids.

Each of the one-iron rubredoxins that have been analyzed have four cysteinyl residues, and of the three proteins on which sequence work has been done all have the cysteines located in the same position. Furthermore, much of the other apparent invariance in the sequences occurs around the cysteinyl residues. This is not surprising since there is now considerable chemical and physical evidence indicating that the four cysteinyl residues provide sulfur ligands for the iron.

In early work it was assumed that the binding of the iron accounted for the visible absorption spectrum of the protein. The work of Lovenberg (1966), Bachmayer *et al.* (1967), and Newman and Postgate (1968) showed that the loss of the visible absorption spectrum occurred simultaneously with reaction of all four cysteinyl residues with mercurial reagents. It appeared, therefore, that all four cysteinyl residues were present with free sulfhydryl groups, and that these SH groups were required for the stability of the iron complex. Furthermore, Lovenberg and Williams (1969) found that the cysteinyl residues in *C. pasteurianum* rubredoxin did not react with iodoacetate unless the iron was first completely removed from the protein. The fact that the four SH groups were required for the maintenance of the chromophore, but that the presence of iron completely blocked the ability of these SH groups to be alkylated, indicated that these groups form ligands for the iron. X-ray diffraction studies (Herriott *et al.*, 1970) have now clearly established that the single iron atom in oxidized, *C. pasteurianum* rubredoxin is indeed bonded to the sulfurs of the four cysteinyl residues in an approximately tetrahedral arrangement, and optical studies (Eaton and Lovenberg, 1970) demonstrated that the tetrahedral geometry is maintained upon one-electron reduction (*vide infra*).

Some insight into the role that other amino acid residues play in maintaining the iron coordination has been obtained from chemical modification experiments. Bachmayer *et al.* (1967) found that the N-terminal methionine is not involved in iron binding. Likewise, the lysine residues do not seem to alter the iron coordination since dinitrophenylation of the lysines or their conversion to homoarginine had no effect on the chromophore. These workers did find, however, that reaction of the apoprotein with N-bromosuccinimide, 2-hydroxy-5-nitrobenzyl bromide, or acylation of the tyrosine residues led to an altered protein in which the iron–sulfur chromophore could not be reconstituted. Although it was originally suggested (Bachmayer *et al.*, 1967) that tyrosine and tryptophan formed the fifth and sixth ligands of an octahedral iron complex, it is now clear from the X-ray diffraction work that this is not the case. Alteration of these residues presumably prevents the protein from assuming a conformation necessary to accommodate the iron atom.

There is a rather wide range of stability observed among the various rubredoxins and the conditions necessary for removing the iron vary considerably with the source of rubredoxin. Rubredoxin from *C. pasteurianum* is perhaps the most stable and requires the most vigorous conditions for complete removal. The iron chromophore is destroyed only slowly in 1% sulfuric acid, and in attempts to prepare aporubredoxin Lovenberg and Williams (1969) found that it was necessary to warm the solution of rubredoxin in 8% trichloroacetic acid and then to dissolve the precipitate in warm 70% ethanol containing 1,10-phenanthroline to remove the iron. The apoprotein can be reconstituted in the presence of iron and 2-mercaptoethanol to form a protein that is indistinguishable from the native protein. A reducing source such as 2-mercaptoethanol is required to reduce cystines to cysteines. This reconstitution procedure has been extremely useful in preparing rubredoxin containing [57]Fe for Mössbauer studies (*vide infra*).

Clostridium pasteurianum rubredoxin has a redox potential of −0.057 V at pH 7.0 (Lovenberg and Sobel, 1965), and the redox potential of the rubredoxin from *D. desulfuricans* appears to be in the same range (Newman and Postgate, 1968). The larger two-iron rubredoxin from *P. oleovorans* has a redox potential of −0.037 V at pH 7.5 (Peterson and Coon, 1968). In no rubredoxin, however, has the pH, temperature, or ionic strength dependence been investigated. Variation in these parameters is necessary for determining the thermodynamic origin of the redox potential and for assessing the net effective charge at the redox center. Although not yet proven, we may assume that the sulfur-bonding species is a mercaptide and not a thiol, i.e., the iron–sulfur complex is not protonated. This would make the net charge of the (III)/(II) couple consisting of iron and the four cysteinyl residues be $(1-)/(2-)$. Consequently, the negative electrostatic environment of the iron could account for a large part of the difference in the redox potential of rubredoxin and the $Fe(III)/Fe(II)$ aquo couple which has a redox potential of $+0.77$ V (Connick and McVey, 1951). Furthermore, *C. pasteurianum* rubredoxin is expected to have 16 negatively charged amino acid residues at neutral pH and only four positively charged ones, which although secondary to the electrostatic effect of the mercaptide ligands may also contribute to lowering the redox potential. These simple electrostatic effects will be reflected in a more positive enthalpy change in the cell reaction relative to the $Fe(III)/Fe(II)$ couple (George *et al.*, 1966). Confirmation of the validity of these comments will have to await a complete thermodynamic investigation.

III. STEREOCHEMISTRY AND ELECTRONIC STRUCTURE

A. Structure by X-Ray Diffraction

The X-ray diffraction studies at a 2.5 Å resolution by Jensen and coworkers on oxidized rubredoxin from *C. pasteurianum* established that the iron is bonded to the sulfurs of the cysteinyl residues in positions 6, 9, 39, and 42 of the 54 amino acid polypeptide chain (Herriott *et al.*, 1970; Jensen, Chapter 4 of this volume). Furthermore, the sulfurs are arranged in an approximately tetrahedral configuration about the iron. Preliminary results from a Fourier difference electron density map at 4 Å resolution indicate that no appreciable change in the iron–sulfur stereochemistry takes place upon reduction of the iron (Jensen, Chapter 4 of this volume). More recent studies on the oxidized protein at 1.5 Å resolution demonstrate considerable deviations from a perfectly tetrahedral arrangement of the iron and four sulfurs (Watenpaugh *et al.*, 1971). Figure 2 shows the iron–sulfur complex of oxidized rubredoxin. Bond angles and bond lengths are given in Table I. Not only do the bond angles differ significantly from the 109.5° value of a perfect tetrahedron, but one of the iron–sulfur bond lengths is considerably shorter than the other three. Furthermore, whereas the three nearly equal iron–sulfur bond lengths fall within the 2.15–2.45 Å range found for small molecule structures, the short Fe–S(42) bond is well outside this range at 2.05 ± 0.03 Å (Watenpaugh *et al.*, 1971). Thus, the most energetically significant distortion would appear to be the abnormally short Fe–S(42) bond.

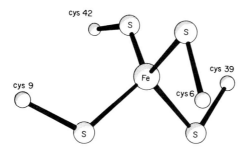

Fig. 2. The iron–sulfur complex of oxidized rubredoxin from *C. pasteurianum* showing the iron, four sulfurs, and four β-carbons (drawn from the 2.0 Å coordinates supplied by L. H. Jensen).

It is highly unusual in protein crystallography to determine such precise values for bond lengths and bond angles, so that one of our major aims in the subsequent discussion will be to correlate the distortions from perfect tetrahedral symmetry observed for the atomic positions by X-ray diffraction with those observed by spectroscopic methods. In the following two sections we present qualitative rationalizations for the electromagnetic properties of the iron–sulfur complex, emphasizing their relation to molecular geometry. Optical properties will be treated in greatest detail, since they are not considered in any of the chapters on methods and because they have been one of our main interests. The first section will be concerned with ligand field properties, i.e., properties which depend

TABLE I

BOND LENGTHS AND BOND ANGLES AT 1.5 Å RESOLUTION WITH
THEIR STANDARD DEVIATIONS[a]

Bond	Bond Length (Å)
Fe–S(6)	2.34 ± 0.02
Fe–S(9)	2.32 ± 0.03
Fe–S(39)	2.24 ± 0.03
Fe–S(42)	2.05 ± 0.03
Bond	**Bond Angle (in degrees)**
S(6)–Fe–S(9)	113 ± 1
S(6)–Fe–S(39)	108 ± 1
S(6)–Fe–S(42)	101 ± 1
S(9)–Fe–S(39)	104 ± 1
S(9)–Fe–S(42)	115 ± 1
S(39)–Fe–S(42)	115 ± 1

[a] From L. H. Jensen (private communication).

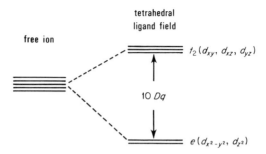

Fig. 3. Splitting of the five $3d$ orbitals by a tetrahedral ligand field. The t_2 and e orbitals consist mainly of the $3d$ orbitals as indicated, but also contain contributions from metal p and ligand orbitals.

primarily on the behavior of the iron $3d$ electrons. These include magnetic susceptibility, Mössbauer, near-infrared optical, and electron paramagnetic resonance spectra. In the second section on the color of rubredoxin, we discuss the visible–ultraviolet spectra and the resonance Raman spectra, both of which depend explicitly on the sulfur electrons as well as the iron electrons.

Symmetry considerations play an important role in understanding all of the electromagnetic properties. The iron–sulfur complex clearly has no strict symmetry. Nevertheless, considerable insight into the origin of the various electromagnetic properties and their relation to molecular structure will come from symmetry considerations alone. We shall frequently be using the term *effective symmetry*, by which we mean the highest possible symmetry that is qualitatively consistent with the experimental observations. The effective symmetry will of course depend on the sensitivity of the property in question to asymmetries in the structure. The highest possible symmetry for the system of iron bonded to four sulfurs is tetrahedral. This will be our zeroth order approximation, accounting for the frequent use of symmetry notations from the point group T_d.

B. Ligand Field Properties

Many of the electromagnetic properties of the iron–sulfur complex in rubredoxin can be rationalized in terms of the behavior of the iron $3d$ electrons in the presence of a distorted tetrahedral ligand field.* A tetrahedral ligand field produces a characteristic splitting of the $3d$ orbitals as illustrated in Fig. 3. The lower degenerate pair consists *mainly* of the

---

* Ligand field theory is presented by Orgel (1960), Ballhausen (1962), Griffith (1964), Figgis (1966), and Lever (1968).

d_{z^2} and $d_{x^2-y^2}$ orbitals, while the upper triply degenerate set is composed of mainly d_{xy}, d_{xz}, and d_{yz}. The energy separation between the e $(d_{z^2}, d_{x^2-y^2})$ and t_2 (d_{xy}, d_{xz}, d_{yz}) orbital levels is the well-known ligand field splitting parameter, 10 Dq or Δ, and is most readily determined from optical measurements (vide infra). For tetrahedral coordination in first-row transition metals, Dq is not large enough to cause spin pairing, no matter what the ligand. Consequently, the iron in oxidized and reduced rubredoxin is expected to behave as a high-spin ferric and high-spin ferrous ion, respectively.

Figure 4 shows the low-lying states of the ferric (d^5) and ferrous (d^6) ion in a weak tetrahedral ligand field with their free ion parentage (Orgel, 1955; Ferguson et al., 1969). The ^6S ground term of the ferric ion is orbitally nondegenerate and, therefore, is not split by a tetrahedral ligand field. A $^6A_1$ ground state derives from ^6S and arises from the configuration $e^2t_2^3$ with five unpaired electrons. In the ferrous case the ^5D term of the free ion is split by a tetrahedral ligand field into an upper orbitally threefold degenerate $^5T_2$ state and a lower orbitally twofold degenerate ^5E state, which, like the t_2 and e orbitals, are separated in energy by 10 Dq. The ^5E ground state arises from the configuration $e^3t_2^3$ with four unpaired electrons. These oxidation and spin states of the iron have been established for rubredoxin from basically four different kinds of measurements—magnetic susceptibility, Mössbauer, optical, and electron paramagnetic resonance spectroscopies.

Most important are the magnetic susceptibility measurements of Phillips et al. (1970). Using a proton magnetic resonance method, they studied the magnetic susceptibility of both oxidized and reduced rubredoxin in solution from 5° to 60°C and found Curie law behavior, as expected in this high temperature range. The effective magnetic mo-

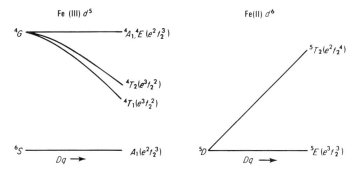

Fig. 4. Schematic energy level diagram for the low-lying states of a d^5 and d^6 ion in a weak tetrahedral ligand field. For $Dq = 0$ the energy levels are those of the free ion. The strong field configurations are indicated in parenthesis.

ments were found to be 5.85 ± 0.20 and 5.05 ± 0.20 μ_B (Bohr magnetons) for the oxidized and reduced proteins, respectively. These results are in good agreement with the spin-only values of 5.92 and 4.90 μ_B expected for high-spin ferric, with five unpaired electrons, and high-spin ferrous, with four unpaired electrons, respectively.* However, the susceptibility data are not sufficiently accurate to assess contributions from orbital angular momentum, which is expected to be quenched in the ferrous case both by delocalization of the iron $3d$ electrons onto the sulfur ligands and by reduction of the symmetry from tetrahedral (Figgis, 1966). Because of the large magnetic moments, contact-shifted resonances in the proton magnetic resonance spectrum of reduced rubredoxin are considerably broadened, and no contact-shifted resonances could be detected for oxidized rubredoxin (Phillips et al., 1970; Chapter 7 of this volume).

While the magnetic susceptibility data establish the total number of unpaired electron spins in the molecule, Mössbauer spectroscopy provides evidence that these spins reside mainly in the iron $3d$ orbitals.† Phillips et al. (1970) examined the Mössbauer spectrum of lyophilized rubredoxin at 4.2°, 77°, and 300°K. The room-temperature isomer shifts were found to be 0.63 and 0.84 mm/second (relative to sodium nitroprusside) for the oxidized and reduced proteins, respectively. The isomer shift for oxidized rubredoxin is near the middle of the range found for ferric high-spin compounds, although it is compatible with other spin and oxidation states (Phillips et al., 1970; Debrunner, 1970; Chapter 6 of this volume). On the other hand, the large isomer shift observed for the reduced protein is characteristic of high-spin ferrous compounds, even though it is somewhat lower than is generally found.

A quadrupole splitting of 0.74 mm/second is found at 300°K for oxidized rubredoxin. The quadrupole splitting is a measure of the deviation from a spherically symmetric charge distribution at the iron nucleus (Chapter 6 of this volume; Debrunner, 1970; Lang, 1970). For a high-spin ferric ion

---

* The spin-only value of the effective magnetic moment is expected in high-spin ferric complexes, even in perfect tetrahedral symmetry. In tetrahedral high-spin ferrous complexes, however, orbital angular momentum may make a substantial contribution to the effective magnetic moment as a result of spin-orbit coupling of the ^5E ground state to the $^5T_2$ excited state. The effective magnetic moment, μ_{eff}, including this contribution can be estimated from the formula (Figgis, 1966) $\mu_{eff} = \mu_{eff}^{so}(1 - 2\lambda/|10Dq|)$ where μ_{eff}^{so} is the effective magnetic moment produced by the unpaired electron spins only, λ is the effective spin orbit coupling constant, and $|10Dq|$ is the magnitude of the energy difference between the ^5E and $^5T_2$ states. Using the free ion value $\lambda = -100$ cm^{-1}, and $|10Dq| = 5000$ cm^{-1}, estimated from the optical measurements discussed below, μ_{eff} is calculated to be 5.10 μ_B.

† Mössbauer spectroscopy of iron–sulfur proteins is discussed by Bearden and Dunham in Chapter 6 of this volume.

in a tetrahedral ligand field the $3d$ electrons have a spherically symmetric distribution, and, consequently, make a zero contribution to the quadrupole interaction. Furthermore, the removal of the degeneracies in the $3d$ orbitals that exist in tetrahedral symmetry does not by itself produce a quadrupole splitting. Therefore, the observed quadrupole splitting in oxidized rubredoxin probably results from asymmetric iron–sulfur covalent bonding. In reduced rubredoxin there is a large quadrupole splitting of 3.36 mm/second at 4.2°K, which is characteristic of a high-spin ferrous ion with an orbitally nondegenerate ground state. In tetrahedral symmetry, five $3d$ electrons are spherically distributed among the five $3d$ orbitals, and the sixth $3d$ electron is equally distributed between the degenerate e (d_{z^2}, $d_{x^2-y^2}$) orbitals. A zero quadrupole splitting results because an electron in a d_{z^2} orbital produces an electric field gradient of equal magnitude but of opposite sign to that produced by an electron in a $d_{x^2-y^2}$ orbital. The large quadrupole splitting observed in reduced rubredoxin indicates that the $d_{x^2-y^2}$ and d_{z^2} orbitals are well separated in energy. From the small decrease in the quadrupole splitting at room temperature, we calculate the e (d_{z^2}, $d_{x^2-y^2}$) orbitals to be split by about 850 cm^{-1}.* Thus, the Mössbauer spectrum in both the oxidized and reduced proteins clearly demonstrates deviations from tetrahedral symmetry.

The optical spectra are not only consistent with high-spin iron in a distorted tetrahedral site, but provide a more detailed picture of the nature of the distortion. That part of the optical spectrum which is in principle most easily understood arises from electronic excitations within the iron $3d$ orbitals. These are the so-called $d \rightarrow d$, crystal field, or ligand field transitions.† In a weak tetrahedral ligand field the lowest energy $d \rightarrow d$ transition, $^5E \rightarrow {}^5T_2$ (Fig. 4), is both spin and orbitally allowed, although it is still expected to have a low absorption intensity because of the inherent center of symmetry possessed by $3d$ orbitals. This transition corresponds to the electronic promotion $e^3 t_2^3 \rightarrow e^2 t_2^4$. A comprehensive

---

* This value is calculated from the relation (Edwards *et al.*, 1967)

$$\Delta E(T) = \Delta E(0) \tanh (\delta/2kT)$$

where $\Delta E(T)$ is the quadrupole splitting of 3.24 ± 0.04 mm/second observed at 300°K, $\Delta E(0)$ is the quadrupole splitting of 3.36 ± 0.04 mm/second observed at 4.2°K, δ is the energy separation of the orbitals deriving from e (d_{z^2}, $d_{x^2-y^2}$), k is Boltzmann's constant, and $T = 300°$K. $\Delta E(T)$ is 3.38 ± 0.04 mm/second at 77°K. Taking into account the experimental uncertainties in the observed quadropole splittings, δ ranges from about 700 cm^{-1} [$\Delta E(T) = 3.20$, $\Delta E(0) = 3.42$] to about 1100 cm^{-1} [$\Delta E(T) = 3.28$, $\Delta E(0) = 3.32$].

† Surveys of ligand field spectra in inorganic complexes are to be found in the books by Lever (1968), Ballhausen (1962), and Jørgensen (1962), and in reviews by McClure (1959) and Ferguson (1970).

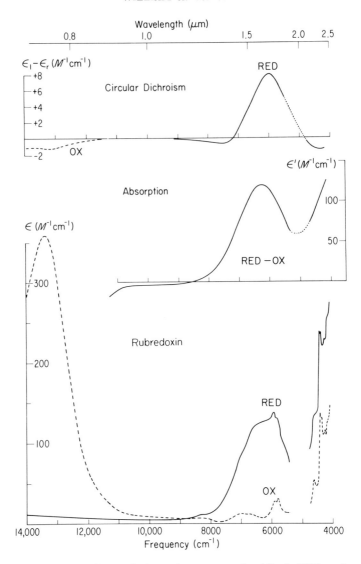

Fig. 5. Circular dichroism and absorption spectra of oxidized (OX) and reduced (RED) *C. pasteurianum* rubredoxin. The middle curve (RED − OX) is the difference absorption spectrum, reduced rubredoxin minus oxidized rubredoxin. Extinction coefficients are based on the value 8800 M^{-1} cm^{-1} for the 4900 Å band of oxidized rubredoxin (from Lovenberg and Williams, 1969). The relatively sharp absorption bands observed between 4000 and 9000 cm^{-1} in oxidized rubredoxin and superimposed on the broad electronic bands of reduced rubredoxin arise from vibrational overtone transitions from the protein and some residual HOD. These vibrational bands are optically inactive. (The figure is reprinted from Eaton *et al.*, 1971, with permission from the National Academy of Sciences.)

discussion of the $^5E \rightarrow {}^5T_2$ transition, including spin orbit coupling, vibrational, and Jahn–Teller effects is given by Slack et al. (1966). Ignoring these effects, a single absorption band is predicted at a frequency corresponding to the energy separation $10Dq$ between the t_2 and e orbitals. From the spectra of inorganic complexes, we expect to find this transition in reduced rubredoxin in the near-infrared spectral region, somewhere between 6000 cm^{-1} (1.6 μm) and 2000 cm^{-1} (5.0 μm), with a maximum extinction coefficient of about 100 M^{-1} cm^{-1}. Figure 5 shows the near-infrared spectrum of oxidized and reduced rubredoxin in ^2H_2O to 4000 cm^{-1} (2.5 μm) (Eaton and Lovenberg, 1970; Eaton et al., 1971). Reduced rubredoxin exhibits an electronic absorption band at 6250 cm^{-1} and the beginning of another electronic band which is estimated to be centered at about 3700 cm^{-1}. The 3700 cm^{-1} estimate is made by fitting the observed data with a Gaussian band of the same width as the 6250 cm^{-1} band. The intensity, bandwidth, and frequencies are all consistent with the assignment of these bands as arising from components of the $^5E \rightarrow {}^5T_2$ ligand field transition.

Convincing additional evidence for this interpretation is obtained from circular dichroism measurements also shown in Fig. 5. Ligand field theory predicts that the $^5E \rightarrow {}^5T_2$ transition is intrinsically *magnetic-dipole-allowed*, and, therefore, should exhibit a large anisotropy factor (Moffitt, 1956), i.e., a large ratio of circular dichroism to absorption $[\approx (\epsilon_l - \epsilon_r)/\epsilon]$.* Mason (1962) pointed out that the anisotropy factor generally exceeds a value of 0.01 for intrinsically magnetic-dipole allowed ligand field transitions and that this could be used as an experimental criterion for making spectral assignments. The criterion of a large anisotropy factor has been extremely useful in assigning ligand field bands in optically active metal complexes (Mason, 1963), including hemoproteins

---

* This can easily be seen from a consideration of the semiclassical expressions for ordinary absorption and natural circular dichroism of solutions (Mason, 1963). The area under an absorption band is proportional to the dipole strength D, which is given by $D = \mu^2$ where μ is the magnitude of the *electric* dipole transition moment vector. The area under a circular dichroism band is proportional to the rotational strength R, which is given by $R = \mu m$ (cos θ) where m is the magnitude of the *magnetic* dipole transition moment vector, and θ is the angle between the two vectors. The anisotropy or dissymmetry factor g is defined as

$$g \equiv \frac{4R}{D} = \frac{4m \ (\cos \theta)}{\mu} \approx \frac{\epsilon_l - \epsilon_r}{\epsilon}$$

Thus $d \rightarrow d$ transitions that are inherently magnetic-dipole allowed and have favorable values of θ are characterized by weak absorption bands with relatively intense circular dichroism bands, resulting in large anisotropy factors.

(Eaton and Charney, 1969, 1971). The point anisotropy factor for the near-infrared bands of reduced rubredoxin is greater than 0.01, and becomes as high as 0.07, confirming the $^5E \rightarrow {}^5T_2$ assignment. Furthermore, the circular dichroism associated with the 6250 cm^{-1} absorption band reveals a splitting of this transition into two components separated by about 1400 cm^{-1}.

We now inquire into the relationship between the observed energy levels and the geometry of the iron–sulfur complex. If all orbital degeneracies are removed, we would expect to observe four excited electronic states in the absence of spin-orbit coupling (Fig. 4). Assuming that the circular dichroism bands at about 6000 and 7400 cm^{-1} correspond to transitions to two different electronically excited states, three excited electronic states are observed optically and a fourth is detected at about 850 cm^{-1} above the ground state by Mössbauer spectroscopy. Thus, in spite of the "blind" region between about 1000 and 4000 cm^{-1}, we are able to construct the complete $3d$ orbital energy level diagram shown in Fig. 6. Since all quintet states derive from the same atomic term (^5D), the mutual electron repulsion parameters are the same for each state and to a first approximation we can equate the observed spectroscopic energy levels to orbital energy level differences. In the simplest model, which considers the ligands as point charges, this orbital level diagram would result from placing a ferrous ion in a weak tetrahedral ligand field with a large axial distortion and a much smaller rhombic distortion. Inclusion of spin-orbit coupling and Jahn–Teller effects in analyzing the spectral results should not alter this conclusion. The axial distortion is indeed quite large, since the axial splitting in the t_2 orbitals is about 3000 cm^{-1}, com-

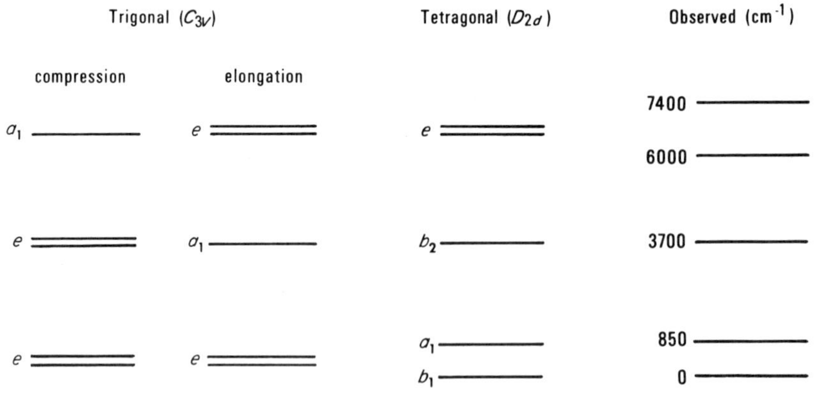

Fig. 6. Energy levels of $3d$ orbitals in various ligand fields. The orbital spacings were chosen so as to coincide as nearly as possible with the orbital energy level diagram "observed" for reduced rubredoxin shown at the extreme right.

pared to the total tetrahedral splitting of about 5000 cm^{-1} ($= -10Dq$).*

The simplest kind of axial distortion from a tetrahedral arrangement of iron and four sulfur atoms arises from an elongation or compression of only one of the iron–sulfur bonds; the tetrahedron is now trigonally distorted, and the altered bond direction coincides with the threefold rotation axis in the new point group C_{3v}. Figure 6 shows the d orbital splitting pattern expected for a trigonal elongation and a trigonal compression in a point charge ligand field model. The "observed" d orbital splitting pattern more nearly resembles that of a trigonal elongation. This result is opposite to that expected if one of the iron–sulfur bonds in reduced rubredoxin were considerably shorter than the other three as is observed in the X-ray structure of oxidized rubredoxin.

If π bonding plays a significant role in determining the d orbital energy levels, the β-carbons of the four cysteinyl residues must also be included in symmetry considerations since the orientation of the sulfur π orbitals depend on the β-carbon positions. The C—S—Fe bonds are not colinear, so that the most symmetric arrangement of the nine-atom system belongs to the tetragonal point group D_{2d}. In D_{2d} symmetry there is a single fourfold rotation–reflection (S_4) axis, which corresponds to one of the three S_4 axes of the parent tetrahedron. The important feature of molecules belonging to the point group D_{2d} (and C_{3v}) is that they possess doubly degenerate energy levels. Figure 6 also shows a d orbital energy level diagram which results from a tetragonal distortion of a tetrahedral ligand field to one of D_{2d} symmetry. This splitting pattern is also consistent with that "observed" in reduced rubredoxin. If we ignore the short Fe—S(42) bond, *oxidized* rubredoxin does in fact have a direction which could conceivably behave like an effective S_4 axis, namely, the common bisector of the S(6)—Fe—S(42) and S(9)—Fe—S(39) bond angles (Fig. 2). Thus, for the present we can only conclude (1) that the effective symmetry of the ligand field is considerably different in oxidized and reduced rubredoxin yet cannot be seen as structural differences in the oxidized–reduced Fourier difference electron density map, which is currently only at 4.0 Å resolution, or (2) that the structures and, consequently, the ligand fields in oxidized and reduced rubredoxin are similar, but that a point charge model is inadequate, and that π bonding plays a dominant role in determining the d orbital energy levels.

Unfortunately, there is very little information from optical studies on

---

* A disquieting feature of this analysis is that the total tetrahedral splitting of about 5000 cm^{-1} is larger than the values usually observed for tetrahedral inorganic complexes. However, this could be the result of conformational constraints imposed by the remainder of the protein.

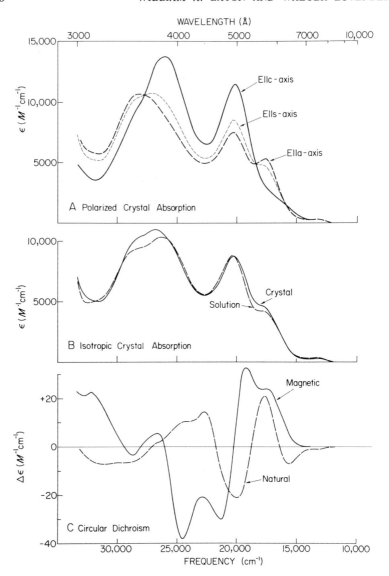

Fig. 7. Room-temperature spectra of oxidized *C. pasteurianum* rubredoxin. (A) Polarized single-crystal absorption spectrum. The spectra were taken on crystals that were flattened on one of the rhombohedral faces using a microspectrophotometer similar to the one described by Eaton and Lewis (1970). The incident beam of plane-polarized light is normal to a rhombohedral crystal face with the electric vector parallel to one or the other of two extinction directions. One of these directions is perpendicular to the *c* (threefold) crystal axis, which we call the *a* axis, and the other direction is intermediate between the *c* axis and the plane perpendicular to *c,* which we call the *s* axis. In order to calculate the *c*-axis polarized spectrum, we

the iron $3d$ orbital energy levels in oxidized rubredoxin. For a high-spin ferric ion the $^6A_1$ ground state is the only sextet ligand field state and, therefore, all $d \rightarrow d$ transitions are forbidden by the strict spin selection rule $\Delta S = 0$. Nevertheless, very weak transitions to the various quartet states that derive from the ^4G atomic term have been observed in inorganic tetrahedral ferric complexes (see Fig. 4), although the specific assignments are still uncertain (Jørgensen, 1962; Lever, 1968; Ferguson, 1970; Gill, 1961; Ginsberg and Robin, 1963; Hathaway and Holah, 1964; Forster and Goodgame, 1965). They are found at frequencies greater than 10,000 cm⁻¹, with molar extinction coefficients in the range 0.5 to 20 M^{-1} cm⁻¹. In oxidized rubredoxin these spin-forbidden ligand field transitions are hidden under the much more intense charge transfer spectrum which begins at about 12,500 cm⁻¹. However, it is not inconceivable that the 13,400 cm⁻¹ band ($\epsilon = 360$ M^{-1} cm⁻¹) arises from a component of the $^6A_1 \rightarrow {}^4T_1(^4G)$ transition (Fig. 5), which is tremendously intensified by interaction with nearby charge transfer states (Fig. 7). If this is so, then we estimate the $^6S - {}^4G$ term separation to be reduced to about 60%

make the assumption that when the electric vector of the incident plane polarized light is parallel to the s axis, it remains parallel to s as it propagates through the crystal. With this assumption, we can calculate the c-axis optical density (OD_c) from the a-axis and s-axis optical densities (OD_a and OD_s) at each wavelength from the relation $OD_c = [OD_s - OD_a(\sin^2 \theta_{s,c})]/(\cos^2 \theta_{s,c})$ where $\theta_{s,c} = 59.6°$ is the angle between the c and s axes and is determined by the geometry of the unit cell (Herriott et al., 1970). Because of the small projection of c onto s, small errors in crystal alignment lead to considerable errors in the calculated c-axis spectrum, which accounts for part of the rather large experimental uncertainties in the polarization ratios reported in Table II. The experimental uncertainty in measuring crystal thicknesses is also large, so that we chose to obtain extinction coefficients by assuming that the solution spectrum and the isotropic spectrum calculated from the crystal data (vide infra) have identical extinction coefficients for the 20,200 cm⁻¹ band, which was taken as 8800 M^{-1} cm⁻¹ (Lovenberg and Williams, 1969). (B) Isotropic absorption spectra. The two spectra shown are the ordinary solution absorption spectrum and the isotropic absorption spectrum calculated from the polarized single-crystal absorption spectrum. The latter spectrum is calculated from the relation (Eaton, 1967) $\epsilon_{\mathrm{iso}} = \frac{1}{3}(\epsilon_c + 2\epsilon_a)$. The solution spectrum was obtained in an approximately 50% saturated ammonium sulfate solution (pH 4), which is close to the composition of the mother liquor in the crystal experiments (pH 4, approximately 70% saturation). Assuming that the extinction coefficients for the two spectra at 20,200 cm⁻¹ are identical (vide supra), then the small differences observed between the solution and crystal isotropic spectra are within the experimental uncertainty in measuring the crystal spectrum. (C) Natural and magnetic circular dichroism spectra (0.1 M tris buffer, pH 7.3). These spectra were taken by Dr. David Ulmer on a Cary 61 circular dichroism instrument equipped with a superconducting magnet. The magnetic field induced circular dichroism spectrum was obtained in a 45 kG magnetic field and is corrected for the zero-field circular dichroism, i.e., the natural circular dichroism.

of its free ferrous ion value (Orgel, 1955; Eaton et $al.$, 1971), which is consistent with the large decrease in interelectronic repulsion parameters expected for sulfur ligands as a result of extensive covalent bonding (Jørgensen, 1962, 1968).

In reduced rubredoxin, the masking of spin-forbidden ligand field transitions by intense charge transfer transitions is much less. However, no specific assignments have been made. Fourteen triplet ligand field states are expected to lie less than 33,000 cm^{-1} above the ground quintet state (Ferguson et $al.$, 1969). With a splitting of most of these triplet states by lower symmetry ligand fields, a quasicontinuum of quintet → triplet, spin-forbidden $d \to d$ transitions is predicted, which probably accounts for the very weak, featureless absorption between 10,000 and 33,000 cm^{-1} (Figs. 5 and 8).

To conclude this section on ligand field properties, we discuss some aspects of the electron paramagnetic resonance (EPR) spectrum. A more complete discussion by Orme-Johnson and Sands is to be found in Chapter 5 of this volume. No EPR has yet been observed for reduced rubredoxin. Oxidized rubredoxin exhibits an EPR spectrum with resonances near $g = 4.3$ (Atherton et $al.$, 1966; Lovenberg, 1966; Palmer and Brintzinger, 1966; Bachmayer et $al.$, 1967) and an additional resonance at $g = 9.4$ (Newman and Postgate, 1968; Peterson and Coon, 1968; Lode and Coon, 1971). Many high-spin ferric complexes show EPR spectra in the $g = 4.3$ region. The symmetry of the ligand field in high-spin ferric complexes is assessed from the values of the spin Hamiltonian parameters, D and E, which describe the EPR spectrum (Orme-Johnson and Sands, Chapter 15; Griffith, 1964a,b; Blumberg, 1967; Dowsing and Gibson, 1969). Blumberg (1967) showed that for $0 \leqslant |E/D| \leqslant \frac{1}{3}$, $E/D = 0$ represents an axially symmetric ligand field, while $E/D = \pm \frac{1}{3}$ occurs in "completely rhombic" symmetry. In cubic symmetry, e.g., tetrahedral or octahedral, $D = E = 0$. According to Griffith (1964a,b), the values of D and E are mainly controlled by spin-orbit coupling between the $^6A_1(^6S)$ ground state and the $^4T_1(^4G)$ state, which is the lowest-energy, excited ligand field state (Fig. 4). In this description the value of E/D depends only on the energies of the three orbital components of the $^4T_1(^4G)$ state relative to the $^6A_1(^6S)$ ground state, and is given by the following relation (Griffith, 1964a,b)

$$\frac{E}{D} = \frac{E_x^{-1} - E_y^{-1}}{2E_z^{-1} - E_x^{-1} - E_y^{-1}}$$

where E_x, E_y, and E_z are the energies of the three orbital components that arise from a rhombic splitting of the triply degenerate $^4T_1(^4G)$ excited state. Notice that in axial symmetry $E_x = E_y \neq E_z$ and therefore $E/D = 0$.

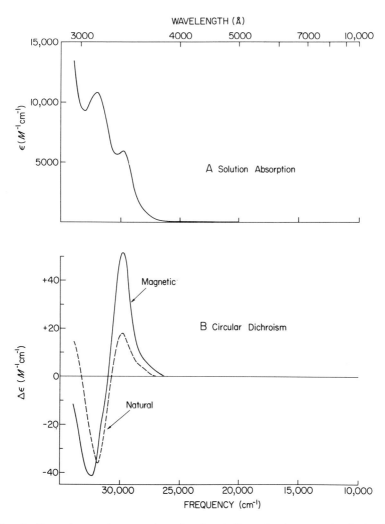

Fig. 8. Room-temperature spectra of reduced *C. pasteurianum rubredoxin.* (A) Solution absorption spectrum (0.05 *M* tris buffer, pH 7.3). The rubredoxin was reduced by hydrogen gas in the presence of a *C. pasteurianum* extract containing hydrogenase. (B) Natural and magnetic circular dichroism spectra (0.1 *M* tris buffer, pH 7.3). The rubredoxin was reduced by excess solid sodium dithionite. Remaining description as in the legend to Fig. 7(C).

"Completely rhombic" symmetry corresponds to an equal energy spacing of the three components, and if this spacing is small compared to the $^4T_1(^4G) - {}^6A_1(^6S)$ separation, then by choosing the z component to be highest or lowest, the above equation gives $|E/D| = \frac{1}{3}$.

Peisach *et al.* (1971) have investigated the EPR spectrum of *Pseudomonas oleovorans* rubredoxin in considerable detail. This EPR spectrum is very similar to that of rubredoxin from *Clostridium pasteurianum* (Lode and Coon, 1971). From the observed g values and the temperature dependence of the resonance amplitudes, these authors find $E/D = 0.28$, and $D = +1.76$ cm^{-1}. An E/D value of 0.28 reflects a ligand field which is almost "completely rhombic." Since the three orbital components of the $^4T_1(^4G)$ state have not been identified in the optical spectrum of oxidized rubredoxin (or apparently in the optical spectrum of any other d^5 high-spin complex where E/D has been determined), we cannot directly compare the ligand field as detected by optical and EPR spectroscopy via Griffith's equation. However, the charge transfer optical transitions in oxidized rubredoxin, discussed in the next section, which presumably involve iron $3d$ orbitals, give rise to a nearly axially symmetric spectrum. Thus, there is an apparent disagreement in the interpretation of the optical and EPR results. A possible solution to this dilemma is that E/D is much more sensitive to deviations from axial symmetry than is evident from Griffith's equation.

C. The Color

We turn now to a consideration of the symmetry properties of the iron–sulfur complex as revealed in the visible and near-ultraviolet optical spectra. Oxidized rubredoxin in moderate concentrations (~ 1 mM) is a deep wine red. Upon one-electron reduction the color becomes pale yellow. A great deal of experimental information about the spectra responsible for these colors is available from solution and polarized single crystal absorption, and natural and magnetic circular dichroism measurements. In contrast to our discussion of the ligand field properties, an orbital-type description of the observed visible and near ultraviolet spectra requires an explicit consideration of electrons localized mainly on the sulfur ligands as well as the iron electrons. There have been, unfortunately, no molecular orbital calculations on the iron–sulfur complex of rubredoxin or any appropriate model compound, so that our understanding of the orbital origin of these spectra is still at a primitive stage. Nonetheless, certain qualitative features are apparent. Because of the moderately high intensity and large bandwidths, the spectrum between 16,000 and 33,000 cm^{-1} (300–600 nm) in oxidized rubredoxin almost certainly arises from charge transfer-type transitions (see previous discussions concerning 13,400 cm^{-1} band). Furthermore, the charge transfer mechanism probably involves promotion of electrons from molecular orbitals localized mainly on the sulfur ligands to molecular orbitals composed primarily of iron

$3d$ atomic orbitals. When electronic charge is added to the central metal upon one-electron reduction, transfer of electrons from sulfur to iron is energetically more difficult, resulting in a shift of the charge transfer spectrum to higher frequencies. Estimates of transition frequencies using Jørgensen optical electronegativity parameters are consistent with a sulfur to iron charge transfer mechanism (Tsibris and Woody, 1970).

Before discussing the polarized single crystal absorption and magnetic circular dichroism spectra, we should comment on the natural circular dichroism shown in Figs. 7 and 8. Although there is potentially a considerable amount of structural information contained in the visible and ultraviolet natural circular dichroism, it has thus far not been very informative; there have been no theoretical investigations, and at the empirical level there have been no systematic studies of the natural circular dichroism or optical rotatory dispersion under a wide variety of conditions. Such studies should be important for assessing the influence of protein conformation on the structure of the iron–sulfur complex. It is worth noting, however, that rubredoxin from several different bacterial species exhibit similar optical activity, indicating similar structures for the iron–sulfur chromophore and its immediate surroundings (Gillard et al., 1965; Lovenberg, 1966; Atherton et al., 1966; Garbett et al., 1967; Peterson and Coon, 1968; Newman and Postgate, 1968; Lovenberg and Williams, 1969; Tsibris and Woody, 1970). Also, because of the somewhat narrower bandwidths, changing sign, and differing anisotropy factors, the circular dichroism more clearly delineates the individual electronic transitions than is apparent in the absorption spectra and, therefore, should eventually be helpful in making detailed spectroscopic assignments.

The spectra of single crystals in plane-polarized light and magnetic circular dichroism of solutions constitute powerful methods for investigating the symmetry properties of chromophores. The structural information derived from the single-crystal spectrum is based on the phenomenon of anisotropic absorption of plane-polarized light by oriented molecules. The directions in which molecules maximally absorb plane-polarized light, so-called transition moment directions, are symmetry determined and are the unique experimental quantities obtained from polarized single-crystal absorption measurements. If the ground- and excited-state geometries are the same, then from a knowledge of the transition moment directions, the symmetry properties of the combining states and, thereby, the symmetry of the chromophore may be determined. For broad-banded spectra at room temperature, the most unambiguous determination of transition moment directions comes from polarization results for the most intense transitions. Since the iron–sulfur chromophores are well separated

from each other in the rubredoxin crystal, the spectrum is uncomplicated
by the effects of intermolecular interactions. Therefore, like the crystal
of cytochrome c (Eaton and Hochstrasser, 1967), myoglobin (Eaton and
Hochstrasser, 1968), and hemoglobin (Makinen and Eaton, 1972), the
rubredoxin crystal may be considered to consist of a collection of non
interacting chromophores—an oriented gas. The oriented gas model i
experimentally justified by the close agreement of the solution spec
trum and the isotropic spectrum calculated from the crystal data
(Fig. 7). Furthermore, the agreement between the crystal and solution
spectra indicates that no large perturbations of the iron–sulfur chromo
phore take place upon crystallization. This result helps to answer th
well-worn question concerning the identity of structure in crystal and
solution.

Since a tetrahedral molecule is a spherically symmetric absorber of
plane-polarized light, the large dichroism observed in the polarized singl
crystal absorption spectrum in Fig. 7 requires that the chromophore pos
sesses less than tetrahedral symmetry. The effective symmetry of the
chromophore is found to be axial from the following considerations. The
transitions at 20,200 cm^{-1} (495 nm) and 17,700 cm^{-1} (565 nm) are intens
enough that the orientation of the transition moments can be directly
obtained from the polarization ratios.* Also these transitions are we

* Rubredoxin crystals belong to the space group $R3$ (point group C_3), and contain
nine molecules in the hexagonal unit cell (Herriott et al., 1970). Since the crystal
are uniaxial, there are only two distinct principal optical directions; these ar
parallel to the threefold c crystal axis and any direction perpendicular to c, a
directions perpendicular to c (i.e., the ab plane) being optically equivalent. We de
fine the polarization ratio as the ratio of the integrated absorption intensity polarized
parallel to the c axis to the integrated absorption intensity polarized perpendicular
to the c axis. The polarization ratio $P(z)$ is related to the orientation of the trans
tion moment by the relation (Eaton, 1967)

$$P(z) = 2n^2/(1 - n^2)$$

where n is the cosine of the angle between the transition moment and the c crystal
axis. The ground state of oxidized rubredoxin is orbitally nondegenerate, so that
this relation applies for transitions to orbitally nondegenerate excited states, when
the chromophore behaves as a linear absorber of plane-polarized light. For allowed
transitions to doubly degenerate excited states, the chromophore is a so-called planar
or circularly symmetric absorber of plane-polarized light and must be axially sym
metric. The expression for the polarization ratio then becomes (Eaton, 1967)

$$P(x, y) = 2(1 - n^2)/(1 + n^2)$$

where n is now the cosine of the angle between the c crystal axis and the (z) norma
to the (x, y) absorbing plane of the chromophore. Thus, in axially symmetric
chromophores, allowed transitions are either polarized parallel (z) to the uniqu

TABLE II

POLARIZATION RATIOS AND SQUARED DIRECTION COSINES OF TRANSITION
MOMENTS RELATIVE TO c CRYSTAL AXIS IN OXIDIZED RUBREDOXIN
FROM POLARIZED SINGLE CRYSTAL ABSORPTION SPECTRUM (FIG. 7)[a]

Transition	Polarization ratio[b]	n^2 for nondegenerate transition[c]	n^2 for degenerate transition[d]
17,700 cm^{-1}	0.22 ± 0.01	0.10 ± 0.04	0.80 ± 0.08
20,200 cm^{-1}	1.55 ± 0.1	0.44 ± 0.02	0.13 ± 0.03

[a] See footnote on p. 152.

[b] The polarization ratio P is defined as the ratio of the c-polarized absorption intensity to the a-polarized absorption intensity.

[c] This value of n^2 is calculated from the relation for nondegenerate transitions $n^2 = P/(P + 2)$.

[d] This value of n^2 is calculated from the relation for degenerate transitions $n^2 = (2 - P)/(2 + P)$.

enough separated from nearby transitions that the polarization ratios can be accurately obtained without recourse to extensive curve-fitting procedures. Table II gives the polarization ratios and the squared direction cosines for the transition moments, assuming a nondegenerate excited state in one case, and a doubly degenerate excited state in the other case. Important restrictions are placed on the transition moment directions by the observed polarization ratios. Both the 17,700 and 20,200 cm^{-1} transitions cannot be degenerate since they would have the same transition moment directions and, therefore, the same polarization ratios. Furthermore, if one of the transitions were degenerate and the other nondegenerate, then the squared direction cosines calculated from the polarization ratios must be identical. Therefore, there are only two straightforward interpretations of the polarization data: (1) both the 20,200 and 17,700 cm^{-1} excited states are nondegenerate, in which case the effective symmetry of the chromophore is rhombic, i.e., there is no symmetry axis higher than a twofold, or (2) the 20,200 cm^{-1} state is doubly degenerate and the 17,700 cm^{-1} state is nondegenerate, so that the chromophore has effectively axial symmetry. The latter interpretation is suggested by the absolute intensities in the solution absorption spectra, since the 20,200 cm^{-1} band is about twice as intense as the 17,700 cm^{-1} band. Also the

axis of the chromophore or are polarized isotropically in the (x, y) plane perpendicular to the unique axis. Notice that for a uniaxial crystal one can only describe the unique (z) direction of the axially symmetrical chromophore in terms of the angle of a cone coaxial with the c crystal axis. For a molecule with cubic symmetry x, y, and z are no longer distinguishable and $P(x, y, z) = 1$, i.e., there is no linear dichroism.

polarization ratios and absolute intensities for the transitions at 28,800 and 26,200 cm^{-1} are in qualitative agreement with the results expected for a nondegenerate and doubly degenerate excited state, respectively. Confirmation of the effective axial symmetry of the chromophore comes from magnetic circular dichroism results.

Comprehensive treatments of the theory and applications of magnetic circular dichroism can be found in the papers by Buckingham and Stephens (1966), Schatz and McCaffery (1969), and Stephens (1970) Here we only present a very brief phenomenological description. All substances become optically active when placed in a magnetic field which has a component parallel to the measuring light beam. The magnetic field causes a Zeeman splitting of degenerate states, and the resulting selection rules require a differential absorption of right and left circularly polarized light. The dispersion of the induced circular dichroism through an absorption band is described by three so-called Faraday terms: A, B, and C The Zeeman splitting of a ground-state degeneracy by the magnetic field leads to a Faraday C term and gives rise to a temperature-dependent magnetic circular dichroism band that peaks at the same frequency as the ordinary absorption band. If the system possesses only an excited state degeneracy, a Faraday A term results, and the magnetic circular dichroism changes sign at the absorption maximum. The band shape for an isolated A term resembles the derivative of the associated absorption band. The B terms result from a "mixing" of the zero-field states by the magnetic field and are present for degenerate and nondegenerate transitions. The magnetic circular dichroism band from a B term peaks at the associated absorption maximum, but can be distinguished from a C term by the absence of a temperature dependence. The B term can be much larger than A or C terms and can prevent their detection. In the event that an absorption band is composed of several electronic transitions, the magnetic circular dichroism becomes more complex For example, two overlapping C terms of opposite signs can generate a "pseudo-A term" magnetic circular dichroism. This happens quite generally in systems with orbitally nondegenerate, spin-degenerate ground states when the transition is to an orbitally degenerate, spin degenerate upper state which is split by spin-orbit coupling (P. J Stephens, personal communication).

Figures 7 and 8 show the magnetic circular dichroism of oxidized and reduced rubredoxin. For reduced rubredoxin the magnetic circular dichroism extrema at 32,000 cm^{-1} (313 nm) and 30,700 cm^{-1} (330 nm closely correspond to the absorption maxima and, therefore, mainly arise from B or C terms, although an A term for the 32,000 cm^{-1} transition could easily be obscured by the larger B and/or C terms. The result on oxidized rubredoxin are much more informative. With an $^6A_1$ ground state, large A or pseudo-A terms are only expected for orbitally degenerate sextet upper states, orbitally nondegenerate states giving only B terms (P. J. Stephens, personal communication). The transitions at 26,200 and 20,200 cm^{-1} exhibit A-term dispersion, strongly indicating orbital degeneracy in the excited states involved in these transitions. The transitions at 28,800 and 17,700 cm^{-1} exhibit B-term dispersion, suggesting that the upper states are orbitally nondegenerate. Thus, the correctness of the interpretation of the polarized single crystal absorption results is reinforced by the magnetic circular dichroism.

The most apparent correlation of the axial charge transfer states with their parent tetrahedral states would be that the 28,800 and 26,200 cm^{-1} states derive from one triply degenerate state in tetrahedral symmetry, and that the 17,700 and 20,200 cm^{-1} pair derive from another triply degenerate state. As with reduced rubredoxin, the splittings of 2600 and 2500 cm^{-1} suggest a considerable axial distortion. From a comparison of the bandwidths for the nondegenerate and doubly degenerate transitions, the rhombic splitting is estimated to be less than 1000 cm^{-1}.

We may now ask what kind of axial distortion is manifested in the charge transfer spectrum. The presence of axial symmetry indicates that all but one of the seven axes of the tetrahedron—four threefold rotation (C_3) axes and three fourfold rotation–reflection (S_4) axes—have been destroyed. We can determine which axis survives by comparing the direction of the unique axis of the axially symmetric chromophore with respect to the c crystal axis, as determined from the single-crystal spectrum, with the possible molecular directions, as determined by the X-ray studies. Since an orbital description of the charge transfer transitions explicitly includes the sulfur atomic orbitals, considerations of effective symmetry for the chromophore should include the β-carbons of the four cysteinyl residues. As discussed earlier, the highest possible symmetry is D_{2d}, and the direction most closely approximating an S_4 axis is the common bisector of the S(6)—Fe—S(42) and S(9)—Fe—S(39) bond angles. This direction makes an angle of about 80° with the c crystal axis, which is compatible with the optically determined angle of about 70° for the unique axis of the chromophore (Table II). The difference of about 10° between the approximate S_4 axis and the unique axis of the chromophore represents a minimum difference, since the optical results only yield the angle of a cone coaxial with the c crystal axis (see footnote on p. 153). We can reject the less plausible assumption that the effective symmetry of the charge transfer chromophore is determined mainly by the positions of only the iron and the four sulfurs. If this were the case, the short (2.05 Å) iron–sulfur(42) bond direction would be expected to behave as a threefold rotation axis, and, therefore, coincide with the unique axis of the chromophore—the short bond direction makes an angle of 35° with the c crystal axis so that it is at least 35° from the unique axis of the chromophore. If our choice of the unique symmetry axis is correct, it is indeed puzzling that the short iron–sulfur(42) bond does not destroy the S_4 axis and thereby cause a much larger splitting of the D_{2d} doubly degenerate states.

Thus far, in order to obtain information concerning the detailed geometry of the iron–sulfur complex from spectroscopic measurements, we have had to assume that the ground and excited electronic state geometries are very similar. Vibrational spectroscopy, on the other hand, is one of the most straightforward methods for investigating ground state molecular geometry. However, the number of vibrational transitions in the infrared spectrum of even a small protein is enormous, and consequently, specific assignments of iron–sulfur transitions would be extraordinarily difficult. Furthermore, there are technical difficulties in obtaining an infrared spectrum in an aqueous medium because of high solvent absorption. Both of these problems can be circumvented by investigating the vibrational spectrum through Raman spectroscopy. Long and Loehr (1970) and Long et al. (1971) have shown that by using excitation frequencies in the region of electronic absorption (the 632.8 nm line of a helium–neon laser and the 488.0 nm line of the argon ion laser) the intensity of the Raman bands associated with the iron–sulfur chromophore in oxidized rubredoxin become considerably enhanced. This resonance or preresonance Raman effect selects out of the exceedingly complex vibrational spectrum of the entire protein only those vibrations which are involved in the electronic transition.* The four expected Raman-active modes for the five-atom tetrahedral system of iron and four sulfurs in oxidized rubredoxin have been assigned by Long et al. (1971) on the basis of their frequencies and polarization properties. In fact, except for one unexplained band at 86 cm⁻¹, these are the only discrete Raman transitions that are observed. The symmetrical stretching mode ν_1 (A_1) is the most intense and appears at 314 cm⁻¹ from the 488.0 nm exciting line, while the triply degenerate stretching mode ν_3 (T_2) appears at 368 cm⁻¹. The two bending modes ν_2 (E) and ν_4 (T_2) were assigned to the much less well-resolved bands at 126 and 150 cm⁻¹, respectively. No splitting of any of the degenerate transitions was observed in these room-temperature spectra, but the nonzero depolarization ratio for the ν_1 (A_1) symmetrical stretching mode could be the result of a distortion from tetrahedral symmetry.

---

* For reviews of the resonance Raman effect see Behringer (1967) and Levin (1972).

Yamamoto *et al.* (1972) have obtained a Raman spectrum of oxidized rubredoxin from *P. elsdenii* at room temperature using the 568.2 nm line of a krypton laser. This solution spectrum has a somewhat improved signal-to-noise ratio and shows three prominent Raman lines at 370, 320, and 158 cm⁻¹. Furthermore, the 370 cm⁻¹ line is split by 18 cm⁻¹ and there is evidence for additional bands at 75 and 175 cm⁻¹. This six-line spectrum suggests that the effective symmetry of the iron–sulfur complex is lower than tetrahedral. Yamamoto *et al.* (1972) carried out a vibrational analysis assuming that a five-atom system is trigonally compressed along one of the iron–sulfur bonds. They obtained a good fit to the observed spectrum by assigning the 158, 320, and 380 cm⁻¹ lines to A_1 modes (in C_{3v} symmetry) and the 75, 175, and 362 cm⁻¹ lines to E modes and by using valence force constants of 1.74 and 1.44 dynes/Å for the one short and three long iron–sulfur bonds, respectively. It is important to note, however, that this vibrational analysis is by no means unique; consequently, a good fit to the observed frequency spectrum does not necessarily provide support for a trigonally compressed tetrahedron. The Raman, optical, and electron paramagnetic resonance spectra of *P. elsdenii* rubredoxin are sufficiently similar to those of *C. pasteurianum* rubredoxin for us to assume that the stereochemistries of the iron–sulfur complexes in these two proteins are essentially the same. We can expect, therefore, that a vibrational analysis of a better resolved spectrum of oxidized *C. pasteurianum* rubredoxin will also be consistent with a trigonally compressed tetrahedron.

IV. SUMMARY AND CONCLUSIONS

Except for the rubredoxin from *P. oleovorans*, there is still no known specific electron transfer function for this protein. Furthermore, there is rather little known about the thermodynamic and kinetic reactivity of the iron–sulfur complex, which is assumed to be the biochemically "active center" of the molecule. Most of the chemical studies preceded the X-ray structure determination and were mainly concerned with elucidating the nature of the iron coordination. The X-ray study, however, stimulated a variety of investigations of the electromagnetic properties, and most of this chapter has been concerned with rationalizing these properties in terms of the X-ray structure of the iron–sulfur complex.

The X-ray investigation has shown that the iron in rubredoxin is bonded to the sulfurs of four cysteinyl residues in an approximately tetrahedral complex. All of the major features of the electromagnetic properties can be understood in terms of this tetrahedral coordination, and the iron appears to be a well-behaved high-spin d^5 ion and high-spin d^6 ion in the oxidized and reduced states, respectively. However, the 1.5 Å X-ray data for oxidized rubredoxin clearly show a distortion from perfect tetrahedral symmetry for the five-atom system of iron, and four sulfurs, the largest distortion corresponding to a trigonal compression. The availability of such accurate X-ray data prompted us to consider the relation between the X-ray structure and spectroscopic properties in more detail. Here the correlation turns out to be no longer straightforward. Only the vibrational spectrum of oxidized rubredoxin *may* directly reflect a trigonal compression in a simple fashion. The charge transfer optical spectrum can be interpreted in terms of an axially symmetrical chromophore, but the axial symmetry is not trigonal. There is, however, a close correspondence between the optically determined unique axis and the direction most nearly approximating an S_4 axis for the nine-atom system of iron, four sulfurs, and four β-carbons. Oxidized rubredoxin exhibits an almost "completely rhombic" electron paramagnetic resonance spectrum, which is as far from axial symmetry as possible. Thus, at microwave frequencies we see a rhombic ligand field for the iron, at infrared frequencies a trigonal collection of balls and springs, and at optical frequencies a tetragonal potential field for the loosely bound iron and sulfur electrons. Although these results may appear at first sight to be mutually contradictory, this is not necessarily the case, since the symmetry determining structural features may differ for the three different kinds of spectra. There is a less optimistic view, namely, that we have given an oversimplified interpretation to some of the spectral data. For example, some of the degeneracies observed in the optical and vibrational spectra may be accidental and, therefore, may not reflect the molecular geometry in a simple fashion.

Stereochemical details are not yet available for reduced rubredoxin from X-ray diffraction, although at 4 Å resolution no differences in the structures of the iron–sulfur complexes in the reduced and oxidized proteins are apparent. From the Mössbauer and ligand field optical spectra a d orbital energy level diagram can be constructed for reduced rubredoxin. In a point charge ligand field model this d orbital splitting pattern could not result from a trigonal compression, but is consistent with a trigonal elongation or tetragonal distortion. However, because π bonding may have a strong influence on the d orbitals, a molecular orbital calculation may be required to relate d orbital levels to the coordination geometry. In fact, a molecular orbital calculation may be extremely worthwhile at this point, since there is now so much experimental information on the electronic structure of the iron–sulfur complex, and in the case of the oxidized species there are accurate atomic positions from the X-ray investigation. Furthermore, we would like ultimately to understand the chemical behavior of rubredoxin not only in terms of the equilibrium positions of its nuclei ("ball and stick" chemistry), but also in terms of electrons in orbitals.

Finally, we turn to two important questions about the structure of the iron–sulfur complex. How is the large distortion in the iron–sulfur bonding brought about and what is its biochemical significance? From a naive examination of CPK molecular models, it would seem possible for the structural unit

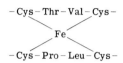

to exist without considerably distorting the iron–sulfur coordination from perfect tetrahedral symmetry. There is, then, the implication that the stereochemical constraints imposed by the conformational requirements in the remainder of the protein are responsible for the large difference in iron–sulfur bond lengths. In fact, Vallee and Williams (1968) have made the general hypothesis that metalloenzymes are "designed" to achieve a distorted geometry at the metal site which approximates the transition state and thereby enhances reaction rates. The distorted geometry could also be important in causing substantial changes in redox potentials from the values for a more symmetrical structure (Vallee and Williams, 1968). Once the biochemically relevant reactions are identified, rubredoxin would be an ideal protein for testing these ideas, not only because of the extensive X-ray structural information, but also because it is the only metalloprotein known so far where all of the ligands are chemically identical. Thus, it will be important to further refine our understanding of how the distortion of the iron–sulfur complex is manifested in its electromagnetic properties, so that we have a rapid means of monitoring the relationship between the iron–sulfur stereochemistry and the thermodynamic and kinetic reactivity of the protein.

NOTE ADDED IN PROOF. Recently, Loew and co-workers (1973) have used iterative extended Hückel molecular orbital theory to calculate a variety of properties of model compounds for the iron–sulfur complex of both oxidized and reduced rubredoxin.

ACKNOWLEDGMENTS

We are indebted to Professor Graham Palmer, Dr. Hideo Kon, Professor Philip J. Stephens, Dr. Ira W. Levin, and Professor Lyle H. Jensen for many helpful and stimulating discussions. We would also like to thank Professor Jensen for supplying us with the unpublished atomic coordinates of rubredoxin from his X-ray diffraction investigation.

REFERENCES

Atherton, N. M., Garbett, K., Gillard, R. D., Mason, R., Mayhew, S. J., Peel, J. L., and Stangroom, J. E. (1966). *Nature (London)* **212**, 590.

Bachmayer, H., Piette, L. H., Yasunobu, K. T., and Whiteley, H. R. (1967). *Proc. Nat. Acad. Sci. U.S.* **57**, 122.

Bachmayer, H., Yasunobu, K. T., Peel, J. L., and Mayhew, S. (1968a). *J. Biol. Chem.* **243**, 1022.

Bachmayer, H., Yasunobu, K. T., and Whiteley, H. R. (1968b). *Proc. Nat. Acad. Sci. U.S.* **59**, 1273.

Ballhausen, C. J. (1962). "Introduction to Ligand Field Theory." McGraw-Hill, New York.

Behringer, J., (1967). *In* "Raman Spectroscopy" (H. A. Szymanski, ed.). Plenum, New York.

Benson, A. M., Haniu, M., Lode, E. T., Coon, M. J., and Yasunobu, K. T. (1970). *Fed. Proc.* **29**, 859.

Blumberg, W. (1967). *In* "Magnetic Resonance in Biological Systems" (A. Ehrenberg, B. G. Mälmstron, and T. Vänngard, eds.), p. 119. Pergamon, Oxford.

Buchanan, B. B., Lovenberg, W., and Rabinowitz, J. C. (1963). *Proc. Nat. Acad. Sci. U.S.* **49**, 345.

Buckingham, A. D., and Stephens, P. J. (1966). *Ann. Rev. Phys. Chem.* **17**, 399.

Connick, R. E., and McVey, W. H. (1951). *J. Amer. Chem. Soc.* **73**, 1798.

Debrunner, P. G. (1970). *In* "Spectroscopic Approaches to Biomolecular Conformation" (D. W. Urry, ed.), p. 209. Amer. Med. Ass., Chicago, Illinois.

Dowsing, R. D., and Gibson, J. F. (1969). *J. Chem. Phys.* **50**, 294.

Eaton, W. A. (1967). Ph.D. Dissertation, Univ. of Pennsylvania.

Eaton, W. A., and Charney, E. (1969). *J. Chem. Phys.* **51**, 4502.

Eaton, W. A., and Charney, E. (1971). *In* "Probes of Structure and Function of Macromolecules and Membranes" (B. Chance, C. P. Lee, and J. K. Blasie, eds.), Vol. I, p. 155. Academic Press, New York.

Eaton, W. A., and Hochstrasser, R. M. (1967). *J. Chem. Phys.* **46**, 2533.

Eaton, W. A., and Hochstrasser, R. M. (1968). *J. Chem. Phys.* **49**, 985.

Eaton, W. A., and Lewis, T. P. (1970). *J. Chem. Phys.* **53**, 2164.

Eaton, W. A., and Lovenberg, W. (1970). *J. Amer. Chem. Soc.* **92**, 7195.

Eaton, W. A., Palmer, G., Fee, J. A., Kimura, T., and Lovenberg, W. (1971). *Proc. Nat. Acad. Sci. U.S.* **68**, 3015.

Edwards, P. R., Johnson, C. E., and Williams, R. J. P. (1967). *J. Chem. Phys.* **47**, 2074.

Ferguson, J. (1970). *Progr. Inorg. Chem.* **12**, 159.

Ferguson, J., Guggenheim, H. J., and Krausz, E. R. (1969). *Aust. J. Chem.* **22**, 1809.

Figgis, B. N. (1966). "Introduction to Ligand Fields." Wiley (Interscience), New York.

Forster, D., and Goodgame, D. M. L. (1965). *J. Chem. Soc.* 268.

Garbett, K., Gillard, R. D., Knowles, P. F., and Stangroom, J. E. (1967). *Nature (London)* **215**, 824.

George, P., Hanania, G. I. H., and Eaton, W. A. (1966). *In* "Hemes and Hemoproteins" (B. Chance, R. W. Estabrook, and T. Yonetani, eds.), p. 267. Academic Press, New York.

Gill, N. S. (1961). *J. Chem. Soc.* 3512.

Gillard, R. D., McKenzie, E. D., Mason, R., Mayhew, S. G., Peel, J. L., and Stangroom, J. E. (1965). *Nature (London)* **208**, 769.

Ginsberg, A. P., and Robin, M. B. (1963). *Inorg. Chem.* **2**, 817.

Griffith, J. S. (1964). "The Theory of Transition-Metal Ions." Cambridge Univ. Press, London and New York.

Griffith, J. S. (1964a). *Biopolym. Symp.* **1**, 35.

Griffith, J. S. (1964b). *Mol. Phys.* **8**, 213.

Hathaway, B. J., and Holah, D. G. (1964). *J. Chem. Soc.* 2408.

Herriott, J. R., Sieker, L. C., Jensen, L. H., and Lovenberg, W. (1970). *J. Mol. Biol.* **50**, 391.

Jørgensen, C. K. (1962). "Absorption Spectra and Chemical Bonding in Complexes." Pergamon, Oxford.

Jørgensen, C. K. (1968). *Inorg. Chim. Acta Rev.* **2**, 65.

Laishley, E. J., Travis, J., and Peck, H. D. Jr. (1964). *J. Bacteriol.* **98**, 302.

Lang, G. (1970). *Quart. Rev. Biophys.* **3**, 1.

LeGall, J., and Dragoni, N. (1966). *Biochem. Biophys. Res. Commun.* **23**, 145.

Lever, A. B. P. (1968). "Inorganic Electronic Spectroscopy." Elsevier, New York.

Levin, I. W. (1972). *In* "Human Responses to Environmental Odors" (J. Johnston *et al.*, eds.). Academic Press, New York.

Lode, E. T., and Coon, M. J. (1971). *J. Biol. Chem.* **246**, 791.

Loew, G. H. *et al.* (1973). *Theoret. Chim. Acta* (in press).

Long, T. V., and Loehr, T. M. (1970). *J. Amer. Chem. Soc.* **92**, 6384.

Long, T. V., Loehr, T. M., Allkins, J. R., and Lovenberg, W. (1971). *J. Amer. Chem. Soc.* **93**, 1809.

Lovenberg, W. (1966). *In Conf. Protides Biolog. Fluids,* 14th (H. Peeters, ed.) p. 165. Elsevier, Amsterdam.

Lovenberg, W. (1972). *Methods Enzymol.* **24**, 477.

Lovenberg, W., and Sobel, B. E. (1965). *Proc. Nat. Acad. Sci. U.S.* **54**, 193.

Lovenberg, W., and Williams, W. M. (1969). *Biochemistry* **8**, 141.

Mason, S. F. (1962). *Proc. Chem. Soc.* 137.

Mason, S. F. (1963). *Quart. Rev. Chem. Soc.* **17**, 20.

Makinen, M. W., and Eaton, W. A. (1972). *Conf. Chem. Phys. Behavior Porphyrin Compounds Related Structures. Ann. N.Y. Acad. Sci.* (in press).

Mayhew, S. G. and Peel, J. L. (1966). *Biochem. J.* **100**, 80P.

McCarthy, K. F. (1972). Ph.D. Dissertation, George Washington Univ.

McCarthy, K., and Lovenberg, W. (1970). *Biochem. Biophys. Res. Commun.* **40**, 1053.

McClure, D. S. (1959). *Solid State Phys.* **9**, 399.

Moffitt, W. J. (1956). *J. Chem. Phys.* **25**, 1189.

Mortenson, L. E. (1964). *Biochim. Biophys. Acta* **81**, 71.

Newman, D. J., and Postgate, J. R. (1968). *Eur. J. Biochem.* **7**, 45.

Orgel, L. E. (1955). *J. Chem. Phys.* **23**, 1004.

Orgel, L. E. (1960). "An Introduction to Transition-Metal Chemistry: Ligand Field Theory." Wiley, New York.

Palmer, G., and Brintzinger, H. (1966). *Nature (London)* **211**, 189.

Peisach, J., Blumberg, W. E., Lode, E. T., and Coon, M. J. (1971). *J. Biol. Chem.* **246**, 5877.

Peterson, J. A., and Coon, M. J. (1968). *J. Biol. Chem.* **243**, 329.

Peterson, J. A., Basu, D., and Coon, M. J. (1966). *J. Biol. Chem.* **241**, 5162.

Peterson, J. A., Kusunose, M., Kusunose, E., and Coon, M. J. (1967). *J. Biol. Chem.* **242**, 4334.

Phillips, W. D., Poe, M., Wieher, J. F., McDonald, C. C., and Lovenberg, W. (1970). *Nature (London)* **227**, 574.

Schatz, P. N., and McCaffery, A. J. (1969). *Quart. Rev. Chem. Soc.* **23**, 552.

Slack, G. A., Ham, F. S., and Chrenko, R. M. (1966). *Phys. Rev.* **152**, 376.

Stadtman, T. C. (1965). *In* "Nonheme Iron Proteins: Role in Energy Conversion" (A. San Pietro, ed.), p. 439. Yellow Springs, Ohio, Antioch Press.

Stephens, P. J. (1970). *J. Chem. Phys.* **52**, 3489.

Tsibris, J. C. M., and Woody, R. W. (1970). *Coordin. Chem. Rev.* **5**, 417.

Vallee, B. L., and Williams, R. J. P. (1968). *Proc. Nat. Acad. Sci. U.S.* **59**, 498.

Watenpaugh, K. D., Sieker, L. C., Herriott, J. R., and Jensen, L. H. (1971). *Cold Spring Harbor Symp. Quant. Biol.* **36**, 359.

Yamamota, T., Rimai, L., Heyde, M. E., and Palmer, G. (1972). unpublished results.

CHAPTER 4

Crystal and Molecular Structure of Rubredoxin from *Clostridium pasteurianum*

L. H. JENSEN

The structure of rubredoxin was initially determined at 3 Å resolution using X-ray diffraction data from crystals of the native protein and *one* derivative only. In order to understand how the structure was solved and to provide a basis for assessing both the power and limitations of X-ray diffraction, it will be necessary to treat briefly the nature of crystals, to cover some of the basic concepts and formulas of X-ray diffraction, and to show how electron densities are derived from X-ray diffraction data.

I. THEORY

True solids are crystalline, i.e., they are characterized by the repetition of a basic unit of structure in three dimensions. The idea is illustrated in Fig. 1(a) for the simplest possible case in two dimensions and is easily generalized to three dimensions. The grid of lines with the same periodicity as the "structure" in Fig. 1(a) and superimposed upon it in Fig. 1(b) is called a *lattice*, in particular the *direct lattice*. The lattice serves as a coordinate system to which the structure is referred. The area between successive grid lines in two dimensions (the volume in three dimensions) is termed the *unit cell*. In Fig. 1(b) the unit cell contains one "comma" which in a real structure could correspond to one molecule.

Most crystals are more complex than the one just illustrated in that the unit cell contains two or more *asymmetric units* (the commas in Fig. 1) related by symmetry such as mirror planes or axes of symmetry. Figure 2 is an example, again in two dimensions, of three asymmetric units about threefold axes, i.e., the members of each group of three are related by rotation of 360°/3 about an axis perpendicular to the plane of the figure. Note that each unit cell in this case contains nine asymmetric units.

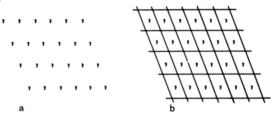

Fig. 1. (a) Two-dimensional "crystal." (b) Lattice superimposed on structure in (a).

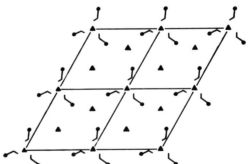

Fig. 2. Two-dimensional structure with threefold axis.

A. X-Ray Diffraction

When exposed to a beam of X rays, crystalline solids show strong diffraction effects (von Laue, 1912) which are easily observed and photographed. Figure 3 is a photograph of a section of the diffraction pattern from a crystal of rubredoxin. The complete pattern could be shown by a set of photographs similar to Fig. 3 stacked above and below it. The diffraction pattern of the three-dimensionally periodic crystal structure is itself three-dimensionally periodic, and being periodic it can be referred to as a lattice, the *reciprocal lattice*. We shall see below that it is "reciprocal" to the direct lattice in the sense that small direct lattices give rise to large reciprocal lattices and vice versa.

A "unit cell" can be chosen in the reciprocal lattice and the spots making up the lattice indexed by a triple of integers designated by the letters h,k,l. One of the letters, h,k,l, corresponds to one of the axial directions of whatever cell is chosen, the numbering beginning with zero at the origin, i.e., the center in Fig. 3, and running sequentially. Considerations

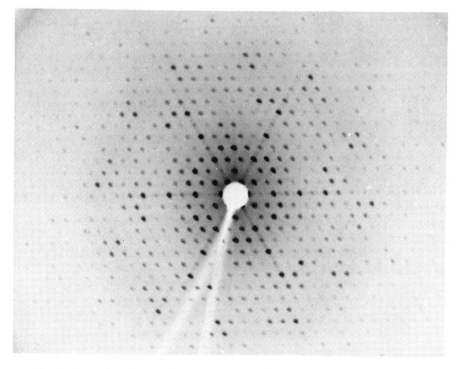

Fig. 3. Precession photograph of rubredoxin, $hk0$ reflections. (Courtesy of L. C. Sieker.)

of symmetry and convention govern the choice of cell in the reciprocal lattice. It is often found that the appropriate choice leads to systematic absence of certain indices. These absences often carry important information about the symmetry of the structure itself.

Each spot in a diffraction pattern can be interpreted as a reflection from sets of parallel planes in the direct lattice (Bragg, 1913). The sets of planes from which "reflection" can be considered to occur are those which can be drawn through the points of intersection of lines in the direct lattice and certain planes parallel to them. It turns out that the indices which can be assigned as described above are simply the reciprocals of the intercepts of the first plane from the origin of any set.

The conditions for diffraction are shown in Fig. 4 for two planes of the set 1,1 (only two indices are needed to define the planes in two dimensions). Two parallel rays, 1 and 2, of the incident beam are shown impinging on the planes at an angle θ. Two parallel diffracted rays, 1' and 2', also make an angle θ with the planes and 2θ with the incident beam extended beyond the point of diffraction. The equation relating the interplanar spacing d of the set of planes, the wavelength λ, and the angle θ is given by Bragg's law.

$$\lambda = 2d \, (\sin \theta) \tag{1}$$

For a given wavelength (often the Cu K_α line with $\lambda = 1.542\text{Å}$), it is clear from Eq. (1) that the smaller the interplanar spacing, the larger $\sin \theta$ and thus θ and 2θ. Therefore, the greater the distance of any spot in the diffraction pattern from the origin, the smaller the spacing between planes in the direct lattice from which "reflection" occurs. This is the reciprocal relation between the direct and reciprocal lattices referred to above.

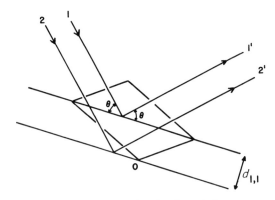

Fig. 4. Construction for Bragg's law.

In the study of physical optics and its application to X-ray diffraction, it can be shown that the *limit of resolution* in an electron density map based on the results of X-ray diffraction is set by the minimum spacing of planes used in calculating the map (James, 1948). The following equation represents the ideal case

$$\text{limit of resolution} = 0.72 d_{min} \qquad (2)$$

for three-dimensional data. In practice, the actual limit of resolution achieved is more nearly equal to d_{min}, and this is the figure commonly used in describing the resolution of electron density maps of proteins.

In order to improve resolution, i.e., decrease the limit of resolution, it is clear that data farther out in the reciprocal lattice must be included. In particular, if the resolution is improved by a factor of 2, reflections twice as far out in the reciprocal lattice will need to be included. Since the reciprocal lattice is three dimensional, this means 2^3 or eight times as many data.

Since most bond lengths are in the range of 1.2–1.5 Å, it would require data with corresponding d_{min} to just barely resolve atoms. For most proteins, the intensity of the diffraction data falls off rapidly with increasing 2θ and become extremely weak or unobservable for reflections with $d < 2.0$ Å. Although atomic resolution in most proteins cannot, therefore, be reached, it is usually possible with good data extending to planes with minimum spacing of 2.0–2.5 Å to recognize in electron density maps many of the side groups from what is already known about their general shape and to describe features of the molecule of basic importance in chemistry and biology.

B. Superposition of Waves

The concept of diffraction as reflection from "planes" is sufficient to explain the direction of all diffracted rays; however, it is necessary to consider how the scattered waves from each atom in the unit cell can be summed for each reflection.

Consider two waves with amplitudes f_1 and f_2 and phases α_1 and α_2 (Fig. 5). Note that the phase is simply the amount by which the crest of any wave differs from the origin, 0. This may be expressed as a fraction of one wavelength, but more often in crystallography phases are expressed in radian measure where one wavelength corresponds to 2π radians. The two waves can be superposed or added point by point to give a resultant wave with amplitude F.

A wave can conveniently be represented by a vector. Its length represents the amplitude of the wave and the angle between it, and the $+x$

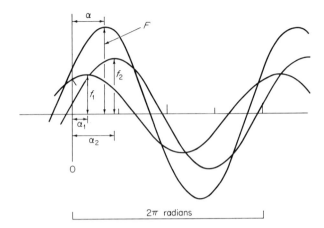

Fig. 5. Superposition of two waves with amplitudes f_1 and f_2 and phases α_1 and α_2 giving a wave with amplitude F and phase α.

axis of a rectangular coordinate system represents the phase. This provides a powerful means of superposing waves. Addition of the vectors representing waves gives a resultant vector representing the superposed waves. Figure 6 shows this construction for the case of the two waves shown in Fig. 5.

It is often convenient to express **f** in terms of its components along the x and y axes, respectively. In Fig. 7 the axial components are labeled **a** and **b**, and it is evident that

$$\mathbf{a} = \mathbf{f} \cos \alpha \tag{3}$$
$$\mathbf{b} = \mathbf{f} \sin \alpha \tag{4}$$
$$\alpha = \tan^{-1}(a/b) \tag{5}$$
$$f = (a^2 + b^2)^{1/2} \tag{6}$$

where **a**, **b**, and **f** are vectors and a, b, and f are the magnitudes of these vectors.

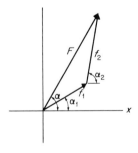

Fig. 6. Superposition of waves by vector addition.

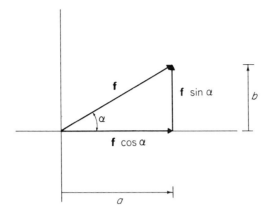

Fig. 7. Axial components $f \cos \alpha$ and $f \sin \alpha$ of $\mathbf{f}$.

Addition of vectors is easily done in terms of their axial components. Thus the case in Fig. 6 is repeated in Fig. 8 in terms of the components of $\mathbf{f}_1$ and $\mathbf{f}_2$ along the x and y axes. It is clear that

$$\mathbf{A} = \mathbf{f}_1 \cos \alpha_1 + \mathbf{f}_2 \cos \alpha_2 \tag{7}$$
$$\mathbf{B} = \mathbf{f}_1 \sin \alpha_1 + \mathbf{f}_2 \sin \alpha_2 \tag{8}$$

where $\mathbf{A}$ and $\mathbf{B}$ are the axial components of the resultant vector $\mathbf{F}$. Addition of axial components is easily adapted to numerical calculation and readily generalized. For the general case of n vectors

$$\mathbf{A} = \mathbf{f}_1 \cos \alpha_1 + \mathbf{f}_2 \cos \alpha_2 + \cdots + \mathbf{f}_n \cos \alpha_n = \sum_n \mathbf{f}_n \cos \alpha_n \tag{9}$$

$$\mathbf{B} = \mathbf{f}_1 \sin \alpha_1 + \mathbf{f}_2 \sin \alpha_2 + \cdots + \mathbf{f}_n \sin \alpha_n = \sum_n \mathbf{f}_n \sin \alpha_n \tag{10}$$

What has been developed for adding waves is directly applicable to X-ray diffraction where we need to add the j waves scattered for the j

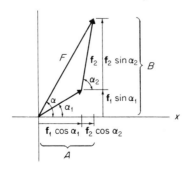

Fig. 8. Vector addition by adding axial components.

atoms in the unit cell of a crystal for each reflection h, k, l. The amplitude of the wave scattered by each atom is taken as f_j and may be considered as a measure of the effective number of electrons scattered by atom j. It can be shown that for the reflection h, k, l the phase α_j of the wave scattered by atom j with coordinates x_j, y_j, z_j is

$$\alpha_j = 2\pi(hx_j + ky_j + lz_j) \tag{11}$$

We can now write for the A and B components of $\mathbf{F}_{hkl}$

$$\mathbf{A}_{hkl} = \sum_j \mathbf{f}_j \cos 2\pi(hx_j + ky_j + lz_j) \tag{12}$$

$$\mathbf{B}_{hkl} = \sum_j \mathbf{f}_j \sin 2\pi(hx_j + ky_j + lz_j) \tag{13}$$

where Σ_j means the sum for all j atoms. The amplitude of the diffracted wave is

$$F_{hkl} = (A_{hkl}^2 + B_{hkl}^2)^{1/2} \tag{14}$$

and the phase

$$\alpha_{hkl} = \tan^{-1}(B_{hkl}/A_{hkl}) \tag{15}$$

It should be noted that it is the intensities of the reflections that are observed. These are proportional to the squares of the amplitudes, and it is impossible at present to observe the phases directly. This loss of information, as we shall see in the next section, is crucial and greatly complicates the work of determining protein structure from X-ray diffraction data.

C. Electron Density and the Phase Problem

It can be shown that the electron density at any point x, y, z in the unit cell is given by the equation

$$\rho(x, y, z) = (1/V) \sum_h \sum_k \sum_l F_{hkl} \cos 2\pi(hx + ky + lz - \alpha_{hkl}) \tag{16}$$

where V is the volume of the unit cell and $\Sigma_h \Sigma_k \Sigma_l$ indicates summation over all indices h, k, l.

All terms on the right-hand side of Eq. (16) are known or observable except α_{hkl}, the phases. Without this information, however, it is impossible to evaluate the electron density ρ. Although the phases cannot be observed directly, it can be shown that two isomorphous derivatives of a structure do provide a basis for determining them.

When proteins crystallize, there are necessarily relatively large spaces between the large molecules. This offers the possibility of attaching heavy atoms to the protein molcules and forming derivatives which are isomorphous with the native protein (Green *et al.*, 1954). This is, in fact, the basis of phase determination which has thus far been successful in solving protein structures.

To determine the phases by using multiple heavy atom isomorphous derivatives, it is first necessary to locate the heavy atoms. This can usually be done by taking the differences, reflection by reflection, between derivative and native data. The following expression can then be evaluated at an appropriate set of points in the unit cell

$$P_{(x,y,z)} = (1/V) \sum_h \sum_k \sum_l (\Delta F_{hkl})^2 \cos 2\pi(hx + ky + lz) \qquad (17)$$

Patterson (1935) showed that peaks in a function of this type occur at distances and directions from the origin corresponding to vectors between atoms in the structure. In the case where the coefficients are the differences between the amplitudes from the derivative and native protein cyrstals, peaks between heavy atoms will tend to dominate the map (Blow, 1958). If one or at most a few heavy atoms are attached to each protein molecule, the map can usually be interpreted in terms of the locations of the heavy atom positions. Having located the positions of the heavy atoms, then by Eqs. (12) and (13), A_H and B_H can be calculated and from these F_H and α_H, where the subscript H means that the quantity calculated is based only on the heavy atoms.

How an unknown phase is determined is shown in Figs. 9 and 10 (Harker, 1956). In Fig. 9(a) a circle with radius F_P is drawn and F_P and α_P for a particular reflection from the native protein are indicated. These are again shown in Fig. 9(b) along with $\mathbf{F}_{H_1}$ and $\mathbf{F}_{PH_1}$ for the derivative. Figure 9(c) reproduces Fig. 9(a) and, in addition, shows $-\mathbf{F}_{H_1}$ drawn from the origin ($\mathbf{F}_H$ is available by calculation as indicated above). With the terminus of $-\mathbf{F}_H$ as center, a circle of radius F_{PH_1} is drawn, where F_{PH_1} is the amplitude

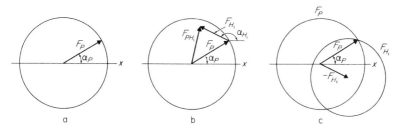

Fig. 9. (a) $\mathbf{F}_P$ and α_P for protein. (b) $\mathbf{F}_P$, α_P, $\mathbf{F}_{H_1}$, α_{H_1}, and $\mathbf{F}_{PH_1}$ for heavy atom derivative 1. (c) Intersection of circle for protein and heavy atom derivative 1 showing ambiguity in phase.

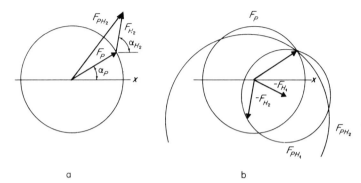

a   b

Fig. 10. (a) $\mathbf{F}_P$, α_P, $\mathbf{F}_{H_2}$, α_{H_2}, and $\mathbf{F}_{PH_2}$ for heavy atom derivative 2. (b) Intersection of circles for protein and two heavy atom derivatives at a point corresponding to phase angle.

of the reflection being considered for heavy atom derivative 1. It will be observed that this circle intersects that for the native protein in two places, one of which corresponds to the actual terminus of $\mathbf{F}_P$ and would serve to determine α_P were there not a second intersection.

The ambiguity in phase for the single derivative can be removed by a second construction similar to Fig. 9(c). Figure 10(a) corresponds to Fig. 9(b) except it is for a second heavy atom derivative. In Fig. 10(b) what appears in Fig. 9(c) has been reproduced with data for the second heavy atom derivative added. It is now seen that both circles for derivative 1 and 2 intersect the native circle at the point corresponding to α_P. The phase for this reflection is, therefore, determined.

D. Anomalous Scattering and the Phase Problem

By reference to Eqs. (12) and (13) we can write

$$\mathbf{A}_{hkl} = \mathbf{A}_{\bar{h}\bar{k}\bar{l}} \qquad (18)$$
$$\mathbf{B}_{hkl} = -\mathbf{B}_{\bar{h}\bar{k}\bar{l}} \qquad (19)$$

since

$$\cos(hx + ky + lz) = \cos(-hx - ky - lz)$$

and

$$\sin(hx + ky + lz) = -\sin(-hx - ky - lz).$$

It is evident that $I_{hkl} = I_{\bar{h}\bar{k}\bar{l}}$. This is Friedel's law.

For heavy atom derivatives of proteins, Friedel's law does not hold because of anomalous scattering by the heavy atoms (light atoms also show the effect but it is usually small and can be neglected). The phenomenon stems from the fact that the tightly bound, inner electrons in heavy atoms do not scatter in phase with the more loosely bound outer electrons. In addition to the usual vector $\mathbf{F}_H$, representing the scattering of a heavy atom, a component at 90° and always in the positive sense must be added.

How the difference between I_{hkl} and $I_{\bar{h}\bar{k}\bar{l}}$ arises is shown in terms of $\mathbf{F}_{hkl}$ and $\mathbf{F}_{\bar{h}\bar{k}\bar{l}}$ in Fig. 11. The heavy atom vector, $\mathbf{F}_{H^+}$ (short notation for $\mathbf{F}_{hkl_H}$) is shown added to that for the native protein $\mathbf{F}_{P^+}$. The component labeled $\Delta\mathbf{f}''^+$ represents anomalous scattering for the heavy atoms for plane h, k, l. In Fig. 11(b) a similar construction is shown for reflection $\mathbf{F}_{\bar{h}\bar{k}\bar{l}}$. Note that $\Delta\mathbf{f}''^-$ is drawn leading $\mathbf{F}_H^-$ by 90°, i.e., turned 90° in a counterclockwise sense. In Fig. 11(c) what is shown in Fig. 11(b) has been reflected across the x axis and superimposed on what is shown in Fig. 11(a). It is clearly evident that $F_{hkl} \neq F_{\bar{h}\bar{k}\bar{l}}$ and therefore $I_{hkl} \neq I_{\bar{h}\bar{k}\bar{l}}$.

For the case shown in Fig. 11(a), how the phases are determined from a single derivative by using measurements of both I_{hkl} and $I_{\bar{h}\bar{k}\bar{l}}$ is shown in Fig. 12. The vectors $-\mathbf{F}_H^+$, $-\Delta\mathbf{f}''^+$ and $-\Delta\mathbf{f}''^-$ [cf. Fig. 11(c)] have been reflected across the x axis. The terminus of $-\Delta\mathbf{f}''^+$ is taken as the center of a circle with radius F_{PH}^+ and that of $-\Delta\mathbf{f}''^-$ as the center of a circle with radius F_{PH}^-. These two circles and that of the reflection from the native crystal intersect at a point corresponding to the phase just as in the case of two derivatives, Fig. 10(b).

Once the phases have been determined, it is a straightforward procedure to evaluate the electron density according to Eq. (3) at intervals over an appropriate volume (often the volume of an asymmetric unit) of the unit cell. The output from programs to calculate electron density maps can usually be made essentially true to scale. Contours representing the electron density can then be drawn directly on transparent plastic

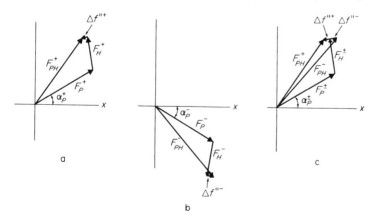

Fig. 11. (a) Vectors for heavy atom derivative including anomalous scattering for $\mathbf{F}_{PH}^-$. (b) Same construction as in (a) for $\mathbf{F}_{PH}^-$. (c) Reflection of (b) across x axis and superimposed on (a) showing difference between $\mathbf{F}_{PH}^+$ and $\mathbf{F}_{PH}^-$.

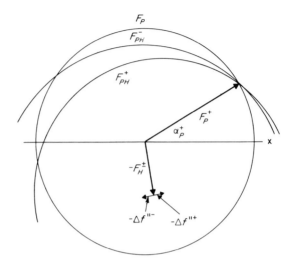

Fig. 12. Resolution of phase ambiguity by use of anomalous scattering. Compare Fig. 10(b).

sheets laid over the computer output. Alternatively, plotters and programs are available to do the contouring automatically, or the display of the map section by section on an oscilloscope or television monitor can be photographed and transferred to plastic sheets as in the case of manual contouring. These sheets stacked together at appropriate spacings provide a view of the molecule in three dimensions.

II. EXPERIMENTAL PROCEDURE

A. Crystallization of Rubredoxin

Isolation and purification of rubredoxin from *C. pasteurianum* has been described by Lovenberg and Sobel (1965). Crystals of the purified protein grow readily from solution by salting out with $(NH_4)_2SO_4$ and appear as well-formed deep red rhombs which develop to sizes of 1 mm or more if allowed to grow for a few weeks. The crystals used for the X-ray work were grown at room temperatures from approximately 0.8 saturated $(NH_4)_2SO_4$ at pH 4.0.

Heavy atom derivatives were obtained by the usual soaking procedure (Green *et al.*, 1954). In this method crystals are transferred to a solution of the heavy atom at appropriate pH and salt concentration. The heavy atoms diffuse into the crystal, and if they bind to the protein molecules at a small number of discrete sites without appreciably altering the crystal structure (isomorphous derivative), the derivative should be satisfactory for phase determination. The following heavy atom reagents formed derivatives with rubredoxin: K_2PtCl_4, K_2HgI_4, and $UO_2(NO_3)_2$.

B. Unit Cell and Space Group

Rubredoxin crystallizes in the trigonal system, space group $R3$. This space group is characterized by a rhombohedral lattice and a threefold axis (see Fig. 2). For computational and descriptive simplicity, it is convenient to refer the structure to a hexagonal rather than a rhombohedral cell. This is shown in Fig. 13 where the view is along the threefold axis (the c axis of the hexagonal cell) and perpendicular to the plane of the a and b axes. The protein molecules are idealized as spheres and seen as circular cross sections in the figure. Molecules occur in clusters of three about the threefold axes. Unshaded circles represent molecules at the level $z = 0$. A single cluster of three stippled circles labeled (2) is from a second level of molecules identical with the first but at $\frac{1}{3}c$ and translated by one-third along the long diagonal of the ab face of the unit cell. Another cluster of three circles, cross-hatched and labeled (3), is from a third level of molecules, again identical with the first, but displaced by $\frac{2}{3}c$ and by two-thirds along the long diagonal of the unit cell face.

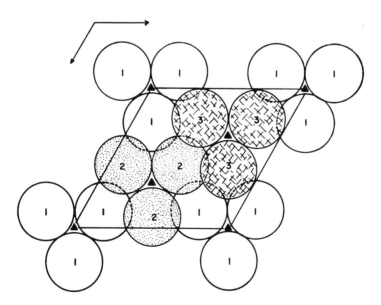

Fig. 13. Packing of spheres in space group $R3$, hexagonal cell shown.

The hexagonal cell contains nine asymmetric units and has the following parameters

$$a = b = 64.45 \text{ Å}$$
$$c = 32.68 \text{ Å}$$

The symmetry of the structure requires a distribution of asymmetric units similar to that shown in Fig. 13. The particular size of the spheres and their distribution about the threefold axis were chosen to satisfy packing requirements. The sphere radius to give contact is 11.91 Å. Such spheres fill 54% of the unit cell volume, a value close to the 56% upper limit based on crystal density for rubredoxin.

C. Data Collection

Crystalline rubredoxin is stable at room temperature and can be left for prolonged periods without noticeable deterioration. When exposed to the X-ray beam, however, the crystals deteriorate at a rate dependent in part on the X-ray flux but also in part on the quality of the radiation (the presence of wavelengths other than the characteristic). Under conditions used to collect the initial data for rebredoxin (Cu K_α radiation, $\lambda = 1.5418$ Å; 0.00035″ Ni filter, 40 kV constant potential generator, 14 mA; crystal 145 mm from target), the native crystals deteriorated at an average rate of 0.12% per hour.

Heavy atom derivative crystals usually deteriorate in the X-ray beam at a rate different from that for the native crystals. In the case of rubredoxin, crystals of both the HgI_4^{2-} and UO_2^{2+} derivatives deteriorated more rapidly than native crystals, and those of the $PtCl_4^{2-}$ derivative, less rapidly. The sensitivity of protein crystals to X rays complicates data collection, and it is usually necessary to use a number of different crystals to collect a set of data.

All data for rubredoxin were collected on a four-circle diffractometer by the $\omega/2\theta$ scan technique. Data for the initial 3 and 2.5 Å resolution maps were collected on a manually set instrument. Subsequently, a computer controlled diffractometer was used to recollect the data and extend it to 1.5 Å resolution.

Differences of absorption of the X rays for different reflections can be large for protein crystals, particularly so if the crystals are large and if they have quite different dimensions in different directions. Absorption of Cu K_α radiation is severe for rubredoxin crystals and all data were corrected by an empirical method (North et al., 1968).

III. DETERMINATION OF THE STRUCTURE

A. Locating the Heavy Atoms

After correcting the data for the effects of absorption and deterioration, derivative data were scaled to those for the native crystals according to the method of Singh and Ramaseshan (1966). Heavy atoms can be located by using the differences

$$(\Delta F)^2 = (F_{PH} - F_P)^2 \tag{20}$$

as coefficients in Eq. (17) as indicated above. With measurements of both I_{hkl} and $I_{\bar{h}\bar{k}\bar{l}}$ for the heavy atom derivatives, other coefficients (Rossman, 1961; Matthews, 1966) have been found useful in calculating vector maps for locating the heavy atoms. Three different types of coefficients were, in fact, used (Herriott *et al.*, 1970) and led to positions for the heavy atoms in the $HgI_4{}^{2-}$ and $UO_2{}^{2+}$ derivatives which refined and were useful in determining phases. No satisfactory model could be found for the $PtCl_4{}^{2-}$ group in the chloroplatinite derivative and no further use was made of the data for that derivative.

In the $HgI_4{}^{2-}$ derivative, the heavy ions are located at a single partially occupied site on the protein molecules. In the $UO_2{}^{2+}$ derivative, on the other hand, the heavy ions are in a cluster of at least four sites within a radius of 2 Å, so close, in fact, that no more than one site can be occupied on a given molecule. If the occupancy for the cluster is assumed to be the maximum possible, i.e., one $UO_2{}^{2+}$ per protein molecule, then the site with maximum occupancy is occupied in 0.45 of the molecules.

B. Determination of Phases

In Figs. 10(b) and 12 the circles for native protein and derivatives are shown to intersect at a point. In practice, however, experimental error in the data obviate the ideal situation shown; the curves do not intersect at a point, and the phase angle is not exactly determined. By applying the theory of errors to the case, Blow and Crick (1959) developed an expression for the probability of the phase as a function of angle for each derivative. In general, the probability functions are bimodal with the modes corresponding to the two intersections of each derivative circle with that for the native protein [Figs. 9(c), 10(b), and 12]. Multiplication of the probability functions for the derivatives gives a single function where the most probable value for the phase is taken as the angle corresponding to the maximum of the function.

C. Solution of the Structure of Rubredoxin at 3 Å Resolution

The structure of rubredoxin was first solved at 3 Å resolution with phases based on the HgI_4^{2-} derivative. The phase ambiguity of the single derivative was resolved as shown in Fig. 12 from measurements of both reflections of each pair, F_{hkl} and $F_{\bar{h}\bar{k}\bar{l}}$ (Blow and Rossman, 1961). A section of the electron density map is shown in Fig. 14(a). The view is in the direction of $-c$ and through a 2-Å-thick section in the vicinity of the Fe atom.

A second 3 Å resolution electron density map was subsequently calculated with phases based on the UO_2^{2+} derivative. A section of this map corresponding to that in Fig. 14(a) is shown in Fig. 14(b). The contours do not correspond exactly, in part because they are at arbitrary intervals, but the essential agreement of the two maps leaves no question in this case about the correctness of the structure based on a single derivative.

Figure 15 is a composite of sections from the 3 Å map (based on the HgI_4^{2-} derivative) covering the whole molecule. Each view is through a quarter of the molecular dimension, 6 Å, as viewed in the $-c$ direction. Although this map is far short of atomic resolution, the Fe position is easily identified with the highest peak in the electron density and the S positions can be inferred from the four prongs of electron density radiating from the Fe and indicating a roughly tetrahedral arrangement. The Fe and S atom positions are indicated in Fig. 15(a).

Some of the general features of the molecule are more easily visualized in the balsa wood model shown in Fig. 16(A). Each thickness of the balsa wood corresponds to 1 Å and the view is normal to c, in the direction of the arrow below Fig. 15(a). It is evident that the molecule is roughly

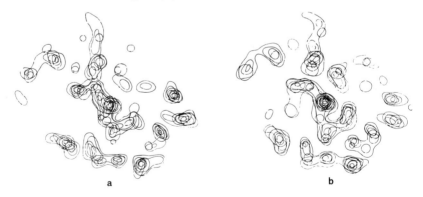

a   b

Fig. 14. Comparison of 2-Å-thick slices from 3 Å resolution electron density maps based on phases from single derivatives: (a) HgI_4^{2-} derivative, (b) UO_2^{2+} derivative (from Herriott *et al.*, 1970).

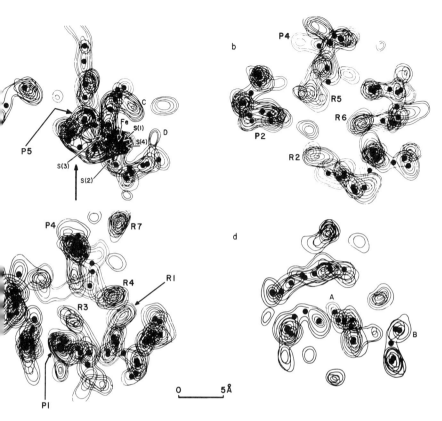

Fig. 15. Composite of sections from 3 Å resolution electron density map based on phases from HgI_4^{2-} derivative only. Each view through 6 Å. Direction of view along $-c$. Black dots show course of the polypeptide chain (from Herriott *et al.*, 1970).

spherical and 20–25 Å in diameter. Three sections of chain indicated by the three straight lines in Fig. 16(A) are roughly parallel and appear to form, in part at least, an antiparallel pleated sheet. Another part of the chain forming the hairpin loop labeled E also appears to form a short section of antiparallel pleated sheet.

The path of the chain is most clearly seen in Fig. 16(B). The direction of view and the labeling correspond to that in Fig. 16(A). Beginning at A, the chain can be traced upward to the region of S(1), then through a small loop to the region of S(2). Thence the chain continues downward across the center of the figure, bends sharply to the left and after a short section bends upward and back down again to form the hairpin loop E. After a short section across the bottom of the molecule, the chain can be followed upward again and in toward the region of S(3), then through

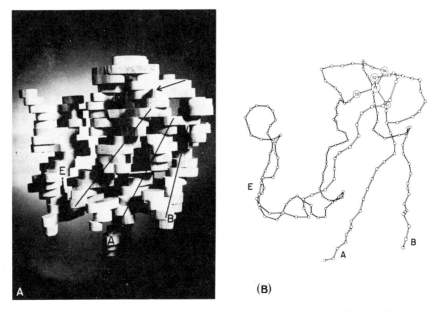

Fig. 16. (A) Balsa wood model based on electron density map in Fig. 16. Direction of view normal to *c*. (B) Model showing iron–sulfur complex and polypeptide chain. View approximately the same as in (a) (adapted from Herriott *et al.*, 1970).

another small loop to the region of S(4) and finally downward behind the iron–sulfur complex and can be observed to terminate near the point labeled B. It is interesting to note that six sections of the chain run vertically in Fig. 16(B), three running upward alternating with three downward (Birktoft, 1970).

On the basis of sequence and other chemical work, Bachmayer *et al.*

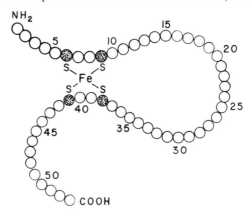

Fig. 17. Diagram of rubredoxin from *M. aerogenes* (after Bachmayer *et al.*, 1967).

(1967) postulated the structure shown in Fig. 17. Comparison with Fig. 16(B) will indicate at once that the arrangement of the chain about the Fe in a large loop, two small loops, and two end segments found in the X-ray work confirms the general features based on chemical work. Furthermore, in the chemical work the shorter of the terminal segments was found to be the N terminus. It is on that basis that A and B in Fig. 16 were initially identified with the N and C termini, respectively.

In a 3 Å resolution map, it is not possible in the absence of sequence information to identify most of the amino acids. Nevertheless, even at this resolution most of the ring amino acids can be recognized as such. From the chemical work, 5 Pro, 3 Tyr, 2 Phe, and 2 Trp had been found, a total of 12 rings. Most of these were recognized in the 3 Å map and are labeled Pro 1–5 and R 1–7 in Fig. 15.

D. Electron Density Map at 2.5 Å Resolution

Figure 18 is a composite of sections from the 2.5 Å resolution electron density map based on phases from both HgI_4^{2-} and UO_2^{2+} derivatives and including measurements for both F_{hkl} and $F_{\bar{h}\bar{k}\bar{l}}$ for both derivatives (Herriott *et al.*, 1970). In determining the phases for this map, therefore, four derivative measurements were available for each reflection. The additional information should improve the phases, and the more extensive data set was expected to provide a map with considerably more detail than was evident in the 3 Å resolution map. That this was realized is clear by comparing Fig. 18 with Fig. 15. The direction of view is the same in the two figures and each view is through the same region of the molecule.

In Fig. 18(a) it is just evident that S(2) and S(3) are now resolved from the Fe atom. In the composite of sections, nothing can be inferred about the resolution of S(1) and S(4) because their position below and above the Fe atom overlaps it. From the individual sections, however, S(1) is resolved from Fe and S(4) almost so.

The Fe—S bond lengths are in the range 2.2–2.4 Å, and the S—Fe—S bond angles range from 96° to 121°. The average value of the six bond angles is 109° and the root mean square deviation from the mean is 10°. Thus within the rather large experimental error of the angles based on the 2.5 Å map, the configuration of the S atoms about Fe does not differ significantly from tetrahedral. Note that this does not mean that the configuration *is* regularly tetrahedral, only that deviations from it were not significant at this point.

The improved resolution of the 2.5 Å map is particularly evident in the rings. Even in the composite of sections in Fig. 18, it is evident in some of the six-member rings seen from the edge that atoms across the

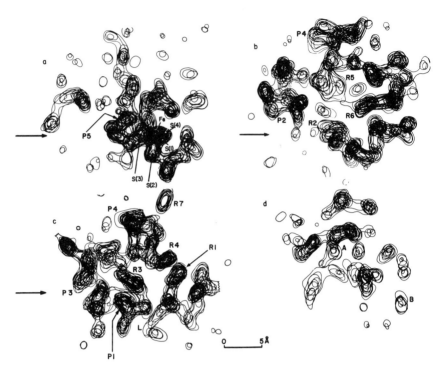

Fig. 18. Composite of sections from 2.5 Å resolution electron density map based on phases from both HgI_4^{2-} and UO_2^{2+} derivatives including anomalous scattering measurements. Each view through 6 Å. Direction of view along $-c$ (adapted from Herriott *et al.,* 1970).

ring are essentially resolved, e.g., R2 in Fig. 18(b) and R3 in Fig. 18(c). Ring R5 in Fig. 18(b) is now easily identified as that of a tryptophan.

It was thought at this point that there were seven ring R groups, and these are identified as R1–R7 in both Figs. 15 and 18. Six of these are on the surface of or buried within the molecule, but R7 appears to project into the solution. In contrast to the other rings as viewed from the edge, there is no indication in Fig. 18(c) of resolution across R7. (It was subsequently shown from the 2 Å resolution map that R7 is not, in fact, a ring but the side chain of an Asx.)

The prominent electron density at A in Fig. 18(d) was identified as the S atom of an N-terminal methionine, Met 1. Successive residues along the chain could be counted over most of the molecule and many side groups identified. Thus, for example, L and R1 were tentatively identified as Lys 3 and Tyr 4 and S(1) and S(2) were identified as the S atoms of Cys 6 and Cys 9, respectively.

E. Electron Density at 2 Å Resolution

In Fig. 19 three sections from the 2 Å resolution electron density map are shown (Watenpaugh *et al.*, 1970a). These are viewed in the direction of $-c$ as in Figs. 15 and 18, but each is through a 3 Å section of the molecule, an eighth rather than a quarter of the molecular dimension. Thus the sections of the molecule shown in Figs. 19(a)–19(c) are just half the thickness of those shown in Figs. 15(a)–15(c) and 18(a)–18(c). Moreover, each view is rotated 90°, the arrows on the left of Figs. 18(a)–18(c) corresponding to those at the bottom of Fig. 19(a)–19(c).

The improved resolution of the 2 Å map compared with the 2.5 Å map is clearly evident by comparing Figs. 19(a) with 18(a). S(2) and S(3) are well resolved, and although S(1) is overlapped by the Fe atom, it is quite apparent. In Fig. 19(c) part of rings R3 and R4 are seen "edge-on" and the dumbell-shaped contours indicating resolution across these rings is characteristic of six-member rings in the 2 Å map. The tryptophan ring viewed almost normal to its plane is seen in Fig. 19(b).

In the three-dimensional map it is possible to count the amino acids from the N-terminal methionine almost to the C terminus with certainty. The C-terminal residue appears to be amino acid 54, although the electron density fades out rapidly in this region. Nevertheless, what appears to be the terminal carboxyl group of the main chain and the carboxyl group of an acid side chain can be seen.

The amino acid count indicates that S(3) and S(4) are the sulfurs in Cys 39 and Cys 42. This is in contrast to the sequences for *M. aerogenes* and *P. elsdenii* where the corresponding residues are Cys 38 and Cys 41. The positions in the sequence of the prolines, P1–P5, and the other ring amino acids, R1–R7, indicated in Figs. 14 and 15, were determined with a high degree of certainty and are given in Table I. It was

TABLE I

IDENTITY OF P1–P5 AND R1–R7 IN FIGS. 15 AND 18

P1	Pro 15
P2	Pro 20
P3	Pro 26
P4	Pro 34
P5	Pro 40
R1	Tyr 4
R2	Tyr 11
R3	Tyr 13
R4	Phe 30
R5	Trp 37
R6	Phe 49
R7	Asp 35

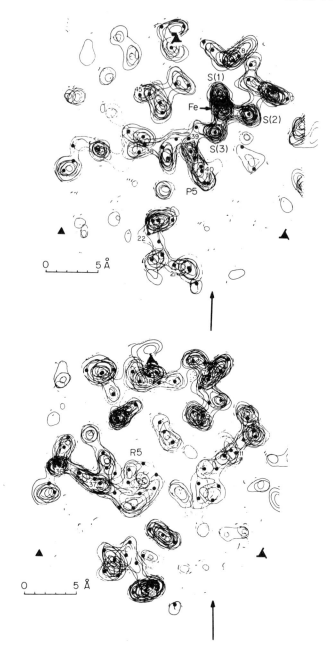

Fig. 19. Composite of sections from 2.0 Å resolution electron density map based on phases from both HgI_4^{2-} and UO_2^{2+} derivatives including anomalous scattering measurements. Each view through 3 Å, half that in the corresponding views in Fig. 18.

at this point that R7 was identified as Asx rather than a ring amino acid as had been thought. The fifth proline, P5 in Fig. 18(a), was easily identified and determined as Pro 40.

Of the 54 amino acids, about 35 could be identified with some certainty and most of the rest were felt to be within an atom or two of correct. This is not, of course, the most effective method of establishing a sequence, but sequence information based on an electron density map can be of great value when considered along with sequence information based on chemical work (e.g., Drenth *et al.*, 1968). In retrospect, it is clear that even a 3 Å resolution map could appreciably decrease the work of chemical sequencing and improve the certainty of the results.

F. Refinement of the Structure

When approximate positions for most of the atoms in a structure have been determined, it is possible to improve their coordinates in one of sev-

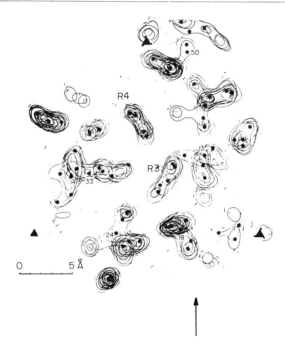

(Fig. 19, continued.) Direction of view along —*c*. Black dots indicate atomic sites. The numbered dots are C α atoms of the residue with that number. Faint, often broken lines is the lowest contour on the map. On the original it was contoured in red which does not show well in the photographic reproduction (adapted from Watenpaugh *et al.*, 1971).

eral ways and to add atoms which may not have been included in the initial model. This is the process of refining a structure.

One method by which a structure may be refined involves calculating the set of F_{hkl} followed by calculating the electron density according to Eq. (15) where the observed F_{hkl} and the calculated α_{hkl} are used. New atomic positions are then derived from the electron density map, and successive cycles of such calculation are carried through until there are no further changes in the calculated phase angles. The refinement is then considered to be complete. This method can also be used to add atoms to an incomplete model, but it is difficult to apply unless the atoms are resolved.

A more powerful method of refining a structure is by means of difference maps. As in the preceding method, this one involves calculating a set of F_{hkl}, but a *difference* electron density map rather than an electron density map is then calculated. A difference map is evaluated by Eq. (15), but in place of the observed F_{hkl}, the differences

$$\Delta F_{hkl} = F_{o_{hkl}} - F_{c_{hkl}} \tag{21}$$

are used. The calculated phases α_{hkl} are used as before.

The appearance of a difference map for an error in an atomic position is illustrated in one dimension in Fig. 20. Suppose an atom to be at the position indicated by ρ_0. Let the position assumed in calculating F_{hkl} be the position indicated by ρ_c. The difference map will give an approximation to the curve $\rho_0 - \rho_c$. Thus a correction in atomic position will be indicated in a difference map by a negative region on one side of the assumed position

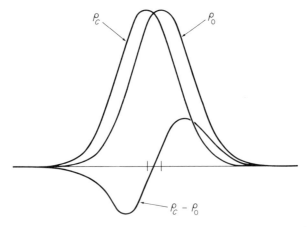

Fig. 20. Appearance of one-dimensional difference "map." Assumed electron density, ρ_0; actual electron density, ρ_c; difference, $\rho_0 - \rho_c$.

and a positive region on the other. It can be shown that the correction in the assumed position of an atom, δ, is given by the expression

$$\delta = -\text{slope/curvature} \tag{22}$$

where the slope is approximately that in the difference map at the assumed atomic position and the curvature is that of ρ_0 (which can be derived from an electron density map). Not only can assumed positions be corrected, but missing atoms appear in difference maps and can be added to the model. Indeed, such maps are valuable in determining any difference from an assumed model, e.g., differences between an enzyme and the enzyme bound to an inhibitor (provided, of course, that diffraction data can be obtained). In fact, difference maps were used in locating the iodine atoms in the HgI_4^{2-} derivative of rubredoxin and the multiple uranium sites in the UO_2^{2+} derivative. In practice, successive cycles of calculating F_{hkl} and difference maps are carried through. The refinement is considered complete when the difference map is as flat as possible.

A third method, one which is both convenient and powerful, is that of least squares. This is an analytical method which minimizes the quantity

$$\sum_w (F_{o_{hkl}} - F_{c_{hkl}})^2 \tag{23}$$

the sum of the weighted $(\Delta F)^2$. If the model is reasonably good, the method of least squares gives excellent corrections to the model. Unfortunately, large problems require enormous amounts of computing, and repeated cycles must be carried through as with the other methods of refinement. Furthermore, this method can only refine a model; new atoms must be added by an electron density or difference electron density map.

The course of refining a structure is commonly monitored by the residual R defined by the expression

$$R = \Sigma ||F_o| - |F_c||/\Sigma |F_o| \tag{24}$$

The numerator is the sum of the differences between the observed and calculated F_{hkl} and the denominator is the sum of the observed F_{hkl}. Thus R is essentially an average error over all the observed reflections. Structures with R values in the range of 0.3–0.4 will usually refine to R values less than 0.1 if the model assumed is a proper one.

The initial atomic positions for refining rubredoxin were derived from the 2 Å resolution electron density map. The black circles in Fig. 19 are, in fact, the atomic positions, and the coordinates were assigned by estimating to 0.1 of a grid interval directly on the computer output. More

TABLE II

Course of the Refinement with 1.5 Å Data

Coordinates	R	Number of reflections	B	Number of H_2O	Occupancy
From 2 Å res. F_0 map	0.389	5033	15	23	1
From 2 Å res. F_0 map	0.376	5027	13.5	23	1
From 2 Å res. F_0 map	0.372	5027	12	23	1
From first ΔF map	0.321	5027	12	23	1
From second ΔF map	0.289	5027	9–20	22	1
From third ΔF map	0.262	5027	7–30	22	1
From fourth ΔF map	0.242	5027	6–40	23	1
From fourth ΔF map	0.224	5027	6–40	100	0.3–1
First L.S. cycle	0.179	5027	−5–50	106	0.3–1

than 95% of the atoms in the molecule were included in the initial model, and an additional 23 oxygen atoms for what appeared to be discrete water molecules in the solution were included (Watenpaugh et al., 1970b).

In attempting to refine a protein structure, there is an advantage in using difference maps. Not only are the computing requirements relatively modest, but interpreting difference maps keeps one tethered in a very direct way to what is happening to the model in space. The initial cycles, therefore, were by means of difference maps and the course of the refinement is evident by following the R values in Table II.

The initial R of 0.389 decreased to 0.372 on omitting six reflections with very low sin θ, where both data and model may be questioned, and adjusting the scale of the observed F_{hkl} and a parameter B which covers thermal motion, disorder in the proteins, and possibly other factors. These adjustments are common in crystallographic calculations and the R of 0.372 that followed from them may be taken as the starting value.

Adjustments in the positions of the atoms made from the first difference map decreased R to 0.321. In the second difference map additional corrections were made in atomic positions, but it was also clear that B values were too high for atoms on the inside of the molecule and too low for those on the outside. This is physically sensible. Low B values indicate low thermal motion, and this is reasonable for atoms on the inside of the molecule where they are packed tightly together. High B values, on the other hand, indicate large thermal motion and possible disorder. This is to be expected for groups on the outside of the molecule particularly those projecting into the solution, and for atoms near the ends of chains.

Corrections in both atomic positions and B values from the third and fourth difference maps decreased R to 0.262 and then to 0.242. Seventy-seven additional water O atoms (with partial occupancy) were added at this point, and R decreased to 0.224.

The refinement had been sufficiently smooth that continuing it by the method of least squares appeared to be warranted. Atomic and B value shifts from the first least-squares cycle along with the addition of twelve water oxygens decreased R to 0.179. This is the status of the refinement at this writing.

Although the refinement is not complete and it is still uncertain how far it can be carried, the following points appear to be justified:

1. The structure of a small protein can be refined in the usual crystallographic sense even though the solvent constitutes almost 50% of the crystals.

2. The B values for some of the atoms on the inside of rubredoxin are as low as those often obtained for small structures.

3. Biochemically useful information has emerged from the refinement in the sense that incorrect atoms have been removed and atoms not initially included have been added in the refinement.

After the first least-squares cycle of refinement, a partial sequence based on chemical work became available (McCarthy, 1970). This in combination with the X-ray work is given in Table III.

G. Reduced Rubredoxin

Rubredoxin in crystalline form can be reduced by dithionite without destroying the crystal structure. Two sets of diffraction data to 4 Å resolution have been collected from a crystal of the reduced protein (Herriott *et al.*, 1969). Although appreciable differences were observed between data from crystals of the oxidized and reduced protein, a difference map showed no appreciable change of the structure *within* the protein molecule, in particular the configuration of the S atoms about Fe had not changed. This should be regarded as a preliminary observation, and the experiment will be repeated. An attempt will be made to collect more extensive data, and the much better phases now available from the refinement will be used in calculating the difference map.

IV. ADDENDUM

Since this chapter was written, the refinement of rubredoxin has been continued through three more least-squares cycles. In the last cycle, 256 H atoms with positions fixed by the nonhydrogen atoms were included

TABLE III
X -Ray, Chemical, and Probable Sequence

No.	Sequence, X ray (July 1970)	Sequence, chemical (July 1970)	Probable sequence (July 1970)
1	Met	Met	Met
2	Lys	Lys	Lys
3	Lys	Lys	Lys
4	Tyr	Tyr	Tyr
5	Thr	Thr	Thr
6	Cys	Cys	Cys
7	Thr	Thr	Thr
8	Val	Val	Val
9	Cys	Cys	Cys
10	Gly	Gly	Gly
11	Tyr	Tyr	Tyr
12	Ile (?)	Ile	Ile
13	Tyr	Tyr	Tyr
14	Asx	Asx	Asx
15	Pro	(Asx)	Pro
16	Glx (?)	(Asx)	Glx
17	Asx (?)	(Asx)	Asx
18	Gly	(Asx)	Gly
19	Asx	(Asx)	Asx
20	Pro	(Glx)	Pro
21	Val (?)	(Pro)	Asx
22	Asx	(Pro)	Asx
23	Gly	(Pro)	Gly
24	Ile	(Gly)	Val
25	Asx	(Gly)	Asx
26	Pro	(Val)	Pro
27	Gly	Gly	Gly
28	Val (?)	Thr	Thr
29	Glu (?)	Asp	Asp
30	Phe	Phe	Phe
31	Lys	Lys	Lys
32	Asx	Asp	Asp
33	Ile	Ile	Ile
34	Pro	Pro	Pro
35	Asx	Asx	Asx
36	Asx	Asp	Asp
37	Trp	Trp	Trp
38	Val (?)	Val	Val
39	Cys	Cys	Cys
40	Pro	Pro	Pro
41	Leu (?)	Leu	Leu
42	Cys	Cys	Cys
43	Gly	(Gly)	Gly

TABLE III (*continued*)

No.	Sequence, X ray (July 1970)	Sequence, chemical (July 1970)	Probable sequence (July 1970)
44	Ile	(Gly)	Val
45	Gly	(Val)	Gly
46	Lys	Lys	Lys
47	Asx	Asp	Asp
48	Glx	(Glx)	Glx
49	Phe	(Glx)	Phe
50	Glx	(Glx)	Glx
51	Glx	(Glx)	Glx
52	Val (?)	(Glx)	Val
53	Asp (?)	(Phe)	Glx
54	Asp (?)	(Val)	Glx

without refinement (Watenpaugh *et al.*, 1973). The residual R [see Eq. (4)] is now 0.126.

Neglect of anomalous scattering when refining a structure in space group $R3$ introduces errors in the phases. In the main course of refinement through four ΔF syntheses and four least-squares cycles, anomalous scattering was neglected in order to conserve time, but it was included for the Fe and four coordinated S atoms in a partial least-squares cycle after the fourth main least-squares refinement cycle. Two of the Fe—S bond lengths changed significantly by including the effects of anomalous scattering. The present bond lengths and angles for the Fe—S complex are shown in Fig. 21. It is evident that the configuration of the S atoms about Fe does differ from tetrahedral; at least four and possibly five of the six S—Fe—S differ significantly from the tetrahedral value.

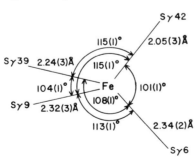

Fig. 21. Bond lengths and angles in the Fe–4 S complex of rubredoxin after fourth least-squares refinement cycle and one partial cycle in which anomalous scattering for the Fe and cysteine S atoms was included.

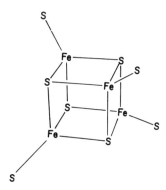

Fig. 22. Model of 4 Fe–8 S complex in a bacterial ferredoxin; model derived from 2.8 Å electron density map.

The refinement with 1.5 Å data has not completely converged and some atoms have moved to positions giving impossible bond lengths and angles. In general, however, the refinement has behaved well in view of the limited data available, and no pronounced tendency of the atoms to oscillate or drift was observed.

Although the intensities of the diffracted beams for protein crystals decrease rapidly with increasing $\sin \theta$, a survey of reflections with $1.25 < d < 1.54$ suggests that it may be possible to observe as much as 40% of the data in this range with intensities greater than 2σ. This will provide a substantial increase in the amount of data which, in turn, can be expected to lead to a considerably better model for rubredoxin, particularly for those atoms with the smallest B values.

Another nonheme iron protein, a bacterial ferredoxin, has now been solved. The most prominent features in the structure are two clusters with four Fe, four inorganic S, and four cysteine S atoms in each (Sieker et al., 1972.) Four Fe and four inorganic S atoms are arranged at opposite corners of a roughly cube-shaped region with four cysteine S atoms coordinated to the four Fe. A model for the 4 Fe–8 S cluster is shown in Fig. 22.

Further work on the ferredoxin structure has shown that the 4 Fe–4 S cubelike region is considerably distorted and better described in terms of two interpenetrating tetrahedra: the smaller one with Fe atoms at the vertices and an Fe—Fe distance of approximately 2.8 Å, the larger one with S atoms at the vertices and an S—S distance of approximately 3.5 Å (Adman et al., 1973). Figure 23 is a schematic view of the main chain and the complexes showing distortion of the 4 Fe–4 S complex from a cube.

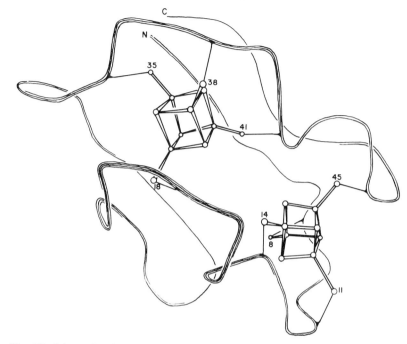

Fig. 23. Schematic diagram of main chain of a bacterial ferredoxin. Two 4 Fe–8 S clusters shown where numbers indicate the cysteine residues bonded to each complex.

ACKNOWLEDGMENTS

I am particularly indebted to my colleagues, L. C. Sieker, Dr. J. R. Herriott, and Dr. Keith Watenpaugh who have done most of the work on which this report is based and to Dr. W. Lovenberg who supplied the rubredoxin. I am also indebted to Professor Philip Wilcox for many helpful discussions and to Professor W. N. Lipscomb for the opportunity to work in his laboratory with the 2 Å resolution carboxypeptidase map.

The work on rubredoxin has been supported by U.S. PHS Grant No. GM 13366 from the National Institutes of Health.

REFERENCES

Adman, E. T., Sieker, L. C., and Jensen, L. H. (1973). *J. Biol. Chem.* **248**, 3987.
Bachmayer, H., Piette, L. H., Yasunobu, K. T., and Whiteley, H. R. (1967). *Proc. Nat. Acad. Sci., Wash.* **57**, 122.
Birktoft, J. (1970). Private communication.
Blow, D. M. (1958). *Proc. Roy. Soc. (London), Ser. A* **247**, 302.
Blow, D. M., and Crick, F. H. C. (1959). *Acta Crystallogr.* **12**, 794.

Blow, D. M., and Rossmann, M. G. (1961). *Acta Crystallogr.* **14,** 1195.

Bragg, W. L. (1913). *Proc. Cambridge Phil. Soc.* **17,** 43.

Drenth, J., Jansonius, J. N., Koekoek, R., Swen, H. M., and Wolthers, B. G. (1968). *Nature (London)* **218,** 929.

Green, D. W., Ingram, V. M., and Perutz, M. F. (1954). *Proc. Roy. Soc. (London)* **A225,** 287.

Harker, D. (1956). *Acta Crystallogr.* **9,** 1.

Herriott, J. R., Sieker, L. C., Jensen, L. H., and Lovenberg, W. (1969). *Int. Congr. Crystallogr, 8th* Abstracts, p. S186.

Herriott, J. R., Sieker, L. C., Jensen, L. H., and Lovenberg, W. (1970). *J. Mol. Biol.* **50,** 391.

James, R. W. (1948). *Acta Crystallogr.* **1,** 132.

Lovenberg, W., and Sobel, B. E. (1965). *Proc. Nat. Acad. Sci., Wash.* **54,** 193.

McCarthy, K. (1970). Private communication.

Matthews, B. W. (1966). *Acta Crystallogr.* **20,** 230.

North, A. C. T., Phillips, D. C., and Matthews, F. S. (1968). *Acta Crystallogr.* **A24,** 351.

Patterson, A. L. (1935). *Z. Krist.* **90,** 517.

Rossmann, M. G. (1961). *Acta Crystallogr.* **14,** 383.

Sieker, L. C., Adman, E., and Jensen, L. H. (1972). *Nature* (London) **235,** 40.

Singh, A. K., and Ramaseshan, S. (1966). *Acta Crystallogr.* **21,** 279.

von Laue, M. (1912). *Sitz. Math. Phys. Kl. Bayer, Akad. Wiss.* p. 303.

Watenpaugh, K., Herriott, J. R., Sieker, L. C., and Jensen, L. H. (1970a). *Amer. Crystallogr. Ass. Abstr.* p. 78. Tulane Univ., New Orleans.

Watenpaugh, K., Herriott, J. R., Sieker, L. C., and Jensen, L. H. (1970b). *Amer. Crystallogr. Ass. Abstr.* p. 44. Carleton Univ., Ottawa.

Watenpaugh, K. D., Sieker, L. C., Herriott, J. R., and Jensen, L. H. (1971). Cold Spring Harbor Symp. on Quant. Biol., **36,** 359.

Watenpaugh, K. D., Sieker, L. C., Herriot, J. R., and Jensen, L. H. (1973). *Acta Crystallogr.* **B29,** 943.

CHAPTER 5

Probing Iron–Sulfur Proteins with EPR and ENDOR Spectroscopy

W. H. ORME-JOHNSON and R. H. SANDS

I. INTRODUCTION

In this chapter we attempt to bring together the results of efforts, made by a number of groups during the past dozen years, to apply electron paramagnetic resonance (EPR) and electron nuclear double resonance (ENDOR) spectroscopy to structural and functional questions in this field. After a section describing salient features of EPR and ENDOR spectroscopy, presently known properties of the simple iron–sulfur proteins are summarized, following which more complex (conjugated) iron–sulfur proteins are described as objects of EPR and ENDOR experimentation. Although the directness, sensitivity, and nondestructive nature of EPR has played a sizable role in its acceptance as a tool in this field, more recently other techniques, such as nuclear magnetic resonance (NMR), ENDOR, Mössbauer, and visible light spectroscopy and magnetic susceptibility measurements have increasingly added to our picture of these substances. In addition to the chapters devoted to other technical

195

approaches, we would draw the reader's attention to the final chapter of this volume in which the results of physical and chemical studies are considered together in a summation of present ideas about the active centers of these proteins. If not the *pièce de résistance* of this book, the final chapter certainly can lay fair claim to the position of the dessert.

II. THE EPR PHENOMENON

A large number of texts, differing both in difficulty and in emphasis, are available to guide the student of electron paramagnetic resonance (EPR). A small selection follows: Carrington and McLaughlan (1969) and Pake (1962) give an introduction to theoretical aspects of the subject; Bersohn and Baird (1966), Ayscough (1967), and Wertz and Bolton (1972) discuss theory and results of interest to the chemists; while Ingram (1957), Poole (1967), and Alger (1968) emphasize experimental techniques. Abragam and Bleaney (1970) comprehensively treat the theory and results of EPR studies on transition metal ions. A book by Ingram (1970) and one edited by Schwartz *et al.* (1972) discuss biological applications of the method, while reviews by Beinert and Palmer (1965) and Palmer (1967a) summarize basic results and techniques of interest to biochemists. A discussion of electron nuclear double resonance (ENDOR) spectrometry may be found in Abragam and Bleaney (1970).

In spite of the availability of extended treatment of the more physical aspects of the subject of this chapter, a summary of matters which at present appear to be germane to our understanding of the EPR and ENDOR of iron–sulfur proteins will be given. This discussion is intended to aid biochemists unfamiliar with the concepts used in this area, and may be skipped with profit by those with a more physical background.

Electron paramagnetic resonance may be observed in materials containing unpaired electronic spins. Because the electron has both a charge and an intrinsic angular momentum (spin) it has a magnetic moment, μ, which is proportional to the spin, S, and can be written

$$\mu = g\beta S \qquad (1)$$

where β is the Bohr magneton ($\beta = eh/4\pi mc = 0.927 \times 10^{-20}$ erg G^{-1}) and g is the electronic g value (2.00232 for a free electron). If the electronic system is placed in a magnetic field H, it has an interaction with the field, called the Zeeman interaction

$$\begin{aligned} \text{Zeeman interaction} &= -\mu \cdot H \\ &= -g\beta S \cdot H \\ &= -g\beta S_z H_z \end{aligned} \qquad (2)$$

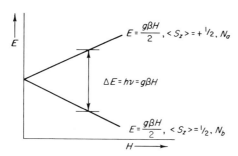

Fig. 1. The electron Zeeman effect. The applied magnetic field H increases from left to right, causing the energy difference between the upper (spins parallel) population and the lower population (spins antiparallel) to increase according to Eq. (3). Transitions are induced, i.e., EPR occurs, when at a given value of the field, H, microwave radiation of frequency ν is supplied.

if the field is in the z direction, where S_z is the component of the electronic spin along the z direction. For a spin-$\frac{1}{2}$ system the allowed values for this projection are $\pm\frac{1}{2}$ giving rise to an energy level diagram as shown in Fig. 1.

Transitions may be induced between these two energy levels at a frequency ν given by

$$h\nu = g\beta H \qquad (3)$$

where h is Planck's constant. Equation (3) may be solved for the g value (sometimes called the spectroscopic splitting factor) and these are often quoted to summarize experimental observations and are given by

$$g = 7.1445 \times 10^{-7} \, (\nu/H) \qquad (4)$$

where ν is given in hertz and H is the field in gauss at which the transition (resonant absorption) is observed. For systems having very little orbital angular momentum, such as free radicals, this g value deviates less than one part in one thousand from the free electron value of 2.00232. On the other hand, if the electron has orbital angular momentum, the g value will deviate markedly from the free electron value. This deviation is a measure of the additional interactions which the electronic spin system has with its surroundings, and quite often the chemical physicist can interpret the exact value of this g factor in terms of the microscopic structure of the site in question.

In the case of spin-$\frac{1}{2}$ systems the presence of an applied magnetic field divides the set of spins in a sample into two populations (as seen in Fig. 1): those with their spins aligned *with* the external field and those with their spins aligned antiparallel to the field. The parallel set of spins are of higher energy, the differences in energy between the two populations is $g\beta H$, and the two sets of spins are connected via a Boltzmann distribution of the form

$$N_a/N_b = \exp{(-g\beta H/kT)}$$

where N_a and N_b are the populations of the upper and lower states and T is the absolute temperature. When $h\nu = g\beta H$, transitions upward and downward between the two states are induced by the applied microwave field with equal probability, so that the net absorption depends upon the fact that there is a greater population in the lower state than in the upper. The microwave field tends to equalize these populations; however, the interactions which the electrons have with the lattice containing them tend to establish and maintain the Boltzmann population. The processes which tend to maintain this population difference are called relaxation processes, and the resonant absorption may be viewed as a continued competition between the tendency of the microwave field to equalize the populations and the tendency of the spin-lattice interactions to maintain the Boltzmann difference population. Provided that the latter processes predominate, the net absorption increases as N_a/N_b gets smaller(i.e., as T decreases.) The size of the resonance signal increases as $1/T$ for $kT >> g\beta H$, which means for $g = 2$ (at the usual frequency of 10^{10} Hz or X band) that this $1/T$ relationship is a good approximation above $2°K$. This dependence of absorption on temperature can be useful when EPR is performed on paramagnetically dilute biological substances at low temperatures ($4°–100°K$) since it allows for greater absorption at these lower temperatures. Even though such conditions are quite different from those in the $300°K$ temperature range in which enzymes are operative, they are often necessary for the observation of EPR because of linewidth considerations to be discussed later. The supposition implicit in the application of these tactics is that there is a continuum of states connecting conditions at the higher and lower temperatures, so that properties observable at low temperatures come from structural features related in an understandable way to those present at higher temperatures. This supposition is not obviously correct, but, as in the case of numerous other physical methodologies, requires considerable effort for its validation.

As was stated earlier, g values for compounds will differ in a way characteristic of the structure of the compound, and, in fact, g is a tensor quantity, and the field required for resonance is a function of the orientation of the molecular axes with respect to the applied magnetic field. Except for certain cases of low symmetry and high spin (see Blumberg, 1967; Dowsing and Gibson, 1969; Aasa, 1970, for a discussion of an important example), principal axes may be chosen such that the off-diagonal terms of the g tensor vanish, and we have to deal with at most three g values (called g_x, g_y, and g_z) for each unpaired spin. In axial symmetry we find a unique g value ($g_\parallel \equiv g_z$) and two resonances at a second position ($g_\perp \equiv g_y = g_x$), while in perfect cubic symmetry (ignoring Jahn–Teller distortions) we would find only one resonance position. Departure from this last condition is referred to as g-value anisotropy. It has become common practice to use g in two senses in publications in this field. As used above, g values characterize the principal components of the g tensor, and they are alternatively used as markers to locate maxima, crossing points, minima, and other positions in EPR spectra. For net spin $= \frac{1}{2}$ systems, g values in this latter descriptive sense are the same as the actual values required for the more rigorous usage as components of a g tensor. For an example from the present field see Palmer *et al.* (1967).

There are a great many factors which affect the shapes of observed spectra, and they are not in general given by just a simple line as might have been concluded from the above discussion. Contributions to the appearance of actual spectra are listed below:

1. In the cases discussed here, the samples are powders (frozen solution) and observed spectra are averages of spectra from all possible orientations of the molecules. If the magnetic field is applied to a molecule such that the direction cosines between the field and the principal axes of the g tensor are l, m, and n, then the g value for absorption by that individual molecule (see Abragam and Bleaney, 1970) is

$$y = (l^2 g_x{}^2 + m^2 g_y{}^2 + n^2 g_z{}^2)^{1/2} \tag{5}$$

From this it is evident that the spectrum will be spread over a field range from g_x to g_z, when an amorphous or polycrystalline substance is examined so that *all* orientations are present.

The synthesis of EPR spectra for amorphous samples has been discussed by several authors (e.g., Kneubühl and Natterer, 1961; Neuman and Kivelson, 1961; Gersmann and Swalen, 1962; Malley, 1965). In brief review, for spin $= \frac{1}{2}$ systems the resonance condition is given by

$$h\nu_0 = g\beta H \tag{6}$$

where ν_0 is the applied microwave frequency, g is the electron g factor, β is the Bohr magneton, and H is the applied magnetic field. For a magnetic field applied at the Euler angles θ, ψ with respect to the molecular g-tensor principal axes

$$g = [g_x{}^2 (\sin^2 \theta) (\cos^2 \Psi) + g_y{}^2 (\sin^2 \theta) (\sin^2 \Psi) + g_z{}^2 \cos^2 \theta]^{\frac{1}{2}} \tag{7}$$

If all molecular orientations are equally likely, then the number of molecules having a magnetic field oriented at angles between θ and $\theta + d\theta$, Ψ

and $\Psi + d\Psi$, is given by the solid angle at these orientations, i.e.,

$$dN = N_0 \, (\sin \theta) \, d\theta \, d\Psi \qquad (8)$$

Equations (6) and (7) may be solved for the magnetic field values at which these molecules undergo resonance absorption. The number of molecules absorbing at magnetic field values between H and $H + dH$ is given by dN/dH. An analytical expression may be obtained from Eqs. (6) and (7) relating $(\sin \theta)d\theta \, d\Psi$ to H and dH. These expressions are given by several authors (e g., Kneubühl and Natterer, 1961) and are plotted versus applied magnetic field as dotted lines in Fig. 2, for a specific set of parameters.

Notice that $H_x = h\nu_0/g_x\beta$ is the magnetic field value at which molecules having their g-tensor x axes collinear with the applied field will absorb microwave power, i.e., undergo EPR. Likewise, $H_z = h\nu_0/g_z\beta$ is the magnetic field value at which molecules having their g-tensor z axes collinear with the applied field will absorb; since $H_z < H_y < H_x$ by assumption, $H_y = h\nu_0/g_y\beta$ is the magnetic field where not only molecules with their y axes aligned collinear with the field will absorb but also molecules of a large number of other orientations (such that $g = g_y$ for those orientations) will absorb. This is the reason for the much greater intensity at H_y.

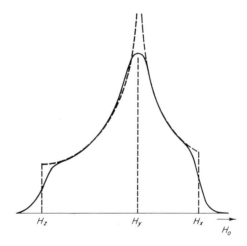

Fig. 2. A calculated EPR absorption spectrum resulting from an amorphous sample for which $g_x < g_y < g_z$. The magnetic field positions of these g values, at the fixed microwave frequency, calculated from Eq. (3), are marked H_z, H_x, and H_y. The dotted curve represents dn/dH, where n is the number of molecules resonant between H and $H + dH$, and the full curve shows the result of including a Gaussian linewidth for each molecule. Note that in practice first derivative spectra are almost always determined, not the absorption spectrum shown here; cf. Fig. 8 (lower spectrum) for an idea of what the first derivative of the curve in the present figure would be like. (Adapted from Fritz et al., 1971.)

To obtain the actual absorption spectrum, it is necessary to plot the spectral intensity versus magnetic field where the absorption line shape for each orientation is multiplied by the transition probability at that orientation and the number of molecules having that orientation. This is most easily accomplished by use of a computer in the cases where the transition probabilities or line shapes differ markedly with orientation (see, for example, Fritz et al., 1971). Furthermore, when one or more hyperfine interactions are present, a computer simulation is almost a necessity.

2. Individual molecules, such as proteins carrying paramagnetic centers, may exist in a range of conformations which are hard to demonstrate by other means but which may yield g values distributed about mean values. Nothing is known a priori about the expected shape of such distributions, often called "g strain," but this constitutes a definite source of linewidth, as will be shown in the discussion of the 2 Fe iron–sulfur proteins.

3. If magnetic nuclei (those with nuclear spin greater than 0) are present in the paramagnetic complex, then the nuclei may produce magnetic fields at the unpaired electronic spin. These interactions are of two types, the sum of which is called the nuclear hyperfine interaction: one is the classical interaction of two magnetic dipoles, $\mathbf{\mu}_s$ and $\mathbf{\mu}_I$, separated by a distance r (this interaction depends on the angle between the line that joins the two dipoles and the external field and is, therefore, anisotropic) and the other interaction is nonclassical and arises from the finite probability of finding the electron inside the nucleus. Since only s-state electrons have a finite density at the nucleus, this latter interaction is proportional to the s-state character of the electronic wave function. In the case of transition element ions this interaction arises by the d-state electrons responsible for the paramagnetism polarizing the s-state electrons, thus producing a net electronic spin polarization at the nucleus. This latter interaction is called the isotropic hyperfine or Fermi contact interaction and can be written as $A\mathbf{I} \cdot \mathbf{S}$ where $\mathbf{I}$ is the nuclear spin and A is a number proportional to the s-state density at the nucleus in question. The Hamiltonian describing such a coupled electron nuclear system is

$$\mathcal{H} = -g\beta\mathbf{S} \cdot \mathbf{H} + A\mathbf{I} \cdot \mathbf{S} - g_n\beta_n\mathbf{I} \cdot \mathbf{H} \tag{9}$$

The last term represents the nuclear Zeeman interaction of the nuclear magnetic moment with the external field. It is some three orders of magnitude smaller than the electron Zeeman term.

In a large applied magentic field the energies of such a system are given by

$$E = -g_e\beta m_s H + A m_I m_s - g_n\beta m_I H \tag{10}$$

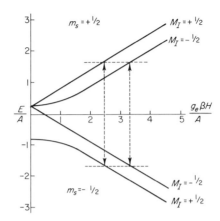

Fig. 3. Coupled electron and nuclear Zeeman interactions, for a nuclear spin of $\frac{1}{2}$. At large magnetic fields compared to $A/g_e\beta$, transitions induced by microwaves of fixed frequency will appear at two values of the applied field H. These transitions are indicated by the two dotted lines. The selection rule governing these transitions is the following: Those transitions are allowed for which $\Delta m_s = \pm 1$, $\Delta M_I = 0$. When $A/g_e\beta$ is larger than the linewidth of the transition in the absence of this coupling, substitution of a nucleus of spin $= \frac{1}{2}$ for a nucleus of spin $= 0$ (e.g., substitution of ^{57}Fe for ^{56}Fe, the natural isotope) will cause a doubling of the number of EPR lines.

where m_I and m_s are the expectation values of the components of the nuclear and electronic spins, respectively, along the applied field direction. These energies are plotted in Fig. 3 for a spin-$\frac{1}{2}$ electronic system coupled to a spin-$\frac{1}{2}$ nuclear system (e.g., ^{1}H, ^{13}C, ^{15}N, ^{19}F, ^{31}P, ^{57}Fe). Notice that there are now two electronic transitions which occur for the same frequency but at two different applied fields. When such peaks are resolved, their presence is a valuable aspect of EPR which can be used to identify components of the paramagnetic center, and when, as is far more common, they are unresolved, they contribute to the linewidth to such an extent that most of the signal shapes encountered in biological EPR are in fact the sums of large number of narrower resonances or spin packets. Under these conditions the method of ENDOR, to be discussed later, is particularly useful in measuring these interactions.

4. As mentioned, the observation of EPR depends on the difference in the two spin populations, created by the external magnetic field. If the incident microwave radiation becomes sufficiently intense, then the rate of transitions to the upper state exceeds the rate at which heat can be emitted to the surroundings, so that the system temperature T_s (now defined from $N_a/N_b = e^{-g\beta H/kT_s}$) increases and the EPR signal diminishes. This is the phenomenon of power saturation. The mechanisms of heat transfer to the lattice (spin-lattice relaxation) depend on the

presence of extended lattice motions or phonons (see Abragam and Bleaney, 1970, for a discussion of this), and these progressively diminish on going to lower temperatures, so that the intensity of microwave power that can be used, and thus the signal intensity obtainable, *diminishes* as the temperature is lowered. The temperature at which biological EPR is done is thus generally the compromise optimum between the saturation effect which suggests higher temperatures, and the Curie law (signal $\propto 1/T$) and linewidth effect (discussed next) which suggest lower temperatures.

5. This relaxation effect, the spin-lattice relaxation, and a similar effect, the spin-spin relaxation, affect the widths of the resonances, according to the uncertainty principle. At room temperature, the relaxation rate is large, the lifetimes of the states are short, and absorption lines are broad. The existence of this phenomenon is the main reason for observing the iron–sulfur proteins at low temperatures.

6. When two paramagnetic species come within about 10 Å of each other, dipolar interactions are large enough to affect the shapes of the signals. A static component, which is anisotropic (depends on the angle between the line connecting the paramagnets and the direction of the applied field), has in amorphous samples the same effect as the isotropic hyperfine interaction, i.e., the resonance position for various molecules is spread out over a finite range, broadening the signal. A time-dependent component is also present which can induce transitions, i.e., the second paramagnet is part of the lattice. This affects the resonance width as described in point (5) above.

7. If orbital overlap between two paramagnetic species occurs, the exchange interaction phenomenon correlates the two spins via the Pauli principle, depending on the degree of overlap. A multiplicity of states differing by one unit in the total spin $S(\mathbf{S} = \mathbf{S}_1 + \mathbf{S}_2)$ then exist, each with an energy given by $-2J\mathbf{S}_1 \cdot \mathbf{S}_2$, i.e., the energy of the coupled state depends upon the relative orientations of the two spins. These states will then be populated according to a Boltzmann population given by

$$\exp\left(\frac{-2J\mathbf{S}_1 \cdot \mathbf{S}_2}{kT}\right) = \exp\left(\frac{-J(S^2 - S_1^2 - S_2^2)}{kT}\right) = A \exp\left(\frac{-JS^2}{kT}\right) \quad (11)$$

As in the case of the Zeeman interaction, this relationship predicts that the upper states will be increasingly populated at higher temperatures resulting in a complex magnetic behavior of such systems because of the opposing temperature dependence of this Boltzmann population due to the exchange interaction and the Curie law. Exchange via intervening ligands is an important feature of the centers in the two-iron (plant-type) ferredoxins and in fact probably operates in all multinuclear clusters in iron–sulfur proteins. This is discussed in subsequent sections.

8. When the electronic spin system has a net spin greater than $\frac{1}{2}$, there are still other interactions which can affect the relative energies of the magnetic levels. These can be written in terms of higher powers of the spin operators (see Abragam and Bleaney, 1970) as follows

$$
\begin{aligned}
\mathcal{3C} &= \beta(g_x S_x H_x + g_y S_y H_y + g_z S_z H_z) + D' S_z^2 + E' S_x^2 + F' S_y^2 + \cdots \\
&= \beta(g_x S_x H_x + g_y S_y H_y + g_z S_z H_z) + D[S_z^2 - \tfrac{1}{3} S(S + 1)] \\
&\qquad\qquad\qquad\qquad\qquad + E(S_x^2 - S_y^2) + \cdots \quad (12)
\end{aligned}
$$

where $D = D' - \frac{1}{2}(E' + F')$ and $E = \frac{1}{2}(E' - F')$. To understand the origins of these extra terms in the energy operator it is necessary to consider the details of a given system.

III. THE PHENOMENON OF ENDOR

Recently a new spectroscopic tool has been applied to the study of iron–sulfur proteins. This is electron nuclear double resonance (ENDOR) spectrometry.

The method of ENDOR involves the detection of induced nuclear spin transitions by measuring the concomitant changes in the intensity of the electron paramagnetic resonance (EPR) signals observed in the sample. The intensity of a partially saturated EPR spectrum is affected by applying to the sample a variable radio frequency field which can induce nuclear spin transitions. The detailed mechanism by which the nuclear transitions affect the EPR spectrum differs for various materials. For an understanding of these mechanisms, the reader is referred to the literature (see Abragam and Bleaney, 1970). A brief discussion here will serve as an introduction to the phenomenon.

As was discussed under item (3) (Section II), for an EPR line whose width is mainly caused by random static interactions with neighboring spins and by a distribution of slightly different conformations (resulting in a distribution of g values), small hyperfine interactions will go undetected; as we shall see, these can be resolved in ENDOR.

Let us consider the phenomenon of ENDOR for a single, unpaired electron ($S = \frac{1}{2}$) interacting with a single nucleus ($I = \frac{1}{2}$). For simplicity let us assume further that there is an isotropic hyperfine (Fermi contact) interaction between these two particles. The energies of this system in an applied static magnetic field H were discussed previously and were given by Eq. (10) and plotted in Fig. 3. The energy plot is repeated in Fig. 4(a).

It is convenient to display the four energy levels existing at some large fixed applied field H_0 in the manner of Fig. 4(b), where each level is labeled at the side by the electron spin quantum number m_s and above by the nuclear quantum number m_I. It is assumed that $A \gg g_n \beta_n H$ which is often the case in these studies. The dotted lines in Fig. 4(b) denote the principal relaxation paths discussed in item (4) (Section II). The relaxation rate at which direct nuclear transitions occur is denoted by $1/\tau_n$, the rate at which electron transitions occur by $1/\tau_1$ and the rate at which cross relaxation occurs by $1/\tau_x$. Most generally, $\tau_1 \ll \tau_x \ll \tau_n$.

Figure 4(c) shows that for the EPR transition noted ($m_I = +\frac{1}{2}$) the effective relaxation rate between these two levels is determined primarily by the direct path ($1/\tau_1$). This is shunted by the indirect path via the ($m_s = +\frac{1}{2}$, $m_I = -\frac{1}{2}$) state which has an effective rate approximately $1/\tau_n$ since $\tau_n \gg \tau_x$ and hence the slower process ($1/\tau_n$) controls the rate via this indirect path. The total effective relaxation between the electronic states of Fig. 4(c) is thus $1/\tau_1 + 1/\tau_n$. If, on the other hand, the nuclear transition is induced instead as in Fig. 4(d), the effective relaxation rate between the nuclear states involved is by the direct path ($1/\tau_n$) shunted by a much more effective indirect path via the ($m_s = +\frac{1}{2}$, $m_I = -\frac{1}{2}$)

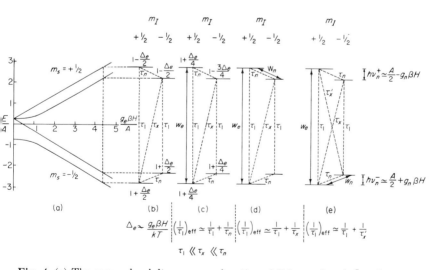

Fig. 4. (a) The energy level diagram as a function of H for an $S = \frac{1}{2}$, $I = \frac{1}{2}$ system with $I \cdot S$ coupling ($A \gg g_n \beta_n H$). (b) The energy levels, relaxation paths and approximate Boltzmann populations at a fixed applied magnetic field. (c) The same as (b) but with the $\Delta m_s = \pm 1$, $m_I = \pm \frac{1}{2}$ transition induced at a rate $W_e \gg 1/\tau_1$. (d) The same as (c) but with $\Delta m_I = \pm 1$, $m_s = +\frac{1}{2}$ transition induced at a rate $W_n > 1/\tau_x$. (e) The same as (d), except that an anisotropic hyperfine coupling is present and $W_n > 1/\tau_e'$. (From Fritz *et al.*, 1971.)

state at a rate approximately $1/\tau_x$ (since $\tau_x \gg \tau_1$). The effective relaxation between nuclear levels is thus $1/\tau_n + 1/\tau_x$ which is dominated by $1/\tau_x$; thus, if the nuclear transition is to be effective in changing the population of the states it must be induced at a rate W_n such that $W_n\tau_x \geq 1$ (not just $W_n\tau_n \geq 1$). Notice that the inducing of the electronic transition does not change this condition. However, the inducing of the nuclear transition does change the effective relaxation between the electronic levels since it influences the relaxation rate via the indirect path; if $W_n \gg 1/\tau_x$, then the electronic relaxation rate via the indirect path is determined by $1/\tau_x$ [instead of $1/\tau_n$ as in Fig. 4(c)]. The application of the nuclear resonance thus changes the effective electronic relaxation rate from $1/\tau_1 + 1/\tau_n$ [Fig. 4(c)] to $1/\tau_1 + 1/\tau_x$ [Fig. 4(d)]; if the EPR signal is partially saturated, this change in the electronic relaxation rate will manifest itself as a change in the EPR signal amplitude. Thus the presence of the nuclear resonance absorption may be detected by monitoring the saturated EPR signal.

It is to be noted that for our simple model displayed in Fig. 4, the inducing of the second nuclear transition ($h\nu_n^-$) has a much smaller effect on the effective electronic relaxation time for the EPR transition chosen. In fact, $\delta\tau_1/\tau_1 \simeq -\tau_1/\tau_n$ for this case, which is a much smaller change than that produced by the transition $h\nu_n^+$, so small that it probably would not be detected.

A more general model can be obtained by allowing the g and A tensors to be anisotropic. When the hyperfine interaction is anisotropic, transitions between the $m_s = +\frac{1}{2}$, $m_I = +\frac{1}{2}$ and $m_s = -\frac{1}{2}$, $m_I = -\frac{1}{2}$ states are allowed and a new relaxation path is created with a characteristic relaxation time τ_x' as shown in Fig. 4(e). This relaxation rate depends on the degree of anisotropy. Since the two nuclear transitions now result in fractional changes in the effective electronic relaxation times of $\delta\tau_1/\tau_1 \simeq -\tau_1/\tau_x$ and $\delta\tau_1/\tau_1 \simeq -\tau_1/\tau_x'$, respectively, the resulting ENDOR signals will not be equal in general. With the above in mind, a hypothetical ENDOR spectrum may be constructed using Eq. (10) to obtain the nuclear transition frequencies as follows

$$
\begin{aligned}
h\nu_n^\pm &= |\Delta E(m_s = \pm\tfrac{1}{2})| \\
&= |E(m_s = \pm\tfrac{1}{2}, m_I = +\tfrac{1}{2}) - E(m_s = \pm\tfrac{1}{2}, m_I = -\tfrac{1}{2})| \\
&= |(+\tfrac{1}{2}g_e\beta H - \tfrac{1}{2}g_n\beta H + \tfrac{1}{4}A) - (+\tfrac{1}{2}g_e\beta H + \tfrac{1}{2}g_n\beta H \pm \tfrac{1}{4}A)| \\
&= |-g_n\beta H \pm \tfrac{1}{2}A| \qquad\qquad\qquad (13)
\end{aligned}
$$

which shows that two lines will be observed corresponding to the two values of m_s and they will be centered at frequencies given by the absolute values of Eq. (13). For protons not directly bonded to the paramagnetic center, $g_n\beta H > \frac{1}{2}A$ and a pair of lines centered at $g_n\beta H$ and separated by A will be observed. For iron-57 in the nucleus of the paramagnetic site,

$A/z \gg g_n\beta H$ and a pair of lines centered at $\frac{1}{2}A$ and separated by $2g_n\beta H$ will result. Figure 5 displays this latter case for a realistic set of parameters for one of the iron sites in the two-iron ferredoxins at $H_0 = 3200$ G, where

$$g_n\beta H_0/h \simeq 0.45 \text{ MHz} \quad \text{and} \quad A/2h \simeq 21 \text{ MHz} \tag{14}$$

It is possible to use the anisotropy in the electron g factor to select molecules of a given set of orientations to undergo ENDOR (Fritz *et al.*, 1971); a brief discussion follows of how this may be done.

As was discussed under item (1) (Section II), setting the magnetic field at some value between H_x and H_z permits only those molecules having a specific set of orientations to undergo EPR. By choosing this field, the set of orientations may be chosen, e.g., if the magnetic field is set below H_z (assuming $H_x > H_y > H_z$), then primarily only those molecules whose z axes are aligned along the applied field will be undergoing EPR. Similarly, if the field is set above H_x, primarily those molecules whose x axes are aligned along the field will be undergoing EPR; if we set the field at H_y (between H_x and H_z), molecules of many orientations will be contributing to the EPR spectrum in addition to those molecules whose y axes are along the applied field. By keeping track of which molecular orientations are contributing to the EPR and hence ENDOR, it is possible to simulate the ENDOR spectrum and by comparison with the experimental spectrum to obtain the components of the A tensor. The application of ENDOR spectrometry to proteins offers the opportunity for the determination of bonding ligands in the paramagnetic sites by the detection and determination of these hyperfine couplings.

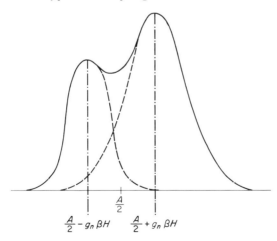

Fig. 5. Predicted spectrum for ^{57}Fe ENDOR from a single site in a two-iron ferredoxin, for one orientation of the molecule. (From Fritz *et al.*, 1971.)

IV. THE PHYSICS OF IRON IN PROTEINS

The paramagnetism of the iron–sulfur proteins is due to the presence of iron. Therefore, in order to understand the EPR and ENDOR of these proteins, it is necessary to discuss the electronic structure of the various valence states of iron and the interactions which these iron electrons have with their surroundings.

Ferric ions, to which much of the discussion in this chapter will be devoted, have a $3d^5$ electronic structure. Thus five electrons are found in the five $3d$ orbitals, and there are two commonly occurring ways in which the electrons can be distributed among these orbitals, depending on the character of the ligands surrounding the ions. If the ions present a relatively weak electrostatic field to the central iron ion, the d orbitals will be separated in energy by an amount small compared to the electrostatic interactions (exchange) between the electrons themselves. Under these conditions, Hund's rule of maximum spin will operate and the electrons will each occupy a separate d orbital, with a resultant spin of $\frac{5}{2}$ for the system. If, on the other hand, a strong ionic electrostatic field or extensive covalent bonding is present, then the orbitals may be separated much more in energy compared to the electron–electron repulsions, and a structure will result in which the five d electrons occupy three orbitals, leaving a net spin of $\frac{1}{2}$. For the strong field (low-spin) cases, the resultant molecule has a spin of $\frac{1}{2}$ at temperatures at which kT is less than the separation of the spin sets, and under these conditions the paramagnetism behaves in the simple way described in the introduction, namely, the spin transition is between a pair of states with a population difference given by a simple Boltzmann factor, so that the signal is proportional to $1/T$. With suitable corrections for g-value anisotropy (Aasa and Vanngard, 1970) the total EPR absorption from such systems can be compared to that of other $S = \frac{1}{2}$ systems such as Cu^{2+} to yield quantitative estimations of the number of spins.

For the high-spin (weak field) ferric compounds, the coupling of the intrinsic spin angular momentum with the orbital angular momentum (spin-orbit coupling) and the electrostatic interactions of the $3d$ electrons with the crystalline electric field result in additional terms in the spin Hamiltonian as indicated in Eq. (12). If the symmetry of the crystalline field at the iron site is axial (the x and y directions are equivalent), then E is zero and the Hamiltonian may be written as

$$H = \beta[g_\parallel S_z H_z + g_\perp(S_x H_x + S_y H_y)] + D[S_z{}^2 - \tfrac{1}{3}S(S + 1)] \quad (15)$$

where $g_\parallel = g_z$ and $g_\perp = g_x = g_y$. In zero applied field, the Hamiltonian consists of the last term only, and if m_s is the expectation value of S_z, then the energies of the different spin states are given by

$$E = Dm_s{}^2 - (\tfrac{35}{12})D \quad \text{(where} \quad m_s = \pm\tfrac{5}{2},\ \pm\tfrac{3}{2},\ \pm\tfrac{1}{2}) \tag{16}$$

The last term is the same for all states and can be ignored in calculating any transitions between states. There is thus a zero-field energy splitting which results in three Kramers doublets. If a magnetic field is now applied along the z axis, for example, then the energies of the spin states become

$$E = g_\parallel \beta H m_s + Dm_s{}^2 \quad \text{with} \quad g_\parallel \simeq 2$$

Such a situation is depicted in Fig. 6. If the magnetic field is oriented perpendicular to the z axis then the energies of the $m_s = \pm\tfrac{5}{2}$ states and the $m_s = \pm\tfrac{3}{2}$ states remain degenerate to first order, and the $m_s = \pm\tfrac{1}{2}$ doublet splits with an effective g value of 6. Two consequences of this are (1) that the energy separation between these Kramers doublets may be comparable to kT [viz., the separation between the $\pm\tfrac{1}{2}$ and $\pm\tfrac{3}{2}$ levels in cytochrome P-450 camphor (Tsai et al., 1970) is equivalent to kT at 11°K] so that only a fraction of the molecules are in the state (usually the $\pm\tfrac{1}{2}$ states) from which EPR is observed, and (2) that there is considerable

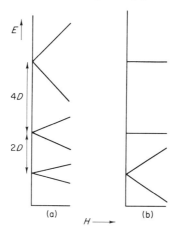

Fig. 6. Magnetic field dependence of the energies of the $m_s = \pm\tfrac{1}{2}$ (lower), $m_s = \pm\tfrac{3}{2}$ (middle), and $m_s = \pm\tfrac{5}{2}$ (upper) states of a high-spin d^5 system for two orientations of the molecule with respect to the applied field: (a) z axis of molecule and field are parallel; (b) z axis of molecule and field are perpendicular. Note that in this latter case the two excited states are degenerate to first order. The EPR transitions observed for such systems as the high-spin ferric hemes are (a) $g_\parallel \cong 2$ and (b) $g_\perp \cong 6$. These transitions arise from the lowest or $m_s = \pm\tfrac{1}{2}$ doublets. Thus at temperatures for which $2D \leq kT$, an appreciable fraction of the molecules will be in upper states and not available for EPR.

g-value anisotropy in such compounds ($g = 2$ to $g = 6$ in this case) so that, for an amorphous sample containing all molecular orientations, the absorption signal is spread over a few thousand gauss and the intensity at any one value of applied magnetic field is weak compared to that from a less anisotropic system of similar concentration.

High-spin compounds of low symmetry may have g-value tensors with nonzero off-diagonal terms (Blumberg, 1967) and yield EPR from two of the Kramers levels (Aasa, 1970), making their study quite complex. The rubredoxins are examples of such a system. In particular, quantitation of these substances in terms of their EPR requires knowledge of the spacing of the Kramers system, obtained from the temperature dependence of the signal intensities, careful integration of broad signals, and a calculation involving Boltzmann factors for the distribution of molecules among EPR-active and EPR-silent states, as well as g-value corrections to the transition intensity observed.

As mentioned above, when two or more iron atoms are present in a complex, additional features are brought in which are particularly important in the case of iron–sulfur proteins. The spins of two iron atoms can be coupled, via polarization of bonding electrons on intervening ligands or by direct exchange in metal–metal bonds, to yield a series of magnetic energy levels, the lowest of which may be of zero net spin or diamagnetic (Thornley $et\ al.$, 1966), even though the individual ions might be considered to be ferric, i.e., $S = \frac{1}{2}$ or $S = \frac{5}{2}$ as discussed earlier. An important point here is that at a temperature where kT is comparable to the energy difference between the lowest and next highest magnetic state, say of spin $= \frac{2}{2}$, the system will begin to exhibit paramagnetism which may $increase$ with temperature in distinction to the usual dependence on $1/T$. When the spins of the two or more ions are coupled in such a way as to make the lowest energy state that of lowest spin, the system is said to be coupled antiferromagnetically. Such is the case for the two-iron ferredoxins. A second feature of such coupled systems is that they may exhibit g values unusual for simpler iron compounds (Brintzinger $et\ al.$, 1966a). Thus, the two-iron (plant-type) ferredoxin may in the oxidized state contain two coupled ferric ions so that the material is diamagnetic, at least at low temperatures, while the addition of an electron to the complex yields a coupled ferric-ferrous pair, of net spin $= \frac{1}{2}$ ($\frac{5}{2} - \frac{4}{2} = \frac{1}{2}$) with observable EPR. If the EPR comes from the lowest magnetic energy level, the signal may exhibit a stronger temperature dependence than the $1/T$ predicted for a simple ($S \pm \frac{1}{2}$) case, and quantitation of EPR in these materials again may be straightforward only at low temperatures where the ground state doublet is essentially the only contribution to the magnetism.

V. RUBREDOXINS

This class of iron–sulfur proteins, characterized by the presence of cysteine iron bonds and the absence of acid-labile sulfur, has yielded most completely to study by physical methods, although until recently (cf. Chapter 6 of Volume I) the physiological role was uncertain. Thus, as described in other chapters of this book, the X-ray structure analysis (Chapter 4 of this volume) has revealed that isolated iron atoms are approximately tetrahedrally coordinated by cysteine mercaptide ligands. The spin state of both the ferric and ferrous forms of the protein are high-spin according to NMR, Mössbauer, and near-infrared spectroscopy (Chapters 3, 6, and 7 of this volume); thus the mercaptide ligand yields a relatively weak crystal field ($Dq \cong -500$ cm^{-1}) as was established by Eaton and Lovenberg (1970). This fact is of importance for understanding the two-iron (plant-type) ferredoxins, as will be seen later on.

Before the X-ray and other analyses were completed, it was appreciated that at least the ferric form of the proteins isolated from *C. pasteurianum* and *P. elsdenii* were high spin and that the environment was of low symmetry. Palmer and Brintzinger (1966) and Atherton *et al.* (1966) observed that the oxidized protein gives a complex signal near $g = 4.3$ and no signal on reduction, and Peterson and Coon (1968) later reported that the rubredoxin of *P. oleovorans* gave in addition an EPR signal near $g = 9$ when low ($< 20°$K) temperatures were employed.

Dowsing and Gibson (1969) have summarized previous theoretical approaches to explaining the origin of the $g = 4.3$ resonance from d^5 systems. If the spin Hamiltonian describing the system is

$$H = \beta H \cdot g \cdot S + D[S_z^2 - \tfrac{1}{3}S(S + 1)] + E(S_x^2 - S_y^2)$$

such resonances arise if (1) $D \cong 0$, $E \neq 0$; D need not be exactly zero if the symmetry of the ligands is lower than tetrahedral (C_{2v}) or octahedral (C_{2v} or D_{2h}), or if (2) D and E are both large, compared to $g\beta H$, and $E/D = \lambda \cong \tfrac{1}{3}$. Blumberg (1967) pointed out that if $\lambda = 0$ represents axial symmetry, then $\lambda = \tfrac{1}{3}$ represents maximal distortion toward rhombic symmetry. Both (1) and (2) lead to sets of three Kramers doublets with separations given by multiples of D. The resonances near $g = 4.3$ arise from transitions in the middle doublet.

Aasa (1970) has shown how the powder line shapes, for $\tfrac{1}{3} > \lambda > 0$, depend on the ratio of D to $g\beta H$. Thus observation of spectra at two or more microwave frequencies can lead to a rather precise characterization of the spin-Hamiltonian parameters. A particularly important feature of this study was that lines arising from nonvanishing off-diagonal terms in the g-value matrix were successfully accounted for.

Peisach *et al.* (1971) have taken a somewhat different approach in their analysis of the spectrum of the rubredoxin from *P. oleovorans*. This protein was studied in its one- and two-iron atom forms, with nearly identical results, indicating that the sites are nearly equivalent and independent. They assumed that if case (2) above was obtained, then it would be possible, by studying the temperature dependence of (X band) EPR signals from rubredoxin in the region of $T \approx D/K$, to determine the spacing $\frac{4}{3}\sqrt{(7)}D$ of the Kramers doublets, based on a Boltzmann distribution of states. They found $D = 1.51$ cm^{-1} $> g\beta H \cong 0.3$ cm^{-1} justifying their assumptions. Their experimental spectra are shown in Fig. 7; in terms of temperature the distance between states is $\sim 8°$K, and it is in this region of temperature that one must work to determine D. Note-

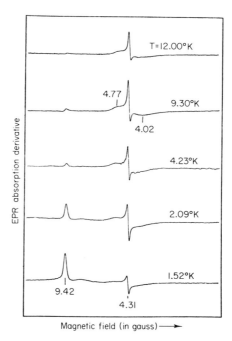

Fig. 7. Temperature dependence of the EPR spectrum of *Pseudomonas oleovorans* rubredoxin. The spectra were obtained at X band at the temperature indicated on the right-hand side of the figure. The g values of various transitions are indicated along the abscissa; the ordinates are an arbitrary function of the first derivative of the microwave absorption with respect to the applied magnetic field, which increases from left to right. (From Peisach *et al.*, 1971.)

worthy in these spectra is that although below 9°K the $g = 4.3$ resonance falls off in amplitude with decreasing temperature, the $g = 9.4$ resonance increases. This fits the picture that the $g = 4.3$ resonance arises from an upper (middle) Kramers doublet which is depopulated as the temperature falls, while the resonance at $g = 9.4$ comes from the ground state, which steadily grows toward unity population as the temperature drops. The reader should keep in mind that superposed on these phenomena is an additional factor, namely, that the individual transitions arise from Kramers doublets, themselves split in the magnetic field according to $h\nu = g\beta H$. The upper and lower states differ in population according to their own Boltzmann distribution; this is why the $g = 4.3$ resonance grows as the temperature of the sample is decreased from 12° to 9.3°K (Fig. 7) and then shrinks again at lower temperatures, when the distribution connecting the Kramers doublets favors the population of the lower ($g = 9.4$) state. This lower state grows *even faster* than $1/T$ because the two phenomena act in the same direction in this case.

Employing the approach of Dowsing and Gibson (1969), Peisach *et al.* have concluded that the best fit of their observed g values and D to theory yields $E/D = 0.28$, which reflects 85% of the maximum possible rhombic distortion expected for ligands unconstrained by attachment to the protein chain. Thus the conformation of the protein chain has energetic requirements that are felt as a perturbation from what would presumably be the equivalent complex, were the cysteines not linked by the intervening amino acids.

Peisach *et al.* have made a further interesting proposal in their study of *P. oleovorans* rubredoxin. They have examined the model compound ferric pyrrolidone dithiocarbamate, where the coordination is primarily to sulfur atoms. They find D for this case to be 1.68 cm^{-1}, which they compare to $D = 0.5$ cm^{-1} for ferrichrome a (Wickman *et al.*, 1965) in which the ligands are oxygen. Since D should depend on the crystal field splitting effect of the ligand plus geometric parameters, they propose that for rhombic ligand fields, it should be possible to distinguish sulfur liganding from weaker ligands such as oxygen, based on the size of D.

The study of the EPR of rubredoxins, at least the *P. oleovorans* case, thus leads to the concept that the ligand field is moderately weak, and of lower symmetry than tetrahedral, a conclusion that could be verified in detail by sufficiently precise crystallographic data (cf. Chapter 4 of this volume). It would also be of interest to check the value of D and E by investigating the EPR of rubredoxin at other frequencies (Aasa, 1970), and to obtain the value of D by the relaxation method (Scholes *et al.*, 1971).

VI. TWO-IRON (PLANT-TYPE) FERREDOXINS

The establishment of these proteins as a class characterized by the fact of having two iron and two acid-labile sulfur atoms per molecule (cf. Chapter 1 of this volume) went on nearly simultaneously with the studies described in this chapter. Taking these properties as given, EPR and allied physical techniques have contributed a great deal in revealing the probable character of the electron transfer centers of these proteins. At this writing, the two-iron ferredoxins, unlike other classes of simple iron–sulfur proteins, have not yielded to crystallographic analysis, so the deductions and predictions made from spectroscopic methods and reported here are presently our best picture of these centers, at least until the day when X-ray analysis succeeds.

It is not certain that the centers in complex systems like mitochondrial particles and xanthine oxidase (Chapters 9 and 10 of Volume I) are of the two-iron plant-ferredoxin type, but the early observation (Beinert and Sands, 1960) of resonances near $g = 1.94$ by low temperature ($\sim 80°K$) EPR drew attention to the possibility of the existence of non-heme iron electron transfer complexes in these materials. Given this impetus, it was found that similar resonances could be seen in proteins containing only iron and labile sulfur in addition to amino acid residues (see, for example, Shethna et al., 1964). The finding that lowering the temperature of observation even further by the use of helium-vapor cooling allowed observation of resonances in reduced spinach ferredoxin (Palmer and Sands, 1966) quickly brought about the realization that there is a large class of proteins having in common the presence of a paramagnetic center with average g value below 2, when the protein is reduced and observed at low temperatures. Figure 8 shows EPR signals from adrenal, C. pasteurianum, and spinach iron–sulfur proteins, illustrating the variations of linewidth and g value observed in these materials. What should also be borne in mind is that there are variations in the temperature range in which these signals can be observed. Depending on the concentration, of course, the adrenal protein signal can be seen at 200°K, while the spinach protein signal is often not easy to detect above 50°K. Malkin and Bearden (1971), in fact, found it necessary to observe illuminated chloroplasts at 25°K in order to detect the ferredoxin resonance, and the variation in temperature dependence of the EPR signals in NADH:CoQ reductase has been put to use (Orme-Johnson et al., 1971b) in resolving four overlapped resonances. Shethna et al. (1968) have used this phenomenon to point out a protein from Azotobacter that is remarkably similar (spectroscopically) to spinach ferredoxin.

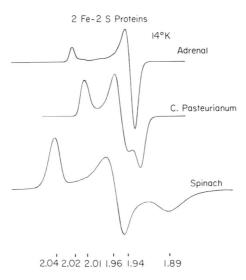

2.04 2.02 2.01 1.96 1.94   1.89

Fig. 8. EPR signals from reduced specimens of plant-type iron–sulfur proteins from bovine adrenals, *Clostridium pasteurianum,* and spinach. The proteins were prepared as described in Orme-Johnson and Beinert (1969a). The protein concentrations were approximately 10^{-4} M; the samples were reduced with sodium dithionite. The ordinate and abscissa are as in Fig. 7. The temperature of observation was 14°K, and other conditions of spectroscopy were microwave frequency, 9.17 GHz; microwave power 0.9 mW; modulation frequency, 100 KHz; modulation width, 6 G; field sweep rate, 100 G min^{-1}; time constant, 0.25 seconds.

Electron paramagnetic resonance signals of the kind shown in Fig. 8 are not commonly observed in well-characterized low molecular weight iron compounds, and in any event low-spin ferrous compounds are diamagnetic, and signals from high-spin ferrous compounds (as even-electron cases) are ordinarily very well relaxed and hard to detect. That the paramagnetic center *does* contain iron was demonstrated for one case by Shethna *et al.* (1964) who observed that an iron–protein fraction from *Azotobacter,* which had been grown on a medium enriched in ^{57}Fe (nuclear spin of $\frac{1}{2}$), yielded an EPR signal broadened in comparison to the control, prepared from cells grown in the presence of natural (low abundance of ^{57}Fe) iron. This broadening could only come from unresolved nuclear hyperfine interactions and thus iron was shown to be a component of the electron transfer center.

These observations were rationalized in theoretical papers by Brintzinger *et al.* (1966b), Gibson *et al.* (1966), and Thornley *et al.* (1966), who pointed out (1) that if two coupled ferric iron atoms are present in the oxidized state, the net spin will be zero at least at low temperatures; (2) that reduction of one atom to the ferrous state will yield a system of net spin of $\frac{1}{2}$; and (3) that reasonable assumptions about ligand field parameters will give g (average) less than 2 for such a coupled system, all in accord with observation. What remained was to show whether two iron atoms are in fact in one complex, what the nature of the other components of the complex is, and what kind of geometry and orbital overlaps are present. Thus the "ball" was returned to the experimentalist's "court."

Anaerobic reductive titrations followed by absorbance (Mayhew et al., 1969) and EPR spectroscopy (Orme-Johnson and Beinert, 1969 contains a discussion of previous evidence on this point) established that one electron was transferred per pair of iron atoms. This electron was accounted for by double integrations (a measure of the total absorption) of the EPR signals, establishing the origin of the resonance as a ground-state doublet.

Incorporation of ^{57}Fe into spinach ferredoxin (Palmer, 1967b) and parsley ferredoxin (Fee and Palmer, 1971) gave slight broadening of the EPR signal, which principally showed that proteins yielding narrower EPR linewidths were required for further progress. Tsibris et al. (1968b) and Beinert and Orme-Johnson (1969) used the P. putida and adrenal iron–sulfur proteins for this purpose. A comparison of the signals of a reduced preparation containing 94% of ^{57}Fe as well as a calculated 94% ^{57}Fe spectrum is shown in Fig. 9. The calculated spectrum was prepared on the assumption that both iron atoms are present in the center with

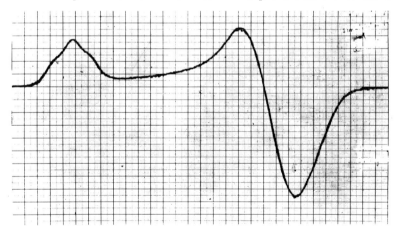

Fig. 9. Comparison of observed and calculated spectra of reduced plant-type ferredoxin from *Pseudomonas putida*. The observed and calculated spectra are superposed. The protein had been enriched with ^{57}Fe by chemical exchange. The spectra were obtained at X band; the ordinate and abscissa are as in Fig. 7. (From Tsibris et al., 1967.)

the unpaired spin, and that they both have the same effective hyperfine coupling constant, about 14 G. It was stated in the original publications and seems worth repeating (cf. Dunham *et al.*, 1971b) that this latter fact does *not* imply anything about the equivalence of the iron atoms. (This matter is discussed further below.) Clearly, however, both iron atoms are present in the center, as postulated, because no calculated spectrum assuming the presence of *one* iron atom in the paramagnetic center will, for 94% ^{57}Fe enrichment, reproduce the experimental spectrum.

The chemical evidence, chiefly that acid-labile sulfur and cysteine residues combine with mercurials with a proportionate loss in chromophore, activity, and potential EPR signal (cf. Chapter 1 of this volume) and that at least four cysteines are present in each iron–sulfur protein of known sequence (Chapter 2 of this volume), as well as the analogy of rubredoxin (*vide supra*), led to speculation that sulfur ligands formed part of the binuclear iron cluster. That this is so was established by the following experiments: Purified proteins from *Azotobacter* and *Pseudomonas putida* showed broadening when the cells were grown on media enriched in ^{33}S (nuclear spin of $\frac{3}{2}$) (DerVartanian *et al.*, 1967). Thus *some* sulfur is present in the paramagnetic centers of these proteins. A further experiment has been possible with the *P. putida* protein, which was grown on either ^{32}S or ^{33}S medium, following which the purified proteins were examined for EPR before and after exchange of the *labile sulfur only* for isotope of the opposite type. This yielded spectra from four species differing in isotopic distribution, which can be seen in Fig. 10. Clearly, broadening is seen from both the stabile (presumably cysteine) and labile (sulfide?, cf. Petering *et al.*, 1971) positions, so that both types of ligands are present. The multiplicity ($\frac{3}{2}$) and enrichment (<50%) of the isotope prevented the determination of the number of ligands of each type, as had been possible with the iron, but the discovery by Tsibris *et al.* (1968a) that selenide can replace sulfide in the reconstitution of ferredoxins allowed further progress to be made (Orme-Johnson *et al.*, 1968). Two atoms of selenium replace two atoms of sulfur in these derivatives, and ^{77}Se (nuclear spin of $\frac{1}{2}$) and ^{80}Se (nuclear spin zero) can be obtained in high (>90%) enrichment. Comparison of the natural, ^{80}Se, and ^{77}Se spectra can be seen in Fig. 11 for derivatives of the adrenal iron–sulfur protein. The low-field portion of the signal shows well-resolved hyperfine lines, which are fit by spectra calculated on the assumption that two selenium atoms are present in the center. Further experiments revealed that derivatives prepared with ^{57}Fe and ^{80}Se showed *iron* hyperfine interactions from *both* iron atoms, so that the paramagnetic center is similar in nature to the native case. Fee and Palmer (1971) have performed experiments with similar results, using parsley ferredoxin.

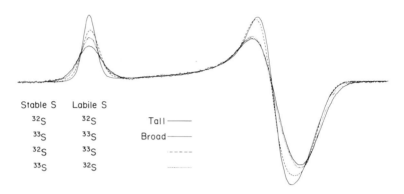

Fig. 10. Comparison of EPR spectra of reduced samples of the plant-type ferredoxin from *Pseudomonas putida*. As indicated in the figure, spectra are shown for samples in which either or both the stable (cysteine + methionine) sulfur had been enriched in ^{33}S content by growth of the organism on a medium containing about 48% of this isotope, the balance being ^{32}S. The labile sulfur was enriched in ^{33}S content by either the same means (^{33}S stable, ^{33}S labile curve) or by chemical exchange (^{32}S stable, ^{33}S labile curve). The ^{33}S stable, ^{32}S labile curve was from a sample grown on ^{33}S medium and back-exchanged with ^{32}S sulfide to remove ^{33}S from the acid-labile sulfur positions. The spectra were obtained at x band; the ordinate the abscissa are as in Fig. 7. The spectra shown represent the same concentration of molecules in each case (from unpublished work of R. Tsai, J. C. M. Tsibris, I. C. Gunsalus, W. H. Orme-Johnson, R. E. Hansen, and H. Beinert).

It should be pointed out that the adrenal and *P. putida* selenoproteins were active (70–100% of controls) in their specific enzymic reactions, and also that the mere fact of the change in the EPR signal on substitution of Se for S implies the presence of the latter in the paramagnetic center. These results strongly suggest that in these proteins *both* labile sulfur atoms as well as at least *some* of the cysteine (or methionine) sulfur atoms are present in the iron–sulfide cluster responsible for electron transfer.

Fritz *et al.* (1971) have applied the ENDOR technique to the study of spinach and parsley ferredoxin as well as the iron–sulfur proteins from pig adrenals and *P. putida*. It has been possible to determine most of the coupling constants for each iron atom in the plant-type ferredoxins. These results are given in Table I. One should note that the coupling constants are anisotropic, and are not equal for the "ferric" and "ferrous" atoms, and that the A tensor is not strictly collinear with the g tensor. These values taken by themselves indicate that the iron atoms are *not* equivalent. Further information on the constitution of these centers was obtained by Dunham *et al.* (1971a), who used the values in Table I in

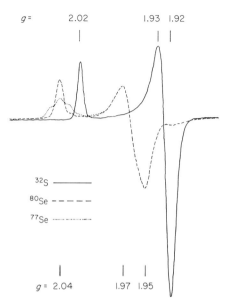

Fig. 11. Comparison of EPR spectra of pig adrenal plant-type ferredoxin in which the labile sulfur atoms had been replaced with selenide atoms, either ^{80}Se ($S = 0$) or ^{77}Se ($S = \frac{1}{2}$) as indicated. The spectrum of the native protein containing labile ^{32}S sulfide is also shown. The spectra are normalized to the same concentration of paramagnetic species. Note the resolution of hyperfine structure from ^{77}Se at $g_\parallel$ ($\simeq 2.04$) while no structure is seen at $g_\perp$. Thus $A_\perp \simeq 0$ in this case. The ordinate and abscissa are as in Fig. 7. (From Orme-Johnson *et al.*, 1968.)

the synthesis of Mössbauer spectra for comparison to experimental data (Chapter 6 of this volume). These effective A values allowed an analysis of the Mössbauer spectra from which it was deduced that antiferromagnetically coupled *high-spin* ferric and ferrous iron atoms are indeed effectively present in the reduced iron–sulfur cluster, as postulated in the theory of Thornley *et al.* (1966) and Gibson *et al.* (1966).

On the framework set up thus far, a number of other experimental approaches, including NMR, optical and X-ray methods, may serve to delineate the ligand geometry, bond distances, and electron distribution in the iron–sulfur clusters. The results to date of magnetic susceptibility measurements on the two-iron ferredoxins should be mentioned here. This is because the postulated antiferromagnetic coupling between pairs of iron atoms necessitates the existence of excited states of spin 1, 2, 3, etc., for the oxidized proteins, and $\frac{3}{2}$, $\frac{5}{2}$, $\frac{7}{2}$, etc., for the reduced proteins. These states should be thermally populated so that high-temperature magnetic susceptibility measurements should show that *both* the oxidized and reduced proteins are paramagnetic and that the paramagnetism increases

TABLE I

EFFECTIVE HYPERFINE COUPLING CONSTANTS, AS DEDUCED FROM ENDOR SPECTRA[a]

A (in G)

Protein	"Ferric" site			"Ferrous" site		
	A_x	A_y	A_z	A_x	A_y	A_z
Spinach ferredoxin	19.3 ± 0.4	$18.2 \begin{array}{l} +0.7 \\ -2.6 \end{array}$	14.6 ± 0.5	n.d.[b]	n.d.	12.4 ± 0.7
Parsley ferredoxin	19.2 ± 0.4	$18.2 \begin{array}{l} +0.7 \\ -2.6 \end{array}$	14.6 ± 0.7	n.d.	n.d.	12.1 ± 0.9
Adrenodoxin	18.5 ± 0.5	$20.7 \begin{array}{l} +0.4 \\ -1.1 \end{array}$	$15.2 \begin{array}{l} +0.4 \\ -0.7 \end{array}$	6.3 ± 1.5	8.9 ± 1.5	12.4 ± 0.5
Putidaredoxin	18.5 ± 0.5	$20.7 \begin{array}{l} +0.4 \\ -1.1 \end{array}$	$15.2 \begin{array}{l} +0.4 \\ -0.7 \end{array}$	6.3 ± 1.5	8.9 ± 1.5	12.4 ± 0.5

[a] From Fritz et al., 1971.
[b] Not determined.

with increasing temperature when the Curie law $(1/T)$ dependence is taken into account. Unfortunately, nothing definite can be said *a priori* how far apart the upper levels should be, i.e., how high a temperature is required. The experimental facts are as follows: Moss *et al.* (1969) and Moleski *et al.* (1970) showed that spinach, parsley, adrenal, and *P. putida* iron–sulfur proteins were diamagnetic in the oxidized state below 4°K, with a minimum distance to the first excited state of about 40 cm^{-1}. Measurements by Palmer *et al.* (1971) in the range 77°–250°K fix this value at 366 cm^{-1}. Comparable measurements on adrenodoxin (Kimura *et al.*, 1970) failed to reveal signs of antiferromagnetism, meaning that the first excited state is at least 700 cm^{-1} above the diamagnetic ground state. Finally, Phillips and Poe (Chapter 7 of this volume) in a study of several plant ferredoxins, find temperature-dependent NMR shifts around room temperature, which they attribute to protons which are contact shifted by an antiferromagnetic center. This was detailed by Dunham *et al.* (1971c). Thus susceptibility data lend support to the concept of an antiferromagnetically coupled iron–sulfur cluster, for the plant ferredoxins.

In summary then, the presence of both iron atoms and both labile sulfur atoms in an iron–sulfur cluster which accepts one electron are firmly established features of these proteins. The reduced complex clearly contains nonequivalent iron atoms, and all evidence supports the presence of a high-spin ferric atom coupled to a high-spin ferrous atom. Other sulfur ligands are present, and on the analogy of the rubredoxin structure, the cysteines seem likely to fill this role. As discussed by Dunham *et al.* (1971b), the ligand field is not octahedral; it is probably tetrahedral. The high-spin nature of the cluster is compatible with the relatively weak-field character of mercaptide $(Dq = -500$ cm$^{-1})$ (see Section V) and sulfide $(Dq = -340$ cm$^{-1})$, although considerable covalency is present so that an ionic interpretation is not strictly valid. A popular structure for the cluster system, employing bridging labile sulfur atoms which are the routes of magnetic coupling between the iron atoms, is shown in Fig. 14 of Chapter 7 (of this volume). Low molecular weight precedents for this general type of structure are known (for example, Connelly and Dahl, 1970). A general discussion of current models for these and other iron–sulfur cluster systems will be found in the final chapter (Chapter 8) of this volume.

One final feature of the EPR spectra of these proteins is worthy of note. The observation of the EPR absorption of the two-iron proteins at markedly different microwave frequencies has led to the demonstration of the major source of the EPR linewidths for a subclass of these proteins, namely, the existence of a distribution of g values caused presumably by a distribution of different protein conformations (Fritz *et al.*,

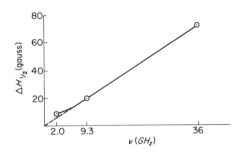

Fig. 12. Dependence of the linewidth ($\Delta H_{1/2}$) at g_z of reduced spinach ferredoxin on the microwave frequency (ν) at which the EPR experiment is performed. Compare this to Fig. 8 (lower curve); the lowest field line at $g \sim 2.04$ is g_z. (From L. Strong, D. Palaith, and R. Sands, in preparation.)

1971). Figure 12 shows the half-width of the EPR spectra at g_z for reduced spinach ferredoxin as a function of the microwave frequency at which it was observed. The linear behavior at the higher frequencies, and hence higher applied fields indicate that the linewidth is contributed to by a term having the form $\Delta H_{1/2} = \Delta g \beta H$; that is, it is exactly what one would expect for a system displaying "g strain." That this is caused by a distribution of different protein conformations and not by some strain introduced by the freezing of the sample is pure conjecture; however, in favor of such an interpretation is the fact that the linewidths are independent of the speed of freezing and of the introduction of glucose to alter the nature of the "solvent matrix." No matter what the interpretation, the experimental fact is that such a linewidth dependence exists and may be used to advantage by the EPR spectroscopist to resolve certain hyperfine splittings in the EPR spectra, i.e., by making measurements at lower frequencies.

VII. IRON–SULFUR PROTEINS WITH FOUR IRON ATOMS

There are two very distinct kinds of these proteins known at present, although admittedly our understanding of these is rather imperfect compared to the rubredoxin and two-iron ferredoxin situations.

The first class are called "high-potential iron proteins." They have very positive oxidation–reduction potentials (pH 7), +0.35 V for the *Chromatium* and +0.33 V for the *Rhodopseudomonas gelatinosa* protein (Dus *et al.*, 1967). Titrations followed by optical and EPR methods show that 1 e^- is transferred per four iron atoms (Mayhew *et al.*, 1969; Flatmark and Dus, 1969; Orme-Johnson and Beinert, 1969). Susceptibility measurements below 4°K, as well as EPR measurements below 50°K, show that the signal

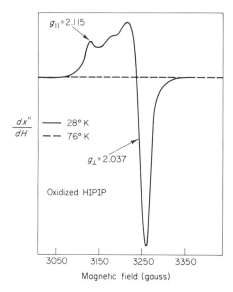

Fig. 13. EPR spectrum at X band of oxidized high-potential iron protein (HIPIP) of *Chromatium* strain D. Spectra were taken at the two temperatures indicated on the figure. The ordinate and abscissa are as in Fig. **7**. (From Palmer *et al.*, 1967.)

accounts for one spin per molecule. The system is thus a ground state doublet, with no excitable states discernable below 50°K. The EPR signal is significantly different from the ferredoxin type, being essentially axial with $g_{\parallel} = 2.2$ and $g_{\perp} = 2.04$ as seen in Fig. 13 (Palmer *et al.*, 1967). The other feature setting these systems apart is that the proteins are paramagnetic in the *oxidized* states, and diamagnetic in the *reduced* states. Both proteins have four cysteine residues, four iron atoms, and four labile sulfur atoms, which crystallographic evidence (Strahs and Kraut, 1968) place in a single complex. The proteins have a molecular weight of about 10,000.

Shethna *et al.* (1971) have reported the isolation of a ferredoxin from *Bacillus polymyxa*. This protein, with a molecular weight of about 9000, appears to be the proximal reductant of nitrogenase in that organism. Further investigation (Orme-Johnson *et al.*, 1972) revealed that the protein contains four iron and four labile sulfur atoms per molecule, and that the protein accepts one electron per molecule on reduction. The oxidation–reduction potential is —0.38 V (pH 7). The EPR signal obtained in the reduced state is shown in Fig. 14. It corresponds to one spin per molecule so that the system is a ground state doublet in the limited temperature range where it can be easily observed. The signal rapidly broad-

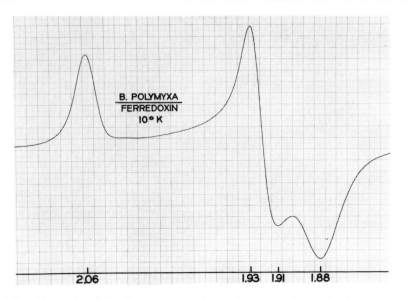

Fig. 14. EPR (*X* band) spectrum of a reduced sample of the ferredoxin of *Bacillus polymyxa*. The temperature of observation was 10°K; the ordinate and abscissa are as in Fig. 7. (From Shethna *et al.*, 1971.)

ens above 20°K and becomes very easily saturated below 10°K. This temperature behavior, the shape of the EPR signal, and the fact that the protein has a light absorption spectrum nearly identical with the bacterial ferredoxins, suggests that the underlying paramagnetic center is similar to one of the two present in the bacterial ferredoxin (*vide infra*). Thus there may exist iron–sulfur clusters containing four iron and four sulfur atoms which function similarly to the two-iron ferredoxins.

What is clearly *not* established at this writing is whether in fact the unpaired spin is associated with one or all of the iron and labile sulfur atoms, nor can anything be said yet about the chemical nature of the clusters, if any, involved. It will be interesting to learn how the iron–sulfur centers that we suppose to be present are constructed so as to allow the diversity in properties presented by these two classes of proteins.

VIII. EIGHT-IRON (CLOSTRIDIAL-TYPE) FERREDOXINS

Chemical features of the iron–sulfur proteins called clostridial or bacterial-type ferredoxins are described in Chapter 1 of this volume. It seems likely at this writing that these proteins contain eight iron and eight labile sulfur residues, and eight or more cysteine residues, and it is with species for which this stoichiometry is well established that these paragraphs will deal. As will be appreciated, we are only at the beginning of detailed investigations of the magnetic properties of these materials.

The initial EPR study of a representative of this class, ferredoxin from *C. pasteurianum*, was made by Palmer *et al.* (1966). They showed that the oxidized protein yields a small, narrow resonance at $g = 2$, while after reduction by dithionite or by NADPH in the presence of ferredoxin reductase and NADPHase a complex resonance between 2.01 and 1.89 is seen. These resonances were found to be quite temperature sensitive; Palmer *et al.* recorded their spectra at 15°K. Using the most recent value of the molar absorbancy of the protein to correct their data, one obtains about 1.6 electrons per molecule, accounted for by double integration of the EPR signal of the reduced protein.

Orme-Johnson and Beinert (1969b) performed a reductive titration of *C. pasteurianum* ferredoxin, monitoring this with EPR spectroscopy at 20°K. It was found that 2 electrons per molecule, provided by sodium dithionite, were required to completely reduce the protein. Also, it was found that *two* resonances appear sequentially during the course of the reduction. The resonance of the oxidized form, near $g = 2$, disappears during the first stages of the titration, being replaced by a signal with $g_\parallel \sim 2.06$ and $g_\perp \sim 1.94$. Further additions of electron equivalents lead to growth of this signal, and the appearance of a second narrower signal between $g = 2.06$ and $g = 1.94$. All changes in the spectrum were complete at 2 electrons per molecule added equivalents. The same sequence of changes was seen when the protein was reduced by hydrogen in the presence of hydrogenase; thus the behavior of the signals is not necessarily an artifact.

The conclusions suggested by the above experiments, namely, that two electrons are accepted by two different sites in the protein, are supported by parallel findings by Mayhew *et al.* (1969) that according to reductive titrations followed by light absorption spectroscopy, two electrons are accepted. Similarly, Eisenstein and Wang (1969) have analyzed their potentiometric titration data, taken with this protein, and have concluded that two electrons are accepted with two different midpoint potentials, viz., −367 and −398 mV, at pH 7.

Similar experiments have recently been performed with *C. acidi-urici* ferredoxin (Orme-Johnson, Sundquist, Bale, and Beinert, unpublished observations). It was found that two electrons are accepted by the protein during a dithionite titration, and that double integration of the EPR signal accounts for two spins per molecule, when the EPR was observed at 4.2°K. Spectra taken during the titration are shown in Fig. 15. The potentials of the two centers are somewhat more separated than in the

case of *C. pasteurianum* ferredoxin, and the potentials are also more negative (−420 to −460 mV, pH 7) than is the case with that protein.
Partial reduction of *C. acidi-urici* ferredoxin with hydrogen in the
presence of hydrogenase allowed the isolation of the nearly pure spectrum
of the first center. Subtraction of this from the spectrum of the fully
reduced protein, followed by a sequence of corrections of the experimental
spectrum of the first signal, to remove the small amount of second signal
present, yielded a spectrum with essentially the same shape as that seen
in part B of Fig. 15. According to this analysis, in which the assumption
is made that each signal accounts for exactly one-half of the spins, the

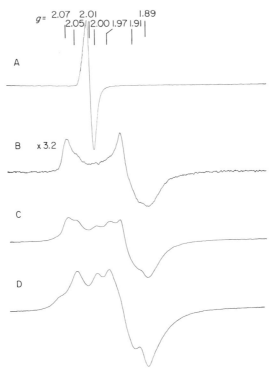

Fig. 15. Spectra taken during titration of *Clostridium acidi-urici* ferredoxin with
sodium dithionite. (See Orme-Johnson and Beinert, 1969a, for details of the method.)
Conditions of EPR spectroscopy: temperature, 4.2°K; microwave frequency, 9.15
GHz; microwave power, 9 mW; modulation frequency, 100 KHz; modulation width,
10 G; field sweep rate, 400 G min^{-1}, time constant, 0.25 seconds. The ordinate
and abscissa are as in Fig. 7. The protein concentration was 8.2×10^{-4} *M*, in
0.1 *M* tris-chloride buffer, pH 7.5 (A) No dithionite, gain 1; (B) 0.44 electrons
per molecule, gain 3.2; (C) 1.44 electrons per molecule, gain 1; (D) 2.0 electrons
per molecule, gain 1. (W. Orme-Johnson, J. Sundquist, J. Bale, and H. Beinert,
unpublished observations.)

first center yields a rhombically distorted but nearly axial spectrum, while the second center shows a set of six apparent g values. The complexity of the EPR from the second center could arise from heterogeneity with respect to the second site, or from large ligand superhyperfine interactions, or from magnetic interactions between the two sites (see note added in proof on p. 238).

The finding of two differentiable electron accepting sites in these two examples of bacterial ferredoxins has a natural explanation in the recent finding by Sieker et al. (1972) that the related ferredoxin from *Micrococcus aerogenes*, for which the X-ray structure has been solved to ~2.5 Å, has two iron–sulfur clusters of equal size, separated by ~12 Å. In this connection it is noteworthy that the ferredoxin of *B. polymyxa* (cf. Section VI) has four iron and labile sulfur atoms, accepts a single electron, and yields an EPR spectrum not unlike that of the first appearing center of the two bacterial ferredoxins. This protein and others like it may well utilize the iron–sulfur cluster of the bacterial-type ferredoxins to accomplish single electron transfers as do the two-iron ferredoxins.

Similar broad resonances have been detected in ferredoxin from *Chromatium* (Hall and Evans, 1969). The investigation of EPR properties of other bacterial-type ferredoxins, the explanation of the significance of the resonance at $g = 2$ in the oxidized protein, the establishment of the nature of the electron-accepting centers (few will doubt but none have proven that they are iron–sulfur clusters), and the utilization of this knowledge in studies of more complex systems remain for the future.

IX. EPR IN MORE COMPLEX IRON–SULFUR PROTEINS

In evaluating the place of EPR in the study of iron–sulfur proteins, the reader should be aware that the finding of the classical $g = 1.94$ resonance is neither a necessary nor a sufficient property of iron–sulfur proteins. Even disallowing the example of the rubredoxins, on the ground that they contain no labile sulfur, there does exist at least one example of an iron–sulfur protein where the EPR properties described for the majority of proteins considered in this book are not found. The Mo–Fe component of nitrogenase (see also further discussion near the end of this section) apparently yields no signal in the reduced state, but does yield a distinctive EPR signal in the oxidized state as isolated and as found in nonrespiring cells (Orme-Johnson, et al., 1972). Whether this is due to the inclusion of Mo in an iron–sulfur cluster system is not yet known. Second, as Beinert et al. (1965b), Brintzinger et al. (1966b), and Blumberg and Peisach (1965) showed, it is possible, in model compounds at least, to generate a signal with average g values below 2, using iron compounds in which the ligands are not of the labile sulfur kind (cf. Chapter 8 of this volume). The ligands used in these model compounds included, in the various cases cited, "unphysiological" types such as cyanide, nitroso groups, and hexamethyl benzene, as well as a more plausible situation in which semiquinones were complexed to ferrous atoms, but the examples do illustrate that it is possible to obtain something like the EPR behavior of the plant and bacterial ferredoxins with other than iron–sulfur clusters. It is, therefore, only the simplest suggestion, and not the required conclusion, that labile sulfur containing iron–sulfur proteins, other than the plant-type ferredoxins, are exhibiting a property of an iron–sulfur cluster when they yield a "$g = 1.94$" EPR signal on reduction.

Nonetheless, the example of the two-iron ferredoxins, together with the historical development of the field, has encouraged the hypothesis that such EPR manifestations are indicative of iron–sulfur clusters as electron transferring groups, in a variety of complex systems. In this area a number of interesting observations have been accumulated, including studies on various oxidases and dehydrogenases as well as components of the mitochondrial electron transport apparatus. Highlights of the EPR properties of some of these substances will be discussed in the following pages; further discussions of chemical and biological properties will be found elsewhere in this book, as well as in a recent review (Orme-Johnson, 1973).

Xanthine oxidase, for example, has eight iron and eight labile sulfur atoms per molecule, and appears to contain at least two kinds of resonances attributable to iron–sulfur centers (Gibson and Bray, 1968; Palmer and Massey, 1969; Orme-Johnson and Beinert, 1969b). One type, observable above 77°K, has apparent g values of 1.90, 1.94, and 2.02, and arises maximally when eight reducing equivalents per molecule have been added during a titration with sodium dithionite. Another signal, for which only a feature at $g = 2.11$ was observed in these experiments, was maximally present when three reducing equivalents were added. This second resonance could only be observed when the temperature of the sample was lower than 30°K. Thus two centers of different midpoint potential are present in the protein, if one assumes that the system is at equilibrium during the titration. The signal giving apparent g values of 1.90, 1.94, and 2.02, when observed above 77°K, shows a broad, unresolved resonance near $g = 1.94$, as well as a second broad feature at $g = 2.02$. When the spectrum is taken at lower temperatures, the features progressively narrow and the two higher field g values become distinguishable. In this respect the resonance has an appearance much like that of spinach ferredoxin (Gibson and Bray, 1968; Palmer and Massey, 1968). The latter authors, allowing for the effect of the resonance at $g = 2.11$, integrated for ferredoxin-like signal and found slightly more than two spins (or four iron atoms, on the plant-type ferredoxin model) per molecule. Thus approximately half the iron atoms in the molecule are accounted for in this type of center. After partial reduction, xanthine oxidase also exhibits an apparently isotropic signal near $g = 2.00$. This signal, on the evidence of its shape, width (about 19 G), absence from preparations depleted in flavin (Komai et al., 1969), and disappearance during complete reduction of the molecule, is due to the semiquinone form of the FAD prosthetic groups. Like other radical species it is easily saturated, so that a combination of high-incident microwave power and low temperature can effectively suppress this signal, which allows its contribution to the complex of signals around $g = 2$ to be evaluated. The maximum size of this signal observed during the steady state amounts to about 30% of the spins expected if all the FAD present were to be converted to the semiquinone form (Bray et al., 1964). A fourth sort of signal is observed in the region from $g = 1.95$ to $g = 1.97$ after partial reduction of the enzyme as well as during the steady state. Bray and Meriwether (1966) isolated xanthine oxidase from the milk of a cow which had been injected with ^{95}Mo. Upon reduction of this enzyme with xanthine for 10 mseconds, the EPR signal was found to be composed principally of the species in the region from $g = 1.95$ to $g = 1.97$, plus hyperfine lines which could be assigned in accordance with the nuclear spin ($\frac{5}{2}$) of ^{95}Mo. This and further experiments and analysis clearly demonstrated the origin of these signals (for a discussion, see Bray, 1971, and Chapter 10 of Volume I). About 35% of the spins expected for Mo (V), if the two atoms of molybdenum per molecule were present in that form in the steady state, were accounted for on integration of the signal. Lowe et al. (1972) have recently shown that there is in addition a splitting of the Mo(V) signal due to a spin–spin interaction between Mo(V) and the iron–sulfur center which yields EPR at $g_{\text{avg}} = 1.95$. For a discussion of the order of appearance of these various species during the approach to the steady state, and the role of the underlying components in the mechanism of the enzyme, see Chapter 9 of Volume I.

Liver aldehyde oxidase is an enzyme of identical composition with respect to cofactors, and it exhibits a similar set of EPR resonances during reduction (Rajagopalan et al., 1968). Of interest here is that the EPR signal attributed to the iron–sulfur moiety of the protein is much more nearly axial than that from xanthine oxidase, even when observed at 25°K. In this regard, this signal, with g values of 2.02 and 1.93, is more nearly like that of adrenodoxin (Fig. 8) than that of spinach ferredoxin. Dihydroorotate dehydrogenase, on the other hand, contains two FAD and two FMN groups, as well as four Fe and four labile sulfur atoms, per molecule. On reduction with NADH, an EPR signal appears with apparent g values of ~ 2.01, 1.94, and 1.92. Integration of the signal reveals the presence of two spins per molecule, equivalent to one electron added per pair of iron atoms. The higher-field features of this signal are well resolved even at 84°K (Aleman et al., 1968). This signal thus resembles that of C. pasteurianum paramagnetic protein (Fig. 8). On the basis of similarity of appearance and temperature behavior of EPR signals, then, one can suggest that something like the three modifications of the two-iron ferredoxin iron–sulfur clusters, seen with simpler proteins, may have been utilized in these more complex enzymes. Whether this speculation is useful or not must of course await further insight into what in fact are the sources of the differences in the properties of those simpler protein models.

The earliest report of EPR resonances, stemming from what are presently thought to be iron–sulfur clusters, concerned observations made with components of mitochondria (Beinert and Sands, 1960). This sort of resonance can, in fact, be observed in several functional locales in the mitochondrial electron transfer system. Succinic dehydrogenase (DerVartanian et al., 1969, and references cited therein) can be isolated in modifications possessing two to eight iron and labile sulfur groups per flavin, and the modification with ca. eight iron atoms has been investigated with the freeze-quenching EPR technique. In addition to a radical signal, an iron–sulfur type signal with apparent g values near 2.01 and 1.94 were shown to appear on reduction and disappear on reoxidation in a time consistent with the turnover rate of the enzyme under the conditions employed. The reduction step was the slower of the two processes. The maximal signal at $g = 1.94$, obtained during a dithionite titration and evaluated by integration, accounted for about one-third of the pairs of iron atoms present. Another portion of the electron transferring apparatus, the cytochrome b–c_1 segment, also contains an iron–sulfur moiety, as shown by Rieske et al. (1964), who were able to isolate a succinylated derivative of a low molecular weight iron–sulfur protein from this region. This protein contains two iron and two labile sulfur atoms, accepts a single electron on reduction, and yields an EPR signal with apparent g values of 2.02, 1.89, and 1.81, on reduction. In the "intact" b–c_1 preparation a similar signal can be elicited, as can signals attributable to cytochromes c_1, b_k, and b_T (Orme-Johnson et al., 1971a). A curious phenomenon was noted during these experiments: under conditions where cytochrome b_k is being reduced, the iron–sulfur protein resonance, which is already maximally present, changes in shape to a form with g values of 2.02, 1.89, and 1.78. Thus the iron–sulfur resonance senses and serves as an indicator of the oxidation state of another paramagnetic group in the enzyme. This sort of subtlety is seen in various experiments with all of the complex proteins so far mentioned in this section, i.e., differences in signal shape and saturation behavior are often seen on moving through intermediate oxidation states of multicomponent enzymes. These phenomena have been noted in detail before (see Beinert and Orme-Johnson, 1967, for references) but their origin remains obscure save for the generalization that such phenomena are certainly evidence for changes in magnetic interaction among paramagnets in these systems and for structural changes associated with oxidation–reduction of various components.

The NADH:CoQ reductase segment of the mitochondrial electron transfer complex has long been recognized (Chapters 9 and 10 of volume I) to contain a large number of (16 to 20) nonheme iron and labile sulfur atoms per flavin. The potential multiplicity of iron–sulfur centers in these parts of the mitochondrion is beginning to be experimentally demonstrated. It was earlier observed (cf. Beinert et al., 1965b) that on reduction with NADH, a signal with apparent g values of 2.02, 1.94, and 1.92 appeared within 10 mseconds. It now appears (Orme-Johnson et al., 1971b) that by observation of resonances that appear during reductive titrations, *four* iron–sulfur type paramagnetic centers can be demonstrated to be present in these materials. This was facilitated by the finding that the different centers have different responses to changes in the temperature of the EPR experiment (Fig. 16). The centers were found to have the following g values: (1) 2.022, 1.938, 1.923, (2) 2.054, 1.922; (3) 2.101, 1.886, 1.864; (4) 2.103, 1.863, all appearing during reduction at a rate consistent with their participation in catalysis. Titrations showed that there is a gradation of potentials among these centers, in the order $2 > 3 + 4 > 1$. Similar findings have been made using yeast submitochondrial particles (Ohnishi et al., 1971), and other, less understood electron acceptors have also been observed during these experiments. As to quantitation, the four iron–sulfur centers appear to account for one electron each per flavin. On the model of the plant-type ferredoxin, this would mean that eight of sixteen or so iron atoms are accounted for. If, however, the type of center postulated in the B. polymyxa protein (cf. Fig. 14) is present (center 2 for example yields a similar signal to that from B. polymyxa ferredoxin), all sixteen of the iron atoms may be in recognized iron–sulfur centers. Leaving aside the possibility of eliciting more signals yet under suitable conditions, the NADH dehydrogenase system, like all the complex proteins discussed in this section (with the exceptions of the b–c₁ iron protein and dihydroorotate dehydrogenase which are the simplest of the group), does not unambiguously give sufficient spins to account for all the nonheme iron atoms, unless in this case the four-iron atom cluster model correctly represents all of the centers. Possible technical

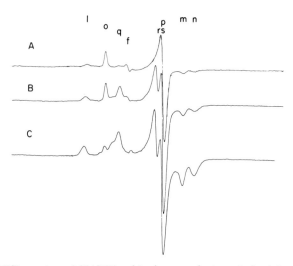

Fig. 16. EPR spectra of NADH: ubiquinone reductase derived from beef heart mitochondria. The protein concentration was 18.2 mg/ml, and the protein was reduced anaerobically with NADH as follows: (A) 0.4 ml of protein was treated with 10.6 electron nEq of NADH; (B), (C) 0.4 ml of protein was treated with 127 electron nEq of NADH. (A) and (B) were at 13°K; (C) was recorded at 7°K. The microwave frequency was 9.2 GHz, the microwave power was 0.27 mW, the modulation frequency was 100 KHz, the modulation amplitude was 7.5 G, the field sweep rate was 200 G min^{-1}, and the time constant was 0.5 seconds. The ordinate and abscissa are as in Fig. 7. The field positions on the g-value scale, indicated by some of the letters above the spectra, are as follows: l, 2.10; o, 2.05; q, 2.02; p, 1.92; m, 1.98; n, 1.86. Resonances q, r, s belong to iron–sulfur center 1; resonances o, p belong to center 2; resonances l, m, n belong to center 3; resonances l and n also contain a fourth center. In (C) the effect of low temperature in enhancing center 3 (l, m, n) compared to center 2 (p, p) can be seen. See the original publication from which this figure is taken (Orme-Johnson *et al.*, 1971b) for further detail on the resolution of the resonances.

reasons for such difficulties have been mentioned in the first section of this chapter; alternatively it seems possible that other centers remain undetected, by reason of being excessively well relaxed and therefore broad, or possibly there are iron–sulfur clusters, like those present in nitrogenase, which may fulfill roles which do not require that they transfer electrons. An intriguing final possibility, in all such cases of "invisible centers," is that they transfer two electrons per complex and so avoid paramagnetic states altogether. The encouraging aspect of studies in these areas has been, however, that repeatedly, refinements in technique followed by renewed efforts at experimentation have brought the accountability of the metal compositions, in terms of potentially paramagnetic clusters, ever closer to a satisfactory state.

In closing, a few novel observations and possibilities in the areas of complex systems should be mentioned. Hydrogenase has recently been purified from both *Desulfovibrio* and *Clostridium* species to a state where it is certain that these are iron–sulfur proteins (Nakos and Mortenson, 1971a,b; LeGall *et al.*, 1971). LeGall *et al.* showed that after a considerable incubation period under H_2, the *Desulfovibrio* enzyme develops a poorly resolved (at 87°K) ERP signal with apparent g values of 2.03 and 1.86. They attribute the slowness of the appearance of the signal to reversal of inactivation of the enzyme, which also manifests itself as an initial lag in kinetic studies. Whatever the explanation for this odd behavior, it appears that this may be another iron–sulfur cluster system. A preparation from *A. vinelandii* with NADH dehydrogenase activity (DerVartanian and Bramlett, 1970) was shown to incorporate molybdenum when the organism was starved of iron. The interesting possibility that under these circumstances molybdenum is able to substitute in a catalytically significant way for an iron–sulfur cluster remains to be explored. *Azotobacter* also yields an iron–sulfur protein which will act as an electron donor to nitrogenase (Yoch *et al.*, 1969) but which exhibits iron–sulfur type EPR signals in oxidized and reduced states. This molecule is reasonably small (about 17,000 molecular weight) and may exemplify a unique further type of iron–sulfur system. Nitrogenase from both *Clostridium* and *Azotobacter* species (cf. Chapter 3 of Volume I) has been separated into two components, both of which are iron–sulfur proteins. Component I, which contains 1 Mo and 12–14 Fe and labile sulfur atoms per molecule, exhibits EPR at $g = 4.3$, 3.6, and 2.0, in the oxidized state. The origin of this resonance is under investigation currently, but it has been found that the resonance at $g = 3.6$ is relatively unobscured by other resonances in whole cells, the interior of which are in a reduced state, so that low-temperature ($<30°K$) EPR can be used to follow the fate of this component of nitrogenase during repression and derepression of this system (Davis *et al.*, 1972). Component II of nitrogenase, which contains 4 Fe and labile sulfur atoms, yields EPR similar to that of the other four–iron proteins in the reduced state (Orme-Johnson *et al.*, 1972). Finally, the report by Uyeda and Rabinowitz (1971) that pyruvate dehydrogenase of *C. acidi-urici* is an iron–sulfur protein with light absorption spectrum not unlike clostridial-type ferredoxin makes it also an attractive candidate for investigation by EPR methods.

In Table II we list g values, temperature of observation, and a recent reference for EPR from a number of iron–sulfur proteins. It is hoped

TABLE II

EPR Signals from Iron–Sulfur Centers in Representative Proteins

Protein	$g_x{}^a$	g_y	g_z	Temperature[b]	Reference
1. Rubredoxin $m_s = \pm\frac{3}{2}$ $\pm\frac{1}{2}$	4.77	4.31	4.02	1.5–77	Peisach et al., 1971
($P.\ oleovorans$) $m_s = \pm\frac{1}{2}$	9.42	1.25	0.9	<15	Fritz et al., 1971
2. Spinach ferredoxin	2.05	1.96	1.89	<77	Fritz et al., 1971
3. Parsley ferredoxin	2.05	1.96	1.90	<77	Fritz et al., 1971
4. Adrenodoxin	2.02	1.935	1.93	<200	Fritz et al., 1971
5. Putidaredoxin	2.02	1.935	1.93	<200	Fritz et al., 1971
6. C. pasteurianum plant-type ferredoxin	2.01	1.95	1.93	<100	Brintzinger et al., 1966b
7. A. vinelandii protein I	2.01	1.94	1.93	<100	Shethna et al., 1968
8. A. vinelandii protein II	2.04	1.96	1.91	<77	Shethna et al., 1968
9. Euglena ferredoxin	2.06	1.96	1.89	<77	Hall and Evans, 1969
10. Chromatium high-potential protein	(features at 2.115, 2.08, 2.04)				
11. B. polymyxa ferredoxin	2.06	1.92	1.88	<77	Palmer et al., 1967
12. C. pasteurianum bacterial-type ferredoxin	(features at 2.04, 2.00, 1.96, 1.92, 1.89, 1.86)			<30	Shethna et al., 1971 Palmer et al., 1966
13. C. acidi-urici ferredoxin	(features at 2.07, 2.05, 2.00, 1.97, 1.91, 1.89)			<30	See Fig. 15, this work
14. Chromatium ferredoxin	(features at 2.09, 2.07, 1.96, 1.89)			<30	Hall and Evans, 1969
15. Azotobacter protein III	(features: oxidized: 2.08, 2.01, 1.97, 1.95; reduced, 2.03, 2.01)			<100	Shethna, 1969
16. Xanthine oxidase (a) (milk) (b)	2.02 2.12	1.94 2.007	1.90 1.91	<100 <30	Lowe et al., 1972 Gibson and Bray, 1968
17. Aldehyde oxidase (liver)	2.02	1.93	1.93	<100	Rajagopalan et al., 1968
18. Dihydroorotate dehydrogenase	2.01	1.94	1.92	<100	Aleman et al., 1968
19. Beef heart mitochondria a. NADH: CoQ reductase					
Center 1	2.022	1.938	1.923	<100	Orme-Johnson et al., 1971b
Center 2	2.054	1.922	1.922	<30	Orme-Johnson et al., 1971b
Center 3	2.101	1.886	1.864	<30	Orme-Johnson et al., 1971b
Center 4	2.103	—	1.863	<30	Orme-Johnson et al., 1971b
b. CoQ: cytochrome c reductase	2.062	1.887	1.809	<100	Orme-Johnson et al., 1971a

[a] Except in cases (1)–(5) these values are measured extrema (g_x and g_z) and midpoint (g_y) positions. The values in cases (1)–(5) represent values derived from spectral calculations. Blumberg (1967), Aasa (1970), and Dowsing and Gibson (1969) discuss the meaning of g values in high spin rhombic cases such as (1). In cases (1) and (10) the signals referred to are for the *oxidized* state of the protein; others are for *reduced* states. In the eight-iron examples (12)–(14) there are variable amounts of a single sharp ($\Delta H\frac{1}{2} \sim 30$ G) signal centered at $g = 2.00$ in oxidized specimens.

[b] This is intended to give a notion of the temperature (°K) range into which a sample must be placed in order to observe EPR. With very concentrated ($\gg 1$ mM) samples, one in general may observe EPR at higher temperatures. For an illustration, see Shethna et al. (1968).

that this compilation will serve as a guidepost and encouragement to experimentation for those who may encounter other iron–sulfur proteins.

ACKNOWLEDGMENTS

We wish to thank the National Institutes of Health for support of research described here, under Grants GM-17170, GM-12394, GM-12176, as well as a Research Career Development Award No. GM-10,236. We also thank our many collaborators, friends, and friendly competitors whose thoughts and experimental contributions we have tried to blend into a coherent story. Dr. H. Beinert gave us the benefit of criticisms of an early draft of this chapter.

REFERENCES

Aasa, R. (1970). *J. Chem. Phys.* **52**, 3919.
Aasa, R., and T. Vänngård. (1970). *J. Chem. Phys.* **52**, 1612.
Abragam, A., and Bleaney, B. (1970). "EPR of Transition Ions," Oxford Univ. Press (Clarendon), London and New York.
Aleman, V., Handler, P., Palmer, G., and Beinert, H. (1968). *J. Biol. Chem.* **243**, 2569.
Alger, R. S. (1968). "Electron Paramagnetic Resonance." Wiley, New York.
Atherton, N. M., Garbett, K., Gillard, R. D., Mason, R., Mayhew, S. J., Peel, J. L., and Stangroom, J. E. (1966). *Nature (London)* **212**, 590.
Ayscough, P. B. (1967). "Electron Spin Resonance in Chemistry." Methuen, London.
Beinert, H., and Orme-Johnson, W. H. (1967). *In* "Proceedings of the Second International Conference on Magnetic Research in Biological Systems" (A. Ehrenberg, B. G. Malmström, and T. Vänngård, eds.). Pergamon, Oxford.
Beinert, H., and Orme-Johnson, W. H. (1969). *Ann. N.Y. Acad. Sci.* **158**, 336.
Beinert, H., and Palmer, G. (1965). *Advan. Enzymol.* **27**, 105.
Beinert, H., and Sands, R. H. (1960). *Biochem. Biophys. Res. Commun.* **3**, 41.
Beinert, H., Palmer, G., Cremona, T., and Singer, T. P. (1965a). *J. Biol. Chem.* **240**, 475.
Beinert, H., DerVartanian, D. V., Hemmerich, P., Veeger, C., and VanVoorst, J. D. W. (1965b). *Biochim. Biophys. Acta* **95**, 530.
Bersohn, M., and Baird, J. C. (1966). "An Introduction to EPR." Benjamin, New York.
Blumberg, W. E. (1967). *In* "Proceedings of the Second International Conference on Magnetic Research in Biological Systems" (A. Ehrenberg, B. G. Malmström, and T. Vänngård, eds.), p. 119. Pergamon, Oxford.
Blumberg, W. E. (1965). *Fed. Proc.* **24**, 580.
Bray, R. C. (1971). *In* "Flavins and Flavoproteins, Third International Symposium" (H. Kamin, ed.), p. 385. Univ. Park Press, Baltimore, Maryland.
Bray, R. C., and Meriwether, L. S. (1966). *Nature (London)* **212**, 467.
Bray, R. C., Palmer, G., and Beinert, H. (1964). *J. Biol. Chem.* **239**, 2667.

Brintzinger, H., Palmer, G., and Sands, R. H. (1966a). *J. Amer. Chem. Soc.* **88**, 623.

Brintzinger, H., Palmer, G., and Sands, R. H. (1966b). *Proc. Nat. Acad. Sci. U.S.* **55**, 397.

Carrington, A., and McLachlan, A. D. (1967). "Introduction to Magnetic Resonance." Harper, New York.

Connelly, N. G., and Dahl, L. F. (1970). *J. Amer. Chem. Soc.* **92**, 7472.

Davis, L. C., Shah, V. K., Brill, W. J., and Orme-Johnson, W. H. (1972). *Biochim. Biophys. Acta* **256**, 512.

DerVartanian, D. V., and Bramlett, R. (1970). *Biochim. Biophys. Acta* **220**, 443.

DerVartanian, D. V., Orme-Johnson, W. H., Hansen, R. E., Beinert, H., Tsai, R. L., Tsibris, J. C. M., and Bartholomaus, R. C., and Gunsalus, I. C. (1967). *Biochem. Biophys. Res. Commun.* **26**, 569.

DerVartanian, D. V., Veeger, C., Orme-Johnson, W. H., and Beinert, H. (1969). *Biochim. Biophys. Acta* **191**, 22.

Dowsing, R. D., and Gibson, J. F. (1969). *J. Chem. Phys.* **50**, 294.

Dunham, W. R., Bearden, A., Salmeen, I., Palmer, G., Sands, R. H., Orme-Johnson, W. H., and Beinert, H. (1971a). *Biochim. Biophys. Acta* **253**, 134.

Dunham, W. R., Palmer, G., Sands, R. H., Bearden, A. J., Beinert, H., and Orme-Johnson, W. H. (1971b). *Biochem. Biophys. Res. Commun.* **45**, 1119.

Dunham, W. R., Palmer, G., Sands, R. H., and Bearden, A. J. (1971c). *Biochim. Biophys. Acta* **253**, 373.

Dus, K., DeKlerk, H., Sletten, K., and Bartsch, R. G. (1967). *Biochim. Biophys. Acta* **140**, 291.

Eaton, W. A., and Lovenberg, W. (1970). *J. Amer. Chem. Soc.* **92**, 7195.

Eisenstein, K. K., and Wang, J. (1969). *J. Biol. Chem.* **244**, 1720.

Fee, J., and Palmer, G. (1971). *Biochim. Biophys. Acta* **245**, 175.

Flatmark, T., and Dus, K. (1969). *Biochim. Biophys. Acta* **180**, 377.

Fritz, J., Anderson, R., Fee, J., Palmer, G., Sands, R. H., Orme-Johnson, W. H., Beinert, H., Tsibris, J. C. M., and Gunsalus, I. C. (1971). *Biochim. Biophys. Acta* **253**, 110.

Gersmann, H. R., and Swalen, J. D. (1962). *J. Chem. Phys.* **36**, 3221.

Gibson, J. F., and Bray, R. C. (1968). *Biochim. Biophys. Acta* **153**, 721.

Gibson, J. F., Hall, D. O., Thornley, J. H. M., and Whatley, F. R. (1966). *Proc. Nat. Acad. Sci. U.S.* **56**, 987.

Hall, D. O., and Evans, M. C. W. (1969). *Nature (London)* **223**, 1342.

Ingram, D. J. E. (1958). "Free Radicals as Studied by ESR." Butterworths, London and Washington, D.C.

Ingram, D. J. E. (1969). "Biological and Biochemical Applications of ESR." Plenum Press, New York.

Kimura, T., Tasaki, A., and Watari, H. (1970). *J. Biol. Chem.* **245**, 4450.

Kneubühl, F. K., and Natterer, B. (1961). *Helv. Phys. Acta* **34**, 710.

Komai, H., Massey, V., and Palmer, G. (1969). *J. Biol. Chem.* **244**, 1692.

LeGall, J., DerVartanian, D. V., Spilker, E., Lee, J. P., and Peck, H. D., Jr. (1971). *Biochim. Biophys. Acta* **234**, 525.

Lowe, D. J., Lynden-Bell, R. M., and Bray, R. C. (1972). *Biochem. J.* **130**, 239.

Malkin, R., and Bearden, A. J. (1971). *Proc. Nat. Acad. Sci. U.S.* **68**, 16.

Malley, M. M. (1965). *J. Mol. Spectrosc.* **17**, 210.

Mayhew, S. G., Petering, D., Palmer, G., and Foust, G. (1969). *J. Biol. Chem.* **244**, 2830.

Moleski, C., Moss, T. H., Orme-Johnson, W. H., and Tsibris, J. C. M. (1970). *Biochim. Biophys. Acta* **214**, 548.

Moss, T. H., Petering, D., and Palmer, G. (1969). *J. Biol. Chem.* **244**, 2275.

Nakos, G., and Mortenson, L. E. (1971a). *Biochemistry* **10**, 455.

Nakos, G., and Mortenson, L. E. (1971b). *Biochemistry* **10**, 2442.

Neiman, R., and Kivelson, D. (1961). *J. Chem. Phys.* **35**, 156.

Ohnishi, T., Asakura, T., Wohlrab, H., Yonetani, T., Chance, B. (1971). *J. Biol. Chem.* **246**, 5960.

Orme-Johnson, W. H., Hamilton, W. D., Ljones, T., Tso, M.-Y. W., Burris, R. H., Shah, V. K., and Brill, W. J. (1972b). *Proc. Nat. Acad. Sci. U.S.* **69**, 3142.

Orme-Johnson, W. H. (1973). *Ann. Rev. Biochem.* **42**, 159.

Orme-Johnson, W. H., and Beinert, H. (1969a). *J. Biol. Chem.* **244**, 6143.

Orme-Johnson, W. H., and Beinert, H. (1969b). *Biochem. Biophys. Res. Commun.* **36**, 337.

Orme-Johnson, W. H., Hansen, R. E., Beinert, H., Tsibris, J. C. M., Bartholomaus, R. C., and Gunsalus, I. C. (1968). *Proc. Nat. Acad. Sci. U.S.* **60**, 368.

Orme-Johnson, N. R., Hansen, R. E., and Beinert, H. (1971a). *Biochem. Biophys. Res. Commun.* **45**, 871.

Orme-Johnson, N. R., Orme-Johnson, W. H., Hansen, R. E., Beinert, H., and Hatefi, Y. (1971b). *Biochem. Biophys. Res. Commun.* **44**, 446.

Orme-Johnson, W. H., Stombaugh, N. A., and Burris, R. H. (1972). *Fed. Proc.* **31**, abs., p. 448.

Pake, G. E. (1962). "Paramagnetic Resonance." Benjamin, New York.

Palmer, G. (1967a). *In Methods Enzymol.* **10**, 594.

Palmer, G. (1967b). *Biochem. Biophys. Res. Commun.* **27**, 315.

Palmer, G., and Brintzinger, H. (1966). *Nature (London)* **211**, 189.

Palmer, G., and Massey, V. (1969). *J. Biol. Chem.* **244**, 2614.

Palmer, G., and Sands, R. H. (1966). *J. Biol. Chem.* **241**, 253.

Palmer, G., Sands, R. H., and Mortenson, L. E. (1966). *Biochem. Biophys. Res. Commun.* **23**, 357.

Palmer, G., Brintzinger, H., Estabrook, R. W., and Sands, R. H. (1967). *In* "Proceedings of the Second International Conference on Magnetic Research in Biological Systems" (A. Ehrenberg, B. G. Malmström, and T. Vänngård, eds.), p. 159. Pergamon, Oxford.

Palmer, G., Dunham, W. R., Fee, J. A., Sands, R. H., Iikuza, T., and Yonetani, T. (1971). *Biochim. Biophys. Acta* **245**, 201.

Peisach, J., Blumberg, W. E., Lode, E. T., and Coon, M. J. (1971). *J. Biol. Chem.* **246**, 5877.

Petering, D., Fee, J. A., and Palmer, G. (1971). *J. Biol. Chem.* **246**, 643.

Peterson, J. A., and Coon, M. J. (1968). *J. Biol. Chem.* **243**, 329.

Poole, C. P. (1967). "Electron Spin Resonance." Wiley (Interscience), New York.

Rajagopalan, K. V., Handler, P., Palmer, G., and Beinert, H. (1968). *J. Biol. Chem.* **243**, 3797.

Rieske, J. S., MacLennan, D. H., and Coleman, R. (1964). *Biochem. Biophys. Res. Commun.* **15**, 338.

Scholes, C. P., Isaacson, R. A., and Feher, G. (1971). *Biochim. Biophys. Acta* **244**, 206.

Schwartz, H. M., Bolton, J. R., and Borg, D. C. (1972). "Biological Applications of ESR." Wiley (Interscience), New York.

Shethna, Y. I. (1970). *Biochim. Biophys. Acta* **205**, 58.

Shethna, Y. I., Wilson, P. W., Hansen, R. E., and Beinert, H. (1964). *Proc. Nat. Acad. Sci. U.S.* **52**, 1263.

Shethna, Y. I., DerVartanian, D. V., and Beinert, H. (1968). *Biochem. Biophys. Res. Commun.* **31**, 862.

Shethna, Y. I., Stombaugh, N. A., and Burris, R. H. (1971) *Biochem. Biophys. Res. Commun.* **42**, 1108.

Sieker, L. C., Adman, E., and Jensen, L. H. (1972). *Nature (London)* **235**, 40.

Strahs, G., and Kraut, J. (1968). *J. Mol. Biol.* **35**, 503.

Strong, L., Palaith, D., and Sands, R., "The Magnetic Field Dependences of the EPR Linewidths of a Variety of Iron-Sulfur Proteins" (in preparation).

Thornley, J. H. M., Gibson, J. F., Whatley, F. R., and Hall, D. O. (1966). *Biochem Biophys. Res. Commun.* **24**, 877.

Tsai, R. L., Tsibris, J. C. M., Gunsalus, I. C., Orme-Johnson, W. H., Hansen, R. E., and Beinert, H., as quoted by Orme-Johnson (1973).

Tsibris, J. C. M., Namtvedt, M. J., and Gunsalus, I. C. (1968a). *Biochem. Biophys. Res. Commun.* **30**, 323.

Tsibris, J. C. M., Tsai, R. L., Gunsalus, I. C., Orme-Johnson, W. H., Hansen, R. E., and Beinert, H. (1968b). *Proc. Nat. Acad. Sci. U.S.* **59**, 959.

Uyeda, K., and Rabinowitz, J. C. (1971). *J. Biol. Chem.* **246**, 3120.

Wertz, J. E., and Bolton, J. R. (1972). "Electron Spin Resonance, Elementary Theory and Practical Applications." McGraw-Hill, New York.

Wickman, H. H., Klein, M. P., and Shirley, D. A. (1965). *J. Chem. Phys.* **42**, 2113.

Yoch, D. C., Benemann, J. R., Valentine, R. C., and Arnon, D. I. (1969). *Proc. Nat. Acad. Sci. U.S.* **64**, 1404.

NOTE ADDED IN PROOF

It has been shown conclusively by R. H. Sands, G. Palmer, R. Mathews, and S. Charleton (in preparation) that the added structure in the EPR spectra of the fully reduced species of the eight-iron ferredoxins is from a triplet state formed presumably by the two exchange-coupled four-iron clusters. The evidence for this is the existence of the half-field resonances at the appropriate intensities and the zero-field splittings in the $g \simeq 1.94$ signals.

CHAPTER 6

Mössbauer Spectroscopy of Iron–Sulfur Proteins

ALAN J. BEARDEN and W. R. DUNHAM

I. THE MÖSSBAUER SPECTROSCOPIC METHOD

The determination of the properties of protein electronic configuration is a step in understanding the processes by which proteins operate. X-Ray protein crystallography affords, in principle, an accurate determination of electron density for those materials which can be obtained and crystallized in sufficient quantity for such analysis. Ferredoxins as a class have long resisted the efforts of protein crystallography. Although the recent work of Sieker *et al.* (1972) presents a high resolution map of the eight-iron, eight-sulfur ferredoxin from *Peptococcus aerogenes*, crystallographic electron-density maps cannot be expected to be sufficiently precise to measure changes in electron density due to oxidation–reduction processes involving one or two electrons. Resonance methods, such as electron paramagnetic resonance (EPR) and nuclear magnetic resonance (NMR) afford the possibilities of contributing data which will allow inferences to be made about the spatial distribution of relatively few electrons. For example, a single *paramagnetic* electron per molecule can be characterized directly as to its environment by EPR, and a group of protons may show an interaction with a paramagnetic center (i.e., a contact interaction) that produces a large shift in the ob-

239

served position of a proton resonance in NMR. Mössbauer spectroscopy, which makes use of the interaction of surrounding electrons with a nucleus, producing shifts in *nuclear* energy levels, is a valuable adjunct to the methods of magnetic resonance for biophysical application. First, it permits information to be gained about diamagnetic states of molecules as well as paramagnetic states. The serious limitation of Mössbauer spectroscopy is that information is available only about nuclear energy levels of Mössbauer isotopes; for biochemical application only ^{57}Fe and two isotopes of I are useful as there are no Mössbauer isotopes of C, N, O, P, and S or of the other transition metals such as Cu, Zn, Mn, or of Mg or Mo. Thus ^{57}Fe investigations of proteins such as hemoglobin, myoglobin, cytochromes, or the iron–sulfur proteins are limited to examining the effects of electronic configuration at the ^{57}Fe nuclear site. This limitation can also be viewed as an experimental asset as there are no interfering signals from other nuclei of the protein molecule.

Nuclear γ-ray resonance (the Mössbauer effect) depends on establishing conditions that permit the natural linewidth of a low-lying nuclear energy state to be observable. This natural linewidth is established by the Heisenberg uncertainty relationship [ΔE (mean lifetime) $\approx h/2\pi$]. For the 14.4 keV isomeric state of ^{57}Fe the mean lifetime of the state is about 1.4×10^{-7} second; the corresponding ΔE is of the order of 10^{-9} eV. This small energy width (high monochromaticity) allows the observation of small energy changes due to the placement of the ^{57}Fe nuclide in electronic environments. The experimental conditions necessary to observe these small energy changes are rather simple; namely, the emitter and absorber of the nuclear γ radiation must be in *solid* form, and small relative velocity changes introduced between the source and the absorber produce an energy scale via the relativistic Doppler shift in energy of the nuclear γ radiation. The physics of the Mössbauer effect is well reviewed at all levels of inquiry, and only those conditions which are special to biophysical application will be discussed here.

Introductory discussions of the Mössbauer effect are to be found in the books by Frauenfelder (1961) and Wertheim (1964). General applications of Mössbauer methods to chemical problems are reviewed in the book by Goldanskii and Herber (1968); the advances in utilization of Mössbauer techniques in many fields of physics, chemistry, and biology are covered by the series edited by Gruverman (1965), and recent reviews of the applications of this spectroscopic method to biological molecules have appeared by Lang (1970), Debrunner (1969), and Bearden and Dunham (1970).

Iron-57 has the following important nuclear properties which allow its use in the current discussion: It is a ground-state radioisotope formed by the successive decay by γ emission from an excited state populated by electron capture from ^{57}Co ($t_{1/2} = 269d$). The nuclear g values for the $I = \frac{1}{2}$ ground state is 0.18048 and for the $I = \frac{3}{2}$ (14.4 keV) excited state is -0.103. The ground state does not possess a nuclear quadrupole moment since $I = \frac{1}{2}$; the 14.4 keV excited state has a nuclear quadrupole moment of 0.3×10^{-24} cm². Protein Mössbauer spectroscopy is performed with the stable ground-state ^{57}Fe isotope present in the natural protein (2.2% natural abundance), protein enriched in ^{57}Fe by chemical exchange, or protein extracted from organisms grown on a higher abundance of ^{57}Fe (in the last method it is important to identify and control all sources of iron metabolism if maximum enrichment is to be achieved).

A Mössbauer spectrometer consists of a source of 14.4 keV radiation, which is usually a ^{57}Co source, the protein absorber containing ^{57}Fe in the ground state as the resonant absorber, a means of providing a periodic variation in relative velocity between the source and absorber, and a γ-radiation detector to measure the transmission of radiation as a function of the relative source–absorber velocity.

The increased absorption when the source and absorber are "on-resonance" may approach 25% for optimum absorbers enriched to 90% in ^{57}Fe. Work with naturally abundant ^{57}Fe proteins is far more difficult, as absorptions are more in the range of 0.5 to 2%. In either case it is important to keep the amount of material present small, as excess amounts of extraneous material, particularly of moderate to high atomic number, decrease the intensity of the Mössbauer beam by way of non-resonant absorption and scattering of the 14.4 keV radiation. In addition to the principal parts of the Mössbauer spectrometer listed above, it is imperative to provide a means of cooling the protein sample and providing a magnetic field of up to several tens of kilogauss at the sample position, as well as providing the necessary electronics (multiscalar, automated control, and readout units) to allow the apparatus to acquire data for 10–20 hours with the minimum of attention other than the refilling of cryogenic fluids. Of the order of 1 μmole of ^{57}Fe is required as an absorber in Mössbauer spectroscopy; there appear to be no methods by which this sensitivity can be raised appreciably.

There are four possible interactions of the Mössbauer nuclide with the electronic surroundings: nuclear isomer shift, nuclear quadrupole interaction, nuclear electronic hyperfine interaction, and the interaction of the paramagnetic nucleus with an applied magnetic field (nuclear Zeeman interaction). An excellent introduction to these effects is contained in the book by Wertheim (1964), and a more extensive application of these ideas is to be found in the book on chemical applications of Mössbauer spectroscopy by Goldanskii and Herber (1968); therefore each effect will only be treated superficially here. The isomer shift produces a change in the nuclear energy levels due to the "electric monopole" interaction between the nucleus and the electronic density at the nuclear position. In general, it is not possible for the magnitudes of the shifts to be calculated absolutely, as this would require greater knowledge of the charge distributions of the ^{57}Fe nuclide than are presently available; however, "isomer shifts" can be useful in a relative sense as a measure of the electron density at the nuclear origin. A "scale of isomer shifts" is involved, as these are also relative to a "standard" source material or a "standard absorber." A valuable compendium of isomer shift and quadrupole data known as the "Mössbauer Effect Data Index" is available (Muir $et\ al.$, 1966).

For ionic iron compounds, the isomer shift for high-spin Fe (II) is significantly distinctive, allowing interpretation directly; this is not the case for high- and low-spin states of ferric ions or for the low-spin state of Fe (II). Thus, spin or oxidation state assignment based solely on isomer shift data is at best a risky procedure for $ionic$ iron compounds and is completely invalid for covalently bound iron.

The $I = \frac{3}{2}$ excited state of ^{57}Fe has a nonzero nuclear quadrupole moment which can produce nuclear energy levels giving rise to the characteristic two-line "quadrupole pair" Mössbauer spectra when the ^{57}Fe nucleus is located in an electric field gradient. This would be the case when there is nonspherical symmetry at the ^{57}Fe position due either to the electronic configuration of the iron electrons or to the ligand electronic distribution.

Two parameters are of importance in discussions of nuclear quadrupole interactions: the quadrupole coupling constant and the asymmetry parameter, $\eta = (V_{xx} - V_{yy})/V_{zz}$, where the double subscript signifies the second partial derivative of the electrostatic potential at the nuclear position. The parameter η can be determined by observation of the Mössbauer resonance (with a nuclear quadrupole interaction present) by application of an external magnetic field (Collins, 1965). It is important to realize that different electronic configurations both in the immediate vicinity of the ^{57}Fe nucleus (the Fe electronic core) and the distant charges (ligand electronic configuration) can yield similar resultant quadrupole coupling constants. In many cases the temperature-dependent population of orbitals due to Boltzmann factors as the protein temperature is varied provides a valuable clue to the electronic configuration.

Both the 14.4 keV excited state ($I = \frac{3}{2}$) and the ground state ($I = \frac{1}{2}$) of ^{57}Fe are nuclear paramagnets and are capable of interacting with electron spins through nuclear electronic hyperfine interactions. These interactions cause additional splittings and in many cases rather complex Mössbauer absorption when present concomitantly with nuclear isomer shift and nuclear quadrupole interactions. Successful unraveling of nuclear hyperfine interactions in these cases is usually dependent on the pronounced temperature dependencies of nuclear hyperfine interactions; that is, at sufficiently high temperatures (near the ice point) nuclear hyperfine interactions may average to zero owing to electron spin relaxation leaving the nuclear quadrupole interaction as a clear "quadrupole-split" pair of Mössbauer absorption lines. In addition, the information available from other resonance techniques, such as EPR and ENDOR (electron nuclear double resonance) can be very helpful in the interpretation of complex Mössbauer spectra.

Finally, it is possible to observe the nuclear γ-ray analogue of the optical Zeeman effect; namely, that nuclear energy levels in the protein absorber are affected by the application of an external magnetic field. The magnetic fields required are larger (50 kG) than can be provided by iron magnets; typically solenoids wound with superconducting elements are employed. The nuclear Zeeman interaction is valuable in determining populations of magnetic states at temperatures below $10°K$ and as pointed out above, in the determination of the asymmetry parameter in the nuclear quadrupole interaction.

Since all four interactions (nuclear isomer shift, nuclear quadrupole interaction, nuclear hyperfine interaction, and nuclear Zeeman interaction) may be present in concert in more than one iron site in an iron–sulfur protein, it is important to recognize the limitations of elementary single interaction criteria for determining the experimental Mössbauer parameters from a series of spectra. The only procedure which is useful is the computation of the expected Mössbauer spectra for possible electronic configurations as represented by values and orientation of the Mössbauer parameters and the comparison of these computed spectra with the experimental data. The relevant formalism for doing this is the spin Hamiltonian approach (Lang, 1970; Pryce, 1950); an approach carried over from its general usefulness in EPR spectroscopy. Consider the possibilities present in a paramagnetic molecule of low symmetry. The paramagnetism implies a g tensor whose principal values (g_{xx}, g_{yy}, and g_{zz}) could be measured preferably in an oriented single crystal of the material. The same material produces an electric quadrupole tensor and a nuclear electron hyperfine interaction which again is a tensor-represented quantity. In general, it is not to be guaranteed that any of these tensors would have principal axes that are colinear. Thus in the spin Hamiltonian form of the Mössbauer calculation one would have to carry out the required quantum-mechanical, energy level calculations keeping in mind the necessary symmetry conditions imposed. In addition, as Mössbauer spectra are usually not taken on single crystals, but rather on random assortments of molecules in frozen solution, the calculated Mössbauer spectra must contain suitable averages over protein orientations. The imposition of a nuclear Zeeman interaction is an additional problem since the experimenter has the choice of determining its direction (usually parallel or perpendicular to the γ-ray direction of the spectrometer).

The inherent complexity of these procedures is solved by digital computation of the simulated spectra within the spin Hamiltonian framework; this procedure has been carried out with particular concern in the studies of oxygen-binding hemoproteins and of the 2 Fe–2 S ferredoxins in conjunction with other resonance spectroscopic methods (EPR, ENDOR) which produce experimental parameters of the same type and usefulness as Mössbauer spectroscopy.

Formally then, Mössbauer data are compared with computer-simulated spectra calculated for a spin Hamiltonian for ^{57}Fe nuclei for each site in the protein molecule. Each ^{57}Fe nucleus is considered to be coupled to a net electronic spin and also may be in an external magnetic field (nuclear Zeeman field). The spin Hamiltonian is then

$$H = H_i + H_q + \langle \tilde{S}_{\text{eff}} \rangle \cdot \tilde{A} \cdot \tilde{I} + H_{\text{Zeeman}}$$

where H_i is the nuclear isomer shift produced by the monopolar interaction of the nucleus with the electron charge density at the nuclear position. H_i is not formally entered in the calculation, as it is a simple linear factor which can be found by moving the experimental spectrum along the energy (velocity) axis. H_q represents the nuclear quadrupole interaction of the excited state ^{57}Fe ($I = \frac{3}{2}$) with any electric field gradient at the nuclear position and is given by

$$H_q = 2DI_z^2 + (E - D)I_x^2 + (-E - D)I_y^2$$

where $D = \text{QS}/[6(1 + \eta/3)^{1/2}]$, $E = \eta D$, and QS is the observed quadrupole splitting in the absence of any magnetic field at the nuclear position. $I_{x,y,z}$ are the components of the ground ($I = \frac{1}{2}$) and excited ($I = \frac{3}{2}$) nuclear states. $\langle \tilde{S}_{\text{eff}} \rangle \cdot \tilde{A} \cdot \tilde{I}$ represents the electron nuclear hyperfine interaction with the net electron spin $\langle \tilde{S}_{\text{eff}} \rangle$, this quantity being quantized spatially by the anisotropic electron Zeeman interaction ($- \tilde{H} \cdot \tilde{G} \cdot \tilde{S}$). Finally the direct (Zeeman) interaction of the nuclear moments is given by $H_{\text{Zeeman}} = -g_N\beta_N H I_z$.

II. MÖSSBAUER DATA

Mössbauer spectra have been obtained on spinach and parsley ferredoxin, the 2 Fe–2 S proteins from *Euglena*, *Scenedesmus*, and *Clostridium pasteurianum*, and two forms (Azo I and II) from *Azotobacter*. Spectra have also been reported on putidaredoxin and adrenodoxin, and the 8 Fe–8 S bacterial ferredoxins from *Clostridium pasteurianum* and *Clostridium acidi-urici* as well as from *Chromatium*. The high-potential iron protein (HIPIP) from *Chromatium* and rubredoxin from *Clostridium pasteurianum* have been measured. Some measurements exist on the enzyme, xanthine oxidase. By no means have all the studies been exhaustive or have even all the redox forms of the proteins been examined; in some cases, spectra are reported for unenriched (in ^{57}Fe) proteins; but in most cases where the data are complete enough for detailed evaluation, there has been some ^{57}Fe enrichment either by growing the organism on an ^{57}Fe-enriched medium or by means of chemical exchange.

A. The 2 Fe–2 S Proteins

Since the demonstration by ^{57}Fe line broadening in the EPR spectra of spinach ferredoxin (Palmer, 1967), adrenodoxin (Beinert and Orme-Johnson, 1969), putidaredoxin (Tsibris *et al.*, 1968), and the two-iron proteins from *Azotobacter* (Shethna *et al.*, 1964) of the involvement of iron in the paramagnetic center of the reduced form of these proteins, there has been renewed interest in the application of Mössbauer spectroscopy to the determination of the iron electronic configurations in these materials. Earlier measurements on the oxidized forms of spinach ferredoxin and the ferredoxin from *Euglena* all point to the existence of a single iron site, probably Fe (III) with both iron atoms in this state for both proteins (Bearden *et al.*, 1965; Bearden and Moss, 1967; Moss *et al.*, 1968; Johnson and Hall, 1968; Johnson *et al.*, 1968, 1969).

Recent Mössbauer measurements by Dunham *et al.* (1971) on the two-iron ferredoxins from spinach, parsley, pig adrenal cortex, *Azotobacter vinelandii*, and *Clostridium pasteurianum* (not to be confused with the bacterial ferredoxin containing eight iron atoms per molecule from the same organism) present data on both the oxidized and reduced forms of the proteins at temperatures from 4° to 256°K and in applied magnetic fields up to 46 kG. An important part of these studies has been the development of computer simulation of expected Mössbauer absorption as a function of the parameters in the Mössbauer spin Hamiltonian as previously mentioned.

The Mössbauer data for the oxidized forms of all the 2 Fe–2 S proteins studied are remarkably similar; that is, a single "quadrupole pair" absorption persists to the lowest temperature of measurement (4°K) with a QS of about 0.65 to 0.70 mm sec^{-1}. These results extend the observations made earlier on a few of the 2 Fe–2 S proteins; the spectra are shown in Fig. 1. By applying an external magnetic field (46 kG), the asymmetry parameter (η) was determined to be 0.6 ± 0.3. The reduced forms of these proteins displayed a quite different situation as is shown for spinach ferredoxin in Fig. 2. These spectra were taken at temperatures from 4.3° to 253°K in a 580 G magnetic field parallel to the source–detector axis. At the lower temperatures (below about 60°K), magnetic hyperfine lines are evident, while at the highest temperature (253°K) the spectrum has collapsed into two sets of "quadrupole pairs." Similar data have been reported by Johnson *et al.* (1971) and Rao *et al.* (1971) for spinach and *Scenedesmus* ferredoxin, and for adrenodoxin.

By using computer simulation of Mössbauer spectra, the electron nuclear double resonance (ENDOR) data of Fritz *et al.* (1971) and

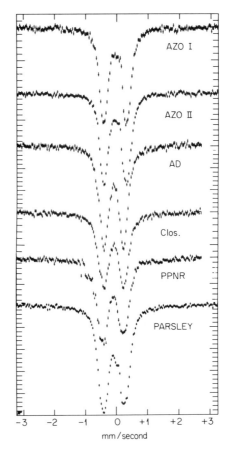

Fig. 1. Mössbauer spectra for oxidized 2 Fe–2 S proteins: parsley, Azo I, Azo II, clostridial (Clos), PPNR, and pig adrenal cortex (AD).

the wide temperature dependence of the magnetic hyperfine interaction, Dunham *et al.* (1971) arrived at the following conclusions on the iron sites in the two-iron, two-sulfur ferredoxins.

1. The oxidized forms of the proteins contain two high-spin ferric iron atoms coupled antiferromagnetically to yield a diamagnetic complex at low temperatures.

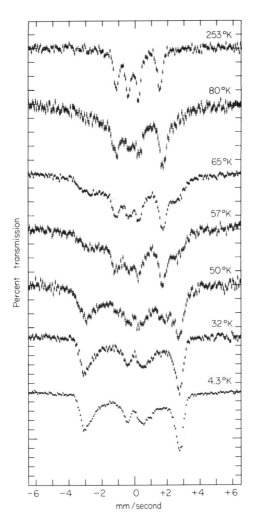

Fig. 2. Mössbauer spectra for reduced spinach ferredoxin. Spectra were taken at 4.3°, 32°, 57°, 65°, 80°, and 253°K.

2. The reduced forms of the proteins contain one ferric site (presumably identical to either site in the oxidized form of the protein) and one high-spin ferrous site. The sites are again antiferromagnetically coupled to produce an electron spin of one-half for the molecule in the ground state.

3. The iron bonding at all sites is covalent.

4. The large value of the quadrupole splitting of the ferrous site indicated that the ground electronic state is orbitally nondegenerate; the temperature dependence of the quadrupole splitting of this site indicated that the first excited state lies at least 500 cm⁻¹ above the ground state.

5. The values of the quadrupole parameters (large QS and small η) suggested tetrahedral ligand symmetry about the iron at all sites, octahedral symmetry being excluded.

The paper by Dunham *et al.* (1971) discusses the detailed interplay between Mössbauer spectroscopy and ENDOR on the same samples, a critical factor in the establishment of the conclusions listed above. The work by Johnson *et al.* (1971) and Rao *et al.* (1971) came to some of these same conclusions but is severely criticized by Dunham and his co-workers on the basis that without computer-simulation techniques, the English workers have based their interpretations on erroneous assignments of absorption lines in their Mössbauer spectra. This matter is also discussed in a short communication by Beinert *et al.* (1971).

The relationship of this work to the ENDOR measurements (Fritz *et al.*, (1971), measurements of magnetic susceptibility (Palmer *et al.*, 1971), optical data (Eaton *et al.*, 1972), and high-resolution proton magnetic resonance work, and the consideration of a model for the iron–sulfur region of the 2 Fe–2 S proteins will be discussed in Chapter 8 of this volume.

Mössbauer spectra have also been obtained on the ⁵⁷Fe-enriched 2 Fe–2 S protein putidaredoxin (Debrunner, 1969; Cooke *et al.*, 1968). The spectra of the protein in the oxidized state are very similar to those of the other 2 Fe–2 S proteins previously discussed. The spectra of the reduced protein, again a single electron process, are similar in that at low temperatures (below 80°K) the onset of a magnetic hyperfine interaction is apparent; no spectra have been published at higher temperatures, although it seems clear that the magnetic hyperfine interaction is "averaging" at the higher temperatures. Because of the similarity of putidaredoxin to the other 2 Fe–2 S proteins in the chemical properties, it is perhaps expected that the Mössbauer spectra will be quite similar, although the temperature dependence of the magnetic hyperfine interaction in the reduced state of the protein may be different.

B. Bacterial Iron–Sulfur Proteins

In contrast to the considerable exploration of the two-iron, two-sulfur ferredoxins by Mössbauer spectroscopy, the investigations of bacterial ferredoxins are more limited. *Clostridium pasteurianum* ferredoxin has been examined in the oxidized state (Phillips *et al.*, 1965; Blomstrom *et al.*, 1964), and the ferredoxin from *Chromatium* has been examined in both the oxidized and reduced forms (Moss *et al.*, 1968); these measurements have been done without the application of an external magnetic field, a parameter which is extremely important in deriving maximum information from Mössbauer spectra.

The Mössbauer spectra of the oxidized form of *Clostridium pasteurianum* ferredoxin (MW = 6000, 8 Fe–8 S) show two partially resolved quadrupole pairs with quadrupole splittings of (a) 0.6 mm sec^{-1} and (b) 0.7 mm sec^{-1}; the ratio of $a:b$ is about 2.5 with the assumption of equal Lamb–Mössbauer factors for the two sites. The isomer shifts of both sites were indicative of high-spin Fe (III). No spectra were obtained for the reduced form of the protein. In light of the restricted data, the only conclusion that could be supported is that in the oxidized form, the iron was probably present as Fe (III) in the high-spin state; although as has been pointed out, spin state assignments based on Mössbauer measurements with no applied field can easily be in error, particularly with covalent bonds, as would be expected for iron–sulfur bonding in ferredoxin.

Mössbauer spectra in both the oxidized and dithionite-reduced state of *Chromatium* ferredoxin have been obtained (Moss *et al.*, 1968), although the data for the reduced protein are now somewhat suspect based on later studies of the effects of dithionite reduction on polyiron ferredoxins. In the oxidized state, two iron sites are evidenced by quadrupole splittings of 1.32 and 0.66 mm sec^{-1} at 4°K; no magnetic hyperfine interactions are present down to this temperature. The ratio of the iron sites was about 2:1—the model making implications of this ratio bear reinvestigating, as the present value of the number of iron atoms per molecule is higher by a factor of 2 than the number thought to be valid at the time of the Mössbauer investigations.

Recent investigations by high-resolution proton magnetic resonance of the bacterial ferredoxins from *Clostridium pasteurianum* and *C. acidiurici* by Poe *et al.* (1970, 1971) in both the oxidized and the reduced forms of the proteins show that spin coupling operates between individual iron atoms in both redox states. The basis of this assignment and the model-making implications are discussed in the research papers cited above and in Chapter 8 of this volume.

C. Xanthine Oxidase

Mössbauer data on xanthine oxidase (MW = 360,000 8 Fe, 2 FAD, 2 Mo, 8 S^{2-}, two electrons transferred upon reduction) published by Johnson and his co-workers (1967) show that upon reduction with either salicylaldehyde or dithionite, the Mössbauer spectra at 4°K display a magnetic hyperfine interaction that is not present in the oxidized form of the enzyme. Further work (Johnson et al., 1969), with the availability of an external magnetic field confirms the original observation, but the fact that these measurements were necessarily made on the naturally abundant ^{57}Fe in the enzyme (2.2%) precludes any definitive conclusions about the state of the iron in the reduced material. In this sense, Mössbauer measurements on large numbers of possible sites with unenriched samples present almost insurmountable difficulties.

D. Rubredoxin

Rubredoxin, not a true iron–sulfur protein, as it lacks "inorganic" sulfide, is a single-chain protein of molecular weight 6320, and contains a single iron atom surrounded by four cysteine residues as determined by X-ray protein crystallography at 2.5 Å resolution. The Mössbauer studies, not in applied magnetic field (Phillips et al., 1970), clearly support the results of magnetic susceptibility (Phillips et al., 1970) and high-resolution proton magnetic resonance measurements (Phillips et al., 1970) in assigning high-spin ferric and high-spin ferrous states to the iron of the protein in the oxidized and reduced states of the protein. In the oxidized state, rubredoxin displays an EPR signal of the "g = 4.3" variety, again in keeping with high-spin ferric in a low-symmetry site.

E. *Chromatium* High-Potential Iron Protein (HIPIP)

In contrast to the low reduction potential of the ferredoxins, the high-potential protein from *Chromatium* has a reduction potential of +350 mV and contains four iron and four sulfur atoms in a molecular weight of 10,074. The amino acid sequence of the single-chain polypeptide is known (Dus et al., 1971). The oxidized state of the protein is paramagnetic with $g_{\parallel} = 2.21$ and $g_{\perp} = 2.04$, although no detailed analysis of the paramagnetic state has been published. Upon reduction, a single electron is taken up to yield a diamagnetic reduced form of the protein (Bartsch, 1963; Mayhew et al., 1969; Flatmark and Dus, 1969). The magnetic properties of these states has also been shown by magnetic susceptibility measurements (Moss et al., 1969). Studies have also been made by high-resolution proton magnetic resonance; these studies are discussed in Chapter 7 of this volume. The X-ray structure is now known to high resolution (Carter et al., 1971).

Mössbauer spectra of both the oxidized and reduced forms of HIPIP have been recorded by two groups of experimenters (Bearden et al., 1965; Moss et al., 1968; Evans et al., 1970). In both sets of measurements, the spectra taken on the reduced form of the protein do not show any evidence of a magnetic hyperfine interaction, in contrast to the large magnetic hyperfine interactions found in the reduced forms of the 2 Fe–2 S proteins. In HIPIP, the magnetic hyperfine interaction is evident in the *oxidized* form of the protein, as recorded by Mössbauer spectroscopy and expected from the paramagnetism shown by EPR and magnetic susceptibility measurements.

The measurements by Bearden et al. (1965, 1967) and Moss et al. (1968) did not use an external magnetic field in order to align the paramagnetic electron to produce a simplified magnetic hyperfine interaction. The more recent measurements by Evans et al. (1970) at 1.3°K in fields of 50 G both parallel and perpendicular to the γ-ray observation direction show the presence of peaks within the broad Mössbauer absorption, although the assignment of *two* magnetic hyperfine interactions in their work would be supportable only by calculating the Mössbauer absorption at all points using trial values of magnetic hyperfine interaction and the measured quadrupole parameters and showing that a *single* magnetic hyperfine interaction would not fit the data.

Recent X-ray crystallographic information on HIPIP does show the close proximity of the four iron atoms and the four sulfur atoms. Whether the Mössbauer information supports the high-resolution proton magnetic resonance data in allocating the reducing electron unequally over the total iron–sulfur complex is still an open question.

REFERENCES

Bartsch, R. G. (1963). *In* "Bacterial Photosynthesis" (H. Gest, A. San Pietro, and L. P. Vernon, eds.), p. 315. Antioch Press, Yellow Springs, Ohio.

Bearden, A. J., and Dunham, W. R. (1970). *Structure Bonding* **8,** 1.

Bearden, A. J., and Moss, T. H. (1967). *In* "Magnetic Resonance in Biological Systems" (A. Ehrenberg, B. G. Malmström, and T. Vänngard, eds.). Pergamon, Oxford.

Bearden, A. J., Moss, T. H., Bartsch, R. G., and Cusanovich, M. A. (1965). *In* "Nonheme Iron Proteins: Role in Energy Conversion" (A. San Pietro, ed.). Antioch Press, Yellow Springs, Ohio.

Beinert, H., Orme-Johnson, W. H. (1969). Electronic Aspects of Biochemistry, *Ann. N.Y. Acad. Sci.* **158**, Art. 1, p. 336.

Beinert, H., Orme-Johnson, W. H., Dunham, W. R., Palmer, G., Sands, R. H., and Bearden, A. J. (1971). *Biochem. Biophys. Res. Commun.* **45**, 1119.

Blomstrom, D. C., Knight, E., Jr., Phillips, W. D., and Weiher, J. F. (1964). *Proc. Nat. Acad. Sci. U.S.* **51**, 1085.

Carter, C. W. Jr., Freer, S. T., Xuong, Ng H., Alden, R. A., and Kraut, J., (1971). *Cold Spring Harbor Symp. Quant. Biol.* **36**, 381.

Collins, R. L. (1965). *J. Chem. Phys.* **42**, 1072.

Cooke, R., Tsibris, J. C. M., Debrunner, P. G., Tsai, R., Gunsalus, I. C., and Frauenfelder, H. (1968). *Proc. Nat. Acad. Sci. U.S.* **59**, 1045.

Debrunner, P. (1969). *In* "Spectroscopic Approaches to Biomolecular Conformation" (D. W. Urry, ed.). Amer. Med. Asso. Press, Chicago, Illinois.

Dunham, W. R., Bearden, A. J., Salmeen, I. T., Palmer, G., Sands, R. H., Orme-Johnson, W. H., and Beinert, H. (1971). *Biochim. Biophys. Acta* **253**, 134.

Dus, K., Tedro, S., Bartsch, R. G., and Kamen, M. D. (1971). *Biochem. Biophys. Res. Commun.* **43**, 1239.

Eaton, W. A., Palmer, G., Fee, J. A., Kimura, T., and Lovenberg, W. (1972). *Proc. Nat. Acad. Sci. U.S.* **68**, 3015.

Evans, M. C. W., Hall, D. O., and Johnson, C. E. (1970). *Biochem. J.* **119**, 289.

Flatmark, T., and Dus, K. (1969). *Biochim. Biophys. Acta* **180**, 377.

Frauenfelder, H. (1961). "The Mössbauer Effect." Benjamin, New York.

Fritz, J., Anderson, R., Fee, J., Palmer, G., Sands, R. H., Tsibris, J. C. M., Gunsalus, I. C., Orme-Johnson, W. H., and Beinert, H. (1971). *Biochim. Biophys. Acta* **253**, 110.

Goldanskii, V. I., and Herber, R. H. (1968). "Chemical Applications of Mössbauer Spectroscopy." Academic Press, New York.

Gruverman, I. (1965). "Mössbauer Effect Methodology," a series of annual volumes on Mossbauer technology first published in 1965. Plenum Press, New York.

Johnson, C. E., and Hall, D. O. (1968). *Nature (London)* **217**, 446.

Johnson, C. E., Knowles, P. F., and Bray, R. C. (1967). *Biochem. J.* **103**, 10C.

Johnson, C. E., Elstner, E., Gibson, J. F., Benfield, G., Evans, M. C. W., and Hall, D. O. (1968). *Nature (London)* **220**, 1291.

Johnson, C. E., Bray, R. C., Cammack, R., and Hall, D. O. (1969). *Proc. Nat. Acad. Sci. U.S.* **63**, 1234.

Johnson, C. E., Cammack, R., Rao, K. K., and Hall, D. O. (1971). *Biochem. Biophys. Res. Commun.* **43**, 564.

Lang, G. (1970). *Quart. Rev. Biophys.* **3**, 1.

Mayhew, S. G., Petering, D., Palmer, G., and Foust, G. P. (1969). *J. Biol. Chem.* **244**, 2830.

Moss, T. H., Bearden, A. J., Bartsch, R. G., and Cusanovich, M. A. (1968). *Biochemistry* **7**, 1591.

Moss, T. H., Petering, D., and Palmer, G., (1969). *J. Biol. Chem.* **244**, 2275.

Muir, A. H., Jr., Ando, K. J., and Coogan, H. M. (1966). "Mössbauer Effect Data Index 1958–1965." Wiley (Interscience), New York.

Palmer, G. (1967). *Biochem. Biophys. Res. Commun.* **27**, 315.

Palmer, G., Dunham, W. R., Fee, J. A., Sands, R. H., Iizuka, T., and Yonetani, T. (1971). *Biochim. Biophys. Acta* **245**, 201.

Phillips, W. D., Knight, E., Jr., and Blomstrom, D. C. (1965). *In* "Nonheme Iron

Proteins: Role in Energy Conversion" (A. San Pietro, ed.). Antioch Press, Yellow Springs, Ohio.

Phillips, W. D., Poe, M., Weiher, J. F., McDonald, C. C., and Lovenberg, W. (1970). *Nature (London)* **227**, 574.

Poe, M., Phillips, W. D., McDonald, C. C., and Lovenberg, W. (1970). *Proc. Nat. Acad. Sci. U.S.* **65**, 797.

Poe, M., Phillips, W. D., McDonald, C. C., and Orme-Johnson, W. H. (1971). *Biochem. Biophys. Res. Commun.* **42**, 705.

Pryce, M. H. L. (1950). *Proc. Phys. Soc. London* **63A**, 25.

Rao, K. K., Cammack, R., Hall, D. O., and Johnson, C. E. (1971). *Biochem. J.* **122**, 257.

Shethna, Y. T., Wilson, P. W., Hansen, R. E., and Beinert, H. (1964). *Proc. Nat. Acad. Sci. U.S.* **52**, 1263.

Sieker, L. C., Adman, E., and Jensen, L. H. (1972). *Nature (London)* **235**, 40.

Tsibris, J. C. M., Tsai, R. L., Gunsalus, I. C., Orme-Johnson, W. H., Hansen, R. E., and Beinert, H. (1968). *Proc. Nat. Acad. Sci. U.S.* **59**, 959.

Wertheim, G. K. (1964). "Mössbauer Effect: Principles and Applications." Academic Press, New York.

CHAPTER 7

NMR Spectroscopy of the Iron–Sulfur Proteins

W. D. PHILLIPS and MARTIN POE

I. INTRODUCTION

Improvements in instrumentation have led to increased use over the past five years of proton magnetic resonance (PMR) spectroscopy in studies of the structures and interactions of proteins in solution. Ribonuclease (Roberts and Jardetzky, 1970), lysozyme (McDonald and Phillips, 1970), and the heme proteins (the cytochromes c, the myoglobins, and the hemoglobins) (Wüthrich, 1970) are especially amenable to the PMR approach and have been studied most extensively. The heme proteins are of particular interest because in certain redox forms and states of ligation they are paramagnetic. The presence of this paramagnetism and its influence on the characteristics of nuclear resonances have been central to the successful application of PMR to the heme proteins.

255

Electron spin resonance (ESR) and magnetic susceptibility studies had demonstrated that some of the redox forms of the iron–sulfur proteins are paramagnetic. It was to be hoped that manifestations of the effects of paramagnetism in the PMR spectra would be useful in elucidating the geometrical, electronic, and magnetic properties of this class of proteins in solution. Application of PMR to the iron–sulfur proteins is still at an early stage. Much remains to be done in merely surveying the PMR characteristics of the range of iron–sulfur proteins and in the basic interpretation of their PMR spectra. Proton magnetic resonance studies of the iron–sulfur proteins are made in aqueous solution, generally over the relatively narrow temperature range of 4°C to about 40°C. Higher temperatures usually are impractical because of instabilities of the molecules, particularly in solution. Many of the complementary physical measurements that have been made (X ray, magnetic susceptibility, ESR, Mössbauer, and ENDOR) must be performed on the molecules in solid phase and often at temperatures between 70° and 4°K. In view of the exchange coupling that apparently exists between the component iron atoms, effects of temperature can be expected to be particularly profound on the electronic and magnetic properties of the iron–sulfur proteins. The PMR studies, thus, could provide, in principle at least, information under environmental conditions not otherwise available.

We will review briefly here results of recent PMR studies on the iron–sulfur proteins. In some respects this account will be a progress report with interpretations and conclusions subject to revision and expansion as new information from PMR and other techniques becomes available on this fascinating class of proteins.

II. PARAMAGNETISM AND NMR

Effects of unpaired electrons on the characteristics of nuclear magnetic resonance (NMR) have been recognized since the discovery of the phenomenon (Bloembergen et al., 1948). Of particular interest to the physicist have been the Overhauser effect in nuclear spin polarization (Overhauser, 1953a,b) and the resonance field shift in metals induced by coupling between nuclei and conduction electrons (Knight shift) (Knight, 1949). Molecular spectroscopists have been concerned with such manifestations of interactions between nuclei and unpaired electrons as changes in nuclear relaxation times (Bloembergen et al., 1948) and NMR shifts induced by macroscopic polarization effects (Dickinson, 1951), and by isotropic hyperfine contact and pseudocontact interactions (McConnell and Chesnut, 1958). Applications of these effects to paramagnetic complexes and coordination compounds of low molecular weight have been reviewed elsewhere (Eaton and Phillips, 1965; de Boer and van Willigen, 1967). Effects of interactions between nuclei and unpaired electrons, insofar as they affect the characteristics of PMR absorption of the iron–sulfur proteins, will be briefly outlined in this section.

A. Relaxation Times

Nuclear magnetic resonance absorption may be characterized by the parameters T_1 (longitudinal relaxation time) and T_2 (transverse relaxation time). The return to a Boltzmann distribution of a nuclear spin system upon saturation by a strong radio frequency pulse is governed by T_1. T_2 is the linewidth parameter. In a paramagnetic molecule, both electron nucleus dipolar interactions and hyperfine contact interactions can contribute to T_1 and T_2. Considering only a dipolar contribution, nuclear relaxation times in the presence of paramagnetic centers are given by (Bloembergen et al., 1948) Eqs. (1) and (2).

$$\frac{1}{T_1} = \frac{4}{3} S(S+1) \frac{(g^2\beta^2 g_N^2 \beta_N^2)}{\hbar^2 d^6} \tau_c \tag{1}$$

and

$$\frac{1}{T_2} = \frac{4}{3} S(S+1) \frac{(g^2\beta^2 g_N^2 \beta_N^2)}{\hbar^2 d^6} \tau_c \tag{2}$$

S and g are, respectively, the spin quantum number and g value of the paramagnetic center, d is the separation between the paramagnetic center and the resonating nucleus under consideration, and τ_c is a correlation time given by Eq. (3).

$$\frac{1}{\tau_c} = \frac{1}{T_{1e}} + \frac{1}{\tau_r} \tag{3}$$

T_{1e} is the electron spin relaxation time, and τ_r is the rotational correlation time. The other symbols have their usual significance.

To the extent, then, that electron–nucleus dipolar interactions dominate, it is seen from Eqs. (1) and (2) that T_1 and T_2 in paramagnetic systems are equal. Hyperfine contact interactions can, however, contribute to relaxation times, and for certain situations the linewidth parameter T_2, is given by Eq. (4) (Bloembergen and Morgan, 1961).

$$\frac{1}{T_2} = \frac{4}{3} S(S+1) \frac{(g^2\beta^2 g_N^2 \beta_N^2)}{\hbar^2 d^6} \tau_c + \frac{1}{3} S(S+1) \frac{A^2}{\hbar^2} \tau_c \tag{4}$$

A is a hyperfine coupling constant.

As will be seen, wide variations in the widths of resonances attributed to a contact interaction origin (pseudocontact or hyperfine contact) are encountered in the iron–sulfur proteins. The very incomplete information on these molecules regarding electronic relaxation times, geometries, and relations between observed contact shifts and hyperfine coupling constants render analysis of line shapes exceedingly difficult. Suffice it to note here that a favorable combination of circumstances appear to be present that permit observation of contact-shifted resonances in the PMR spectra of the iron–sulfur proteins. However, widths of contact-shifted resonances encountered in the iron–sulfur proteins are characteristically considerably greater than those of the cytochromes c and myoglobins (Wüthrich, 1970). Because of very short electronic relaxation times and relatively large values of d [Eq. (4)], effects of paramagnetic relaxation appear to be largely absent in the heme proteins. This clearly is not the case for the iron–sulfur proteins.

B. Pseudocontact Shifts

Electron–nucleus dipolar interactions of paramagnetic molecules in solution can affect not only relaxation times but can strongly perturb positions of nuclear resonances as well. This latter effect has been termed pseudocontact interaction, and for molecules in solution the isotropic pseudocontact resonance shift, ΔH_{pc} is given by Eq. (5) (McConnell and Robertson, 1958).

$$\Delta H_{pc} = -(3 \cos^2 \zeta - 1)(g_\parallel - g_\perp)(g_\parallel + 2g_\perp) \frac{\beta^2 H_0 S(S + 1)}{27kTd^3} \qquad (5)$$

Here, tetragonal symmetry is assumed for the ligand field about the paramagnetic center, d is the separation between the paramagnetic center and the resonating nucleus, ζ is the angle between the distance vector and the tetragonal axis, and the g tensor is defined by the components $g_\parallel$ and $g_\perp$, parallel and perpendicular, respectively, to the symmetry axis. The pseudocontact interaction depends on an anisotropic g tensor ($g_\parallel \neq g_\perp$), and because of the high symmetries of the g tensors involved, probably makes a minor contribution to observed contact shifts for most of the iron–sulfur proteins. A notable exception would appear to be rubredoxin from *Clostridium pasteurianum*, to be discussed later. In practice it is quite difficult to separate contributions to contact shifts attributable to pseudocontact interactions from those arising from hyperfine contact interactions.

C. Hyperfine Contact Shifts

The electron–nucleus hyperfine contact interactions that give rise to the isotropic hyperfine splittings of ESR spectroscopy can be manifested in large contact shifts in NMR spectroscopy. The conditions for observation of such contact shifts in NMR are that $T_{1e}^{-1} \gg A$ or $T_e^{-1} \gg A$, where T_{1e} and T_e are, respectively, electronic relaxation and exchange times, and A is a hyperfine coupling constant. Where NMR hyperfine contact shifts are observed, ESR resonances generally are so broad as to render difficult or impossible resolution of hyperfine splittings. Conditions conducive to observation of PMR contact shifts appear to be present for the iron–sulfur proteins that contain two, four, and eight iron atoms.

Isotropic hyperfine contact shifts ΔH_{hc} for paramagnetic systems that obey the Curie law frequently have been related to hyperfine coupling constants A through the relation (McConnell and Chesnut, 1958)

$$\left(\frac{\Delta H_{hc}}{H_0}\right)_i = -A_i \frac{\gamma_e}{\gamma_N} \frac{g\beta S(S+1)}{3kT} \tag{6}$$

where γ_e and γ_N are, respectively, magnetogyric ratios of the electron and resonating nucleus. Large deviations from Eq. (6) have, however, been observed even for systems whose magnetic susceptibilities exhibit Curie law behavior. As will be seen, some of the iron–sulfur proteins appear not to obey the Curie law, at least over the range of temperature accessible to the solution state PMR studies. It is apparent, however, that considerable further theoretical as well as experimental work is required before adequate correlation of the magnitudes and temperature dependences of contact shifts of the iron–sulfur proteins with their magnetic and electronic properties becomes possible.

Two principal mechanisms by which spin densities in paramagnetic systems are manifested in hyperfine contact interaction shifts in PMR spectra are by spin polarization and hyperconjugation. For an aromatic $\dot{C}$—H fragment, such as occurs as a component of a porphyrin ring of a paramagnetic heme protein, proton contact interaction constants, derived from observed contact shifts and Eq. (6), are related to the spin density ρ centered on the $p\pi$ orbital of carbon by Eq. (7) (McConnell and Chesnut, 1958)

$$A_i = Q\rho_i \tag{7}$$

where Q is a proportionality constant. For the particular bonding situation encountered here, $Q \cong -6.3 \times 10^7$ Hz (Bernal et al., 1962). If, alternatively, a methyl group were bonded to an aromatic carbon atom that contained spin density $\dot{C}$—CH_3, the hyperfine coupling constant of the methyl protons and the spin density centered on carbon have been related by

$$A_i \cong +7.5 \times 10^7 \rho_i \tag{8}$$

but wide variations in the value of the proportionality "constant" have been reported (McLachlan, 1958; Chesnut, 1958; Horrocks et al., 1964).

Although it has not been established unequivocally, it will be suggested that most of the contact shifts observed to date in the PMR spectra of the iron–sulfur proteins arise from the β-CH$_2$ protons of cysteine residues. Spin density is assumed to be transferred to cysteinyl sulfur as the result of iron–sulfur coordinative binding. Observed contact-shifted resonances, then, could arise as a result of hyperconjugative interaction between cysteinyl β-CH$_2$ protons and spin density centered on sulfur. Alternatively, isotropic hyerfine contact interactions can be propagated by delocalization along σ-bond systems (Eaton et al., 1967). Finally, even though the g tensors of most of the iron–sulfur proteins appear rather isotropic, at this stage of our understanding of the geometrical and electronic structures, the pseudocontact interaction cannot be eliminated as a secondary or even primary contributor to observed contact shifts in these proteins.

D. Identification of Contact-Shifted Resonances

The identification of resonances in the PMR spectrum of a protein subject to contact interaction effects is nontrivial and merits some discussion. Three principal criteria exist: absolute resonance positions, relaxation times, and temperature dependences of resonance positions. The PMR spectra of proteins in water usually are referenced with respect to the sharp resonance of the methyl protons of 2,2-dimethyl-2-silapentane sulfonate (DSS). The convention employed in referencing the PMR spectra of the iron–sulfur proteins was that resonances displaced to high field of that of the methyl proton resonance of DSS (assigned a value of 0 ppm) were given negative values, and those displaced to low field were assigned positive values. For diamagnetic proteins in the native conformation, protons bound to carbon exhibit a range of resonances on this scale that extends between −4 and +9 ppm (Roberts and Jardetzky, 1970; McDonald and Phillips, 1970). In H$_2$O solution where the exchangeable OH and NH protons become observable in PMR spectra, resonance absorption may extend as far as +15 ppm to low field (Glickson et al., 1969; Patel et al., 1970). Thus, in D$_2$O solutions where all exchangeable protons are replaced by deuterons, there is a good possibility that resonances occurring outside the −4 to +9 ppm range originate from protons subject to contact interaction effects. This is not to imply, of course, that contact-shifted resonances do not occur in the −4 to +9 ppm region. However, this region of resonance absorption of proteins usually is so complex that unambiguous identification of contact-shifted resonances that appear here can be extremely difficult.

As was indicated earlier, relaxation times of protons of a given molecule that exhibit contact-shifted resonances generally are shorter than those of protons not subject to paramagnetic influence. This reduction of T_1 and T_2 results from proximity to the paramagnetic center. Resonances subject to dipolar relaxation, thus, are less prone to saturation at high levels of radiofrequency energies. More significant, however, for diagnostic purposes, is the fact that resonance widths of protons sufficiently near a paramagnetic center to be subject to contact interaction effects usually are appreciably greater than those of protons unaffected by such interactions. In the iron–sulfur proteins, widths of resonances of single protons of up to 250 Hz are encountered. These are to be contrasted with resonance widths of 5–15 Hz that are expected for diamagnetic proteins of these molecular weights. Anomalously large resonance widths, thus, are compatible with the presence of a paramagnetic center in a molecule and the presence of isotropic hyperfine and/or pseudocontact interaction effects. It should be noted that reductions of T_2 by paramagnetic centers militate against the detection of contact-shifted resonances in the presence of narrower resonances arising from protons unaffected by contact perturbations. This broadening, for example, often makes difficult the resolution of contact-shifted resonances in the −4 to +9 ppm region of resonance absorption of proteins.

Finally, the temperature dependences of contact-shifted resonances are expected to reflect the local magnetic susceptibilities of paramagnetic centers (Eaton and Phillips, 1965; de Boer and van Willigen, 1967). Temperature dependences of contact-shifted resonances may further be modified in striking fashion by protein conformational perturbations over the temperature range studied. Both isotropic hyperfine and pseudocontact interactions can be highly sensitive functions of small, local geometrical readjustments. This sensitivity of the magnitudes of contact shifts to structural perturbations can be useful for studying protein structure, but greatly complicates analysis of temperature dependences of contact shifts in terms of electronic and magnetic parameters (McDonald and Phillips, 1969).

E. Magnetic Susceptibility Shifts

The influence of bulk magnetic susceptibility on the positions of nuclear resonances provides a convenient and moderately sensitive means of measuring magnetic susceptibilities of liquid or solution samples (Bartle et al., 1968). The method has been employed to measure the magnetic susceptibilities of the rubredoxin from *C. pasteurianum* (Phillips *et al.*, 1970) and the eight-iron ferredoxins from *C. pasteurianum* (Poe *et al.*, 1970) and *C. acidi-urici* (Poe *et al.*, 1971). Since details of the determinations for the iron–sulfur proteins have been given elsewhere (Phillips and Poe, 1972), we will only outline the principles involved.

Dickinson (1951) classically computed the Lorentz cavity field produced on a uniform distribution of magnetizable material surrounding a paramagnetic species. The resonance field shift, ΔH induced in the diamagnetic medium by the paramagnetic solute is given by Eq. (9)

$$\Delta H/H = (\tfrac{4}{3}\pi - \alpha)\,\Delta\kappa \qquad (9)$$

where α is the demagnetization or shape factor and $\Delta\kappa$ is the change in volume susceptibility of the sample caused by introduction of the solute. α is $4\pi/3$ for a spherical sample. For the cylindrical sample container conventionally employed in NMR, α is 2π when the sample axis and magnetic field are orthogonal and vanishes when the magnetic field and cylinder are coaxial. The latter geometry is appropriate for a spectrometer based on a superconducting solenoid, and confers a twofold sensitivity advantage, at constant resonance frequency, for susceptibility determinations over the more conventional electromagnet-based spectrometers. A solenoidal-based spectrometer operating at a resonance frequency of 220 MHz was employed for the susceptibility determinations to be reported later.

III. RUBREDOXIN

Rubredoxin from *Clostridium pasteurianum* consists of a single polypeptide chain of molecular weight 6320, contains a single iron atom and four cysteine residues, but lacks "inorganic" sulfur (Lovenberg and Sobel, 1965). In this latter respect, rubredoxin is not a true iron–sulfur protein. The X-ray structure of the protein has been completed to 2.5 Å, and the iron appears to be bound to the polypeptide chain by coordinate linkages to the sulfur atoms of the four cysteine residues (Herriott *et al.*, 1970). The sulfur atoms appear to be arrayed approximately tetrahedrally about the iron atom.

Rubredoxin undergoes a reversible one-electron oxidation reduction with a potential of -0.057 V. (Lovenberg and Sobel, 1965). The magnetic susceptibilities of the protein in the two oxidation states were determined by the NMR method previously discussed and were found to obey a Curie law temperature dependence and to correspond to $5.85 \pm 0.2 \ \mu_\mathrm{B}$ for the oxidized form and $5.05 \pm 0.2 \ \mu_\mathrm{B}$ for the reduced form (Phillips *et al.*,

1970a). These results are compatible with high-spin ferric iron ($S = \frac{5}{2}$) for oxidized rubredoxin and high-spin ferrous iron ($S = 5$) for the reduced protein. Mössbauer (Phillips *et al.*, 1970a) and circular dichroism (Eaton and Lovenberg, 1970) studies concur in assigning high-spin Fe (III) and Fe (II) to the redox states of rubredoxin.

We turn now to consideration of the PMR spectra of rubredoxin. Earlier studies established that the PMR spectra of denatured, diamagnetic proteins are essentially those of the component amino acids, appropriately weighted with respect to intensities by the amino acid composition. Such a calculated, random coil spectrum for rubredoxin is shown in Fig. 1. Proton magnetic resonance spectra for native rubredoxin, in oxidized and reduced forms, dissolved in D_2O and at 45°C, are shown in Fig. 2 (Phillips *et al.*, 1970a). It is seen that the spectra of the oxidized and reduced forms differ between themselves, and both are different from that of the calculated random coil spectrum. For diamagnetic proteins, differences betweeen the spectra of native and denatured conformations appear attributable to resonance displacements that result from intramolecular environmental perturbations that accompany protein folding (McDonald and Phillips, 1969; McDonald *et al.*, 1971). These perturbations undoubtedly are responsible, at least in part, for the differences in PMR spectra between native and denatured rubredoxin. In addition, for rubredoxin there exists the possibility in both redox states that resonances are shifted by contact interaction and broadened by dipolar relaxation. These effects are difficult to separate in the complex and severely overlapped -1.5 to $+9.0$ ppm region of resonance absorption of the protein and will not further concern us here since we are principally inter-

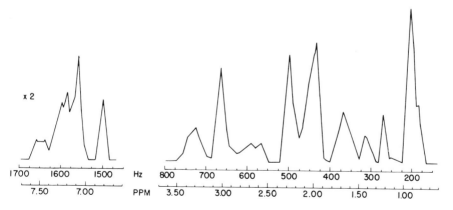

Fig. 1. Calculated PMR spectrum for extended, random-coil configuration of *C. pasteurianum* rubredoxin. This spectrum was computed from the amino acid composition of rubredoxin according to the algorithm of McDonald and Phillips (1969).

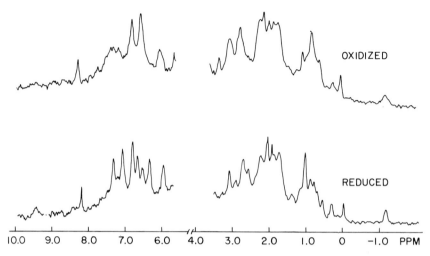

Fig. 2. PMR spectra at 220 MHz for oxidized and reduced *C. pasteurianum* rubredoxin. The 6 mM rubredoxin is dissolved in unbuffered 99.77% D_2O at pD 5.6, and the spectra were accumulated on a computer of average transients for the following numbers of passes: high field (right-hand side), 18 passes; low field (left-hand side), 55 passes. The vertical scales on these four spectra are not directly comparable; the horizontal scales are in parts per million of the polarizing field from the methyl resonance of sodium 2,2-dimethyl-2-silapentane sulfonate (DSS), with down-field shifts assigned positive values, temperature 45°C. Reproduced by permission (Phillips *et al.*, 1970a).

ested in the possibility of observation of resonances displaced by contact interaction from this spectral region.

Searches were made in the +9 to +40 and −1.5 to −27 ppm regions of the PMR spectra of both redox forms of rubredoxin. The only additional resonances detected for *either* redox form of the protein were those designated ϵ, φ, and η in the −2 to −5 ppm region of the reduced form of the protein (Fig. 3). Because of breadths, positions, and temperature dependences, protons giving rise to these resonances almost certainly are subject to contact interaction effects, probably of the pseudocontact variety.

The quality of the contact shifted spectra of the two redox forms of rubredoxin can only be characterized as disappointing. The paucity of identifiable contact shifts in the PMR spectra of rubredoxin would appear to be attributable to the very large magnetic moments possessed by the high-spin iron in both redox states and strong associated dipolar relaxation [Eq. (2)]. Possibly the only reason the three contact-shifted resonances were observed in the reduced form of the protein in contrast to none definitively identified in the spectrum of oxidized rubredoxin, is the

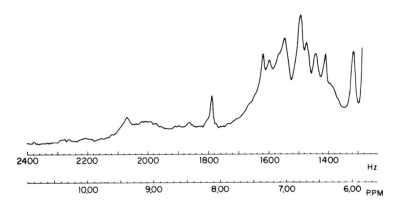

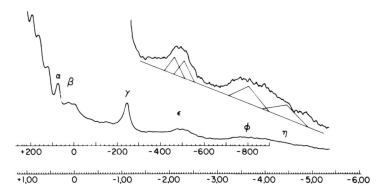

Fig. 3. The 220-MHz PMR spectra of the high-field and low-field regions of reduced *C. pasteurianum* rubredoxin. The 5.45 mM proteins, which have an absorption ratio $A_{280}/A_{490} = 2.4$, was dissolved in 0.1 M tris ^{2}HCl, pD 7.8 (in D$_2$O) at +23°C. The low-field spectrum was accumulated on a computer of average transients for 300 passes. The fourfold enlarged version of the high-field spectrum is underlayed with triangles of width and intensity appropriate for the data analysis presented. The lower horizontal scale is in parts per million (ppm) from DSS, while the upper scale is in Hz. Reproduced by permission (Phillips *et al.*, 1970a).

lesser value of the magnetic moment exhibited by the ferrous ion. For fixed geometries, resonance widths of given protons would be expected to be about 50% greater in oxidized rubredoxin than in the reduced protein. In any event, if the quality of contact-shifted spectra encountered in rubredoxin were representative of that to be encountered for the class of iron–sulfur proteins, the contact shift approach to the structures of these proteins most likely would have been abandoned. Fortunately, this turns out not to be the case.

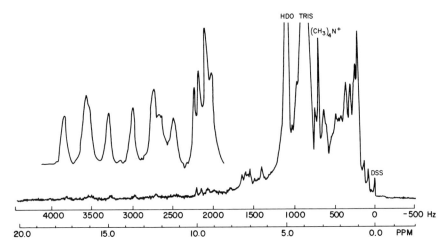

Fig. 4. PMR spectrum at 220 MHz of oxidized ferredoxin from *C. pasteurianum*. The ferredoxin is dissolved in a solution of D_2O containing tris buffer with tetramethyl ammonium chloride and DSS as internal references; the ferredoxin concentration is 16.5 mM. The lower spectrum in the figure is a single trace, the insert on the left-hand side is spectrum computer averaged over 75 scans. Temperature, 23°C. Reproduced by permission (Poe *et al.*, 1970).

IV. EIGHT-IRON FERREDOXINS

Ferredoxin from *Clostridium pasteurianum* was the first of the bacterial ferredoxins to be isolated (Mortenson *et al.*, 1962). The molecular weight of the protein is 6000, and it contains eight iron atoms,* eight inorganic sulfur atoms,* and eight cysteine residues (Lovenberg *et al.*, 1963). The ferredoxin undergoes a reversible two-electron oxidation reduction with a potential of about −0.420 V. Our discussion will deal primarily with the more stable oxidized form. Some results will be presented on both the oxidized and reduced forms of the related ferredoxin from *C. acidi-urici*.

The 23°C PMR spectrum of the oxidized form of ferredoxin from *C. pasteurianum* is shown in Fig. 4 (Poe *et al.*, 1970). The strong absorption in the 0–8 ppm region is typical of that encountered for diamagnetic pro-

---

* The iron and inorganic sulfur contents of *C. pasteurianum* ferredoxin have been variously reported to be from six to eight per molecule. However, in view of the convincing value of eight iron and eight inorganic sulfur atoms obtained recently for the ferredoxin from *C. acidi-urici* (Hong and Rabinowitz, 1970) and the apparent similarities of the two ferredoxins with respect to other chemical and physical properties, a value of eight is accepted here for the iron and sulfur contents of *C. pasteurianum* ferredoxin.

teins such as lysozyme and ribonuclease. Upon spectral accumulation by means of a computer of average transients, the partial spectrum between 8 and 18 ppm shown in the upper left-hand inset of Fig. 4 emerges from the background. Careful intensity comparisons reveal that a total of six-

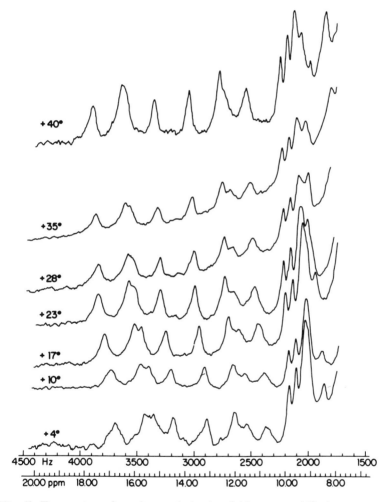

Fig. 5. Temperature dependence of the low-field, contact-shifted resonances of oxidized ferredoxin from *C. pasteurianum*. These averaged spectra were obtained from a single D₂O solution of 15.4 m*M* oxidized ferredoxin. The spectra were averaged for the following number of scans at the indicated temperatures: 5°C, 100 scans; 10°C, 130 scans; 17°C, 70 scans; 23°C, 70 scans; 28°C, 50 scans; 35°C, 50 scans; 40°C, 50 scans. The vertical scales at the various temperatures are not comparable.

teen protons per ferredoxin molecule contribute intensity to this region of resonance absorption. The extreme low-field resonance at 17.7 ppm, in fact, arises from a single proton, the partially split resonance at 16.3 ppm, from two protons, the two resonances at 15.0 and 13.8 ppm, from one proton each, etc. The temperature dependences of the resonances of the 8 to 18 ppm region over the range 4°–40°C are shown in Fig. 5 and plotted in Fig. 6. The resonances are seen to trend uniformly to lower resonance fields with increasing temperature.

The anomalous positions, widths, and temperature dependences of the low-field resonances of *C. pasteurianum* ferredoxin suggest a contact interaction origin of the isotropic hyperfine and/or pseudocontact varieties. For this to be the case, a paramagnetic center or centers must be present in the molecule. And indeed, in solution and over the 4°–65°C temperature range, the paramagnetic contribution to the magnetic susceptibility shown in Fig. 7 was observed for the oxidized form of the protein. Thus, the paramagnetism required to produce the contact shifts of the ferredoxin would appear to be present.

Two points regarding the magnetic susceptibility are worthy of note. An effective magnetic moment per iron atom, μ_{eff}, can be derived from

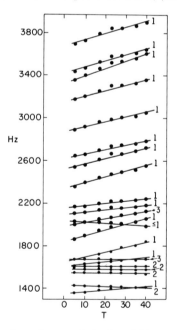

Fig. 6. Temperature dependences of the low-field resonances in oxidized *C. pasteurianum* ferredoxin at 220 MHz. Numbers of protons giving rise to each resonance are indicated on the figure. Reproduced by permission (Poe *et al.,* 1970).

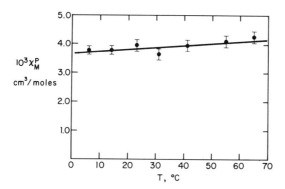

Fig. 7. Temperature dependence of the paramagnetic contribution to the molar magnetic susceptibility of oxidized ferredoxin. The data were obtained upon a ferredoxin solution which contained 7.02 mM ferredoxin, buffer, and references, and had an absorbance ratio A_{390}/A_{280} of 0.805.

the results of Fig. 7 and Eq. (10).

$$\mu_{\text{eff}}^2 = 3kT\chi_m^p/8N\beta^2 \tag{10}$$

under the assumption that all eight iron atoms contribute equivalently to the paramagnetic susceptibility. μ_{eff} per iron atom increases from 1.0 to 1.2 μ_B over the 4°–65°C temperature range investigated (Poe et $al.$, 1971). These values are significantly less than the 1.73 μ_B expected if each iron atom possessed only a single, unpaired electron and much less than the magnetic moments for iron of rubredoxin. The low magnetic moments for this ferredoxin could be accounted for by extensive antiferromagnetic exchange coupling between the component iron atoms. Temperature dependencies of the magnetic susceptibility and the contact-shifted resonances also are compatible with such a model.

The problem remains of identification of the observed contact-shifted resonances of oxidized $C.$ $pasteurianum$ ferredoxin with specific CH protons of the polypeptide chain. The iron of rubredoxin from $C.$ $pasteurianum$ is bound to the polypeptide through coordinate linkages with the sulfur atoms of the four cysteine residues (Herriott et $al.$, 1970). It appears that the four iron atoms of the high-potential iron protein from $Chromatium$ similarly are bound to the polypeptide chain through Fe–S bonds involving cysteinyl sulfur (Carter et $al.$, 1971). If we suppose that the eight iron atoms of $C.$ $pasteurianum$ ferredoxin are bound to the polypeptide chain by the eight cysteine residues, the 16 β-CH$_2$ protons of the cysteine residues would be expected to experience the strongest contact interaction effects of all CH protons of the protein. Tentatively, then, the sixteen contact-shifted resonances observed for the oxidized form of this protein are attributed to the β-CH_2 protons of the cysteine residues. β-CH_2 protons of cysteine unperturbed by contact interaction exhibit resonances at 3.0 ppm (McDonald and Phillips, 1969; McDonald $et\ al.$, 1971) with respect to the internal reference employed in all the reported studies, namely, the methyl proton resonance of sodium 2,2-dimethyl-2-silapentane sulfonate (DSS).

It is tempting to ascribe the contact shifts observed in the PMR spectrum of oxidized $C.\ pasteurianum$ ferredoxin to β-CH_2 protons of cysteine subject to isotropic hyperfine contact interaction effects. However, as discussed above, assignment of these resonances to cysteine protons, while extremely probable, must be regarded as tentative. Furthermore, the possibility of a sizable, even dominating, pseudocontact contribution to the contact shifts cannot easily be dismissed. While the g tensor of the reduced form appears fairly isotropic (Palmer $et\ al.$, 1966; Orme-Johnson and Beinert, 1969a), with only relatively minor pseudocontact contributions to contact shifts consequently expected, nothing is known for certain about the g tensor of the oxidized form and possible pseudocontact contributions to the contact shifts.

An interesting feature of the above results, if the assignments are correct, is the resolution of separate contact shifts for each of the two β-CH_2 protons of each of the eight cysteine residues. Rotation about the C_β—S bond of each cysteine residue presumably is prevented because of coordinate binding of iron to sulfur and attachment of the C_β carbon to the polypeptide chain (Fig. 8). The two β-CH_2 protons of each cysteine residue then would be expected in general to be nonequivalent with respect to contact interaction effects and to exhibit different contact shifts

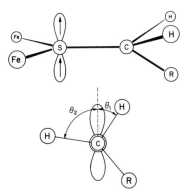

Fig. 8. Possible mode of cysteine-iron binding in the eight-iron ferredoxins. To the extent that isotropic contact contributions dominate contact interactions, the contact shifts of the cysteinyl β-CH_2 protons would depend on the angles θ. Reproduced by permission (Poe $et\ al.$, 1970.)

for either an isotropic-hyperfine or pseudocontact interaction. If pseudocontact interaction were the dominating contact interaction mode, nonequivalences of the two β-CH$_2$ protons of each cysteine residue would be expected because of the sensitive angular and distance dependences of pseudocontact interactions [Eq. (5)]. If hyperfine contact interactions propagated by a hyperconjugative mechanism dominated in these systems, magnitudes of contact shifts would depend on angular orientations about the C$_\beta$—S bond of cysteine residues. For heuristic purposes, we suppose here that as a result of coordinative binding, spin density is transferred from iron to cysteinyl sulfur. Spin density on sulfur is manifested in contact shifts of the β-CH$_2$ protons by the hyperconjugative mechanism discussed earlier. For such a model, contact interaction constants, A, would depend on the dihedral angle θ about the C$_\beta$—S bond axis by Eq. (11) (Stone and Maki, 1967).

$$A = A_0 \cos^2 \theta \qquad (11)$$

Only for $\theta_1 = \theta_2$ (Fig. 8) would contact shifts for the two β-CH$_2$ protons of a cysteine residue be equal.

The ferredoxin from *C. acidi-urici*, like that of *C. pasteurianum*, possesses a molecular weight of 6000 and contains eight iron atoms and eight inorganic sulfur atoms (Hong and Rabinowitz, 1970). The eight cysteine residues of the ferredoxin are located at the same positions along the polypeptide chain as the eight of *C. pasteurianum* ferredoxin (Rall *et al.*, 1969). Other physical and chemical properties of the two ferredoxins are similar. There is a paramagnetic contribution to the magnetic susceptibility of the oxidized form *C. acidi-urici* ferredoxin (Poe *et al.*, 1971). Contact-shifted resonances are observed in the PMR spectrum of the oxidized form of the protein (Poe *et al.*, 1971). The contact shift spectra of the oxidized forms of the two clostridial ferredoxins, while similar, differ in detail. This is to be expected if, indeed, the resonances derive from the β-CH$_2$ protons of the cysteine residues and if, as suggested, orientations about C$_\beta$—S bonds of cysteine residues play a significant role in modulating contact interaction effects in these as well as the other iron–sulfur proteins.

The two-electron reduction of *C. acidi-urici* ferredoxin was accomplished by dithionite, and a series of contact-shifted resonances, identified by position and temperature dependence and each with an intensity corresponding to one proton per molecule, was observed in the 3400–13,000 Hz range (Poe *et al.*, 1971). Temperature dependences of these resonances are plotted in Fig. 9. The two resonances of Fig. 9 that occur between 12,000 and 13,000 Hz were not reported in the initial study (Poe *et al.*, 1971) because they were outside the range of the spectrometer employed as it

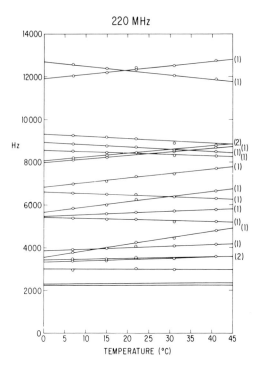

Fig. 9. Temperature dependences of the contact-shifted resonances of reduced
C. acidi-urici ferredoxin at 220 MHz. Numbers of protons per ferredoxin molecule
giving rise to these resonances are indicated to the right on the figure.

then existed. It is, of course, not certain that additional resonances will not
be found as searches are extended to even lower resonance fields. From results on the model of the Fe_4S_4 clusters $[(C_2H_5)_4N]_2[Fe_4S_4(SCH_2C_6H_5)_4]$,
to be discussed shortly, it is almost certain that the contact-shifted
resonances observed in the PMR spectrum of the oxidized forms of the
bacterial ferredoxins derive from the β-CH_2 protons of the cysteinyl
residues (see Section VI). However, it is likely because of the larger
contact interactions involved that the α-CH protons of the cysteinyl
residues undergo also significant contact interaction displacement in the
reduced forms of the ferredoxins and contribute, along with the cysteinyl
β-CH_2 protons, to the observed contact shifted resonances.

Two superimposed electron spin resonance (ESR) signals were observed in the reductive titration of the two clostridial ferredoxins (Orme-
Johnson and Beinert, 1969a). This clearly suggests the existence of two
inequivalent paramagnetic centers in each of the reduced proteins. This
may or may not imply the separation of the eight iron atoms into two

or more clusters on the protein. Attempts were made to follow the reductive titrations of the clostridial ferredoxins by PMR (Poe *et al.*, 1971). "Averaged" resonances intermediate in position between those of fully oxidized and fully reduced ferredoxin were observed over the entire titration range. Apparently intermolecular electron exchange, fast on the PMR time scale, is taking place between oxidized and reduced forms of the proteins. In partially reduced systems, electron exchange between redox species must be taking place at rates that exceed about 10^3 sec^{-1} to yield the observed effects. If more than one redox center exists in the ferredoxins, intramolecular as well as intermolecular electron exchange may be present. The behavior of the clostridial ferredoxins is in contrast to that of the four-iron and two-iron iron–sulfur proteins to be discussed later. In the latter, superimposed and not averaged PMR spectra of the separate forms are observed for solutions that contain both redox species. Because of the "fast" electron exchange in the clostridial ferredoxins, at least under the solution conditions employed, little can be said from the PMR results concerning the existence of multiple iron sites.

V. HIGH-POTENTIAL IRON PROTEIN

Among the iron–sulfur proteins that can be isolated from the photosynthetic bacterium *Chromatium* is an electron transfer agent with an unusually high, positive redox potential ($E_m' = +0.35$ V) known as high-potential iron protein (HIPIP). This protein has a molecular weight of

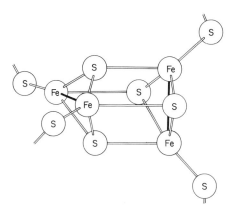

Fig. 10. Probable structure for the redox center of *Chromatium* HIPIP. This structure is suggested from preliminary X-ray analysis and is closely analogous to that of $(C_5H_5)_4Fe_4S_4$ (Schunn *et al.*, 1966; Wei *et al.*, 1966). Reproduced by permission (Phillips *et al.*, 1970b).

10,074, contains four atoms each of iron and inorganic sulfur and four cysteine residues (Bartsch, 1963; Dus *et al.*, 1967). X-Ray diffraction studies indicate the structure of the iron–sulfur moiety of HIPIP to be that depicted in Fig. 10 (Carter *et al.*, 1971; Palmer *et al.*, 1966) in close analogy to the organometallic compound $Fe_4S_4(C_5H_5)_4$ in which cyclopentadienyl groups rather than cysteine residues are coordinatively bound to iron (Schunn *et al.*, 1966; Wei *et al.*, 1966). The protein has been reported to be diamagnetic in the reduced form and to possess a paramagnetic susceptibility in the oxidized form that obeys the Curie law and corresponds to a single unpaired electron ($S = \frac{1}{2}$) (Moss *et al.*, 1969). ESR absorption has been observed for the oxidized protein below 28°K ($g_{\parallel} = 2.21$, $g_{\perp} = 2.04$) (Orme-Johnson and Beinert, 1969b; Palmer *et al.*, 1967).

Proton magnetic resonance absorption of the oxidized form of *Chromatium* HIPIP is shown in Fig. 11 (Phillips *et al.*, 1970b). The envelope of resonances between −1 and +9 ppm are those characteristic of proteins unperturbed by magnetic interactions. As discussed earlier, protons subject to contact interaction effects may also exhibit resonance absorption in this region of the spectrum. However, because of extensive overlap and complexity, identification of the relatively broad and weak contact-shifted resonances in this region is virtually impossible. Upon extensive computer averaging, the additional series of resonances between 23 and 43 ppm in the upper left-hand inset of Fig. 11 are revealed. Temperature dependences and numbers of contributing protons per HIPIP molecule for this set of five contact-shifted resonances are shown on the left-hand side of Fig. 12.

The contact-shifted resonances in the PMR spectrum of oxidized *Chromatium* HIPIP are assigned tentatively to the β-CH_2 protons of the

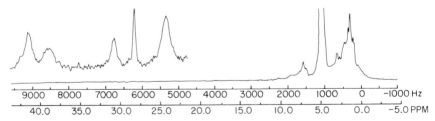

Fig. 11. The 220-MHz PMR spectrum of oxidized *Chromatium* HIPIP at +5°C. Spectrum referenced with respect to internal 2,2-dimethyl-2-silapentane sulfonic acid. The strong peak at 5.0 ppm arises from residual [1-²H]H₂O protons. The inset is a 100-pass, computer-averaged spectrum of the 22 to 43 ppm region of resonance absorption. Reproduced by permission (Phillips *et al.*, 1970b).

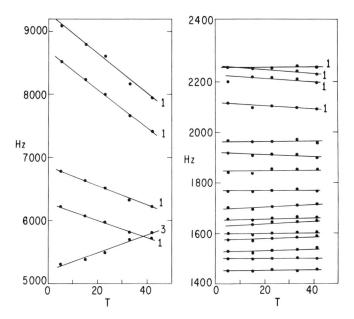

Fig. 12. Temperature dependence of the low-field resonances of oxidized HIPIP. Numbers of protons associated with certain of these resonances are indicated. Reproduced by permission (Phillips *et al.*, 1970b).

four cysteine residues that bind the iron–sulfur moiety to the polypeptide chain. A total intensity corresponding to eight protons rather than seven would be expected for the contact-shifted resonances. Unless our assignment is incorrect, a resonance corresponding to one proton either is too broad for detection or is to be found in a region of resonance absorption where identification would be difficult, i.e., the −1 to +9 ppm region.

Assuming the correctness of the assignment, the β-CH$_2$ groups of the four cysteine residues are seen to be distributed into two classes of two each (or possibly three classes) based on the temperature dependences of contact shifts. The proton contact shifts of two β-CH$_2$ groups increase with temperature and the other two decrease with temperature. It would seem likely, then, that the unpaired electron of the oxidized form of *Chromatium* HIPIP is not distributed uniformly over the Fe$_4$S$_4$ center, but rather is at least somewhat localized at one end of the redox cluster. Recent Mössbauer results (Johnson *et al.*, 1970) indicate that, indeed, two [57]Fe-electron hyperfine coupling constants are exhibited by oxidized HIPIP, i.e., that the unpaired electron is not distributed uniformly over the four iron atoms.

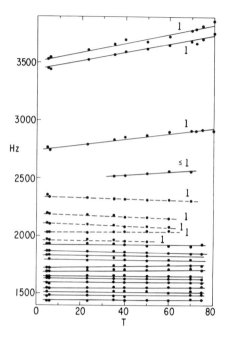

Fig. 13. Temperature dependences of the low-field resonances of reduced HIPIP. Numbers of protons associated with certain of these resonances are indicated. The dotted lines represent resonances that disappear with time in D_2O solution and presumably, therefore, arise from exchangeable protons. Reproduced by permission (Phillips *et al.*, 1970b).

Contact-shifted resonances also are observed in the PMR spectrum of the ostensibly diamagnetic, reduced form of *Chromatium* HIPIP. The temperature dependences of the three observed contact-shifted resonances of reduced HIPIP, each of intensity corresponding to one proton per molecule and occurring between 2700 Hz (12.3 ppm) and 3700 Hz (16.8 ppm), are plotted in Fig. 13. As was the case for the oxidized form of *C. pasteurianum* ferredoxin, the magnitudes of the contact shifts of reduced *Chromatium* HIPIP increase with temperature. It is suggested that the iron atoms of reduced HIPIP are paramagnetic, but are antiferromagnetically exchange coupled. Contact shifts would be manifested to the extent that magnetic states with $S' \neq 0$ were thermally populated. Populations of such states could be sufficiently small that a paramagnetic component to the magnetic susceptibility would be undetected, particularly at low temperatures. On the other hand, contact interaction perturbations on PMR spectra from rather small amounts of net unpaired spin often can be detected.

VI. A SYNTHETIC ANALOGUE OF THE Fe_4S_4 CLUSTERS

Recently Herskovitz, Averill, and Holm have synthesized a series of anions of general formula $[Fe_4S_4(SR)_4]^{2-}$ whose structures and properties appear to be closely related to the iron–sulfur components of the bacterial ferredoxins and high-potential iron protein (Herskovitz et al., 1972). The structure of the anion $[Fe_4S_4(SCH_2C_6H_5)_4]^{2-}$ as determined by Ibers by X-ray crystallography is shown in Fig. 14. The Fe_4S_4 cluster possesses D_{2d} symmetry and the four iron atoms are crystallographically equivalent.

Carter et al. have determined to 2.25 Å resolution the structure of the high-potential iron protein of Chromatium (Carter et al., 1971) and the symmetry and distances of the iron–sulfur cluster appear to be very similar to those of $[Fe_4S_4(SCH_2C_6H_5)_4]^{2-}$. Sieker et al. have demonstrated that the eight iron atoms and eight "inorganic" sulfur atoms of the ferredoxin from Micrococcus aerogenes are distributed into two Fe_4S_4 clusters whose geometries are similar to that of Chromatium HIPIP (Sieker et al., 1972) and in turn to that of $[Fe_4S_4(SCH_2C_6H_5)_4]^{2-}$. For both the bacterial ferredoxin and the HIPIP, X-ray studies show the Fe_4S_4 clusters to be bound to the polypeptide chain through the coordination of cysteinyl sulfur to iron (Carter et al., 1971; Sieker et al., 1972).

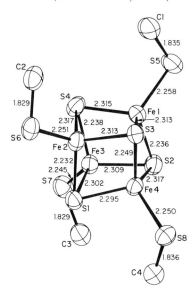

Fig. 14. Structure of the iron–sulfur cluster of $[(C_2H_5)_4N][Fe_4S_4(SCH_2C_6H_5)_4]$. Reproduced by permission (Herskovitz et al., 1972).

Magnetic susceptibility, Mössbauer, NMR, photoelectron spectroscopic, and optical spectral studies have established the close electronic
and magnetic similarities between the Fe_4S_4 clusters of the oxidized forms
of the bacterial ferredoxins, the reduced form of HIPIP and the
$[Fe_4S_4(SR)_4]^{2-}$ anions (Herskovitz et al., 1972). For example, in Fig.
15 the temperature dependence to 4°K of the magnetic susceptibility of
$[Fe_4S_4(SCH_2C_6H_5)_4]^{2-}$ indicates the four iron atoms to be antiferromagnetically spin exchange coupled. Magnetic susceptibility studies of the
oxidized forms of the ferredoxins from C. pasteurianum (Poe et al., 1970)
and C. acidi-urici (Poe et al., 1971) in aqueous solution suggest antiferromagnetic spin exchange coupling between component iron atoms. The
magnetic moments per iron atom of the anion and those of the two bacterial ferredoxins are very similar (1.05 μ_B) at room temperature. This
correspondence between magnetic properties appears to be a most delicate
reflection of the basic similarities of electronic structures of the synthetic
and naturally occurring Fe_4S_4 clusters.

The temperature dependence of the CH_2 proton resonance of

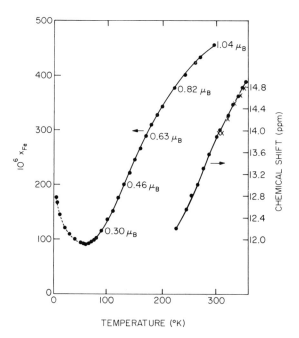

Fig. 15. Temperature dependences of the magnetic susceptibility and methylene
proton resonance of $[(C_2H_5)_4N][Fe_4S_4(SCH_2C_6H_5)_4]$. Reproduced by permission
(Herskowitz et al., 1972). Effective magnetic moments per iron atom are indicated
at selected temperatures.

$[Fe_4S_4(SCH_2C_6H_5)_4]^{2-}$ in solution over the range of $-48°$ to $+77°C$ is plotted in Fig. 15. It is seen that the resonance is displaced to low field with increasing temperature, and, in fact, the temperature dependence of the resonance parallels rather well that of the magnetic susceptibility. In addition, the CH_2 proton resonance of $[Fe_4S_4(SCH_2C_6H_5)_4]^{2-}$ falls near the centers of gravity of the resonances attributed to β-CH_2 protons of cysteinyl residues subject to contact shift perturbation for the oxidized forms of the ferredoxins from *C. pasteurianum* (Fig. 6) and *C. acidi-urici* (Poe *et al.*, 1971); temperature dependences of the positions of resonances of the CH_2 protons of the anion and those assigned to the β-CH_2 cysteinyl protons of the oxidized forms of the bacterial ferredoxins also are similar. Similar parallels are evident from comparison of positions and temperature dependences of the CH_2 proton resonance of $[Fe_4S_4(SCH_2C_6H_5)_4]^{2-}$ and the resonances attributed to β-CH_2 protons of cysteine residues of the *reduced* form of the high-potential iron protein from *Chromatium* (Fig. 13).

On the basis of the X-ray, magnetic susceptibility, and NMR evidence (as well as Mössbauer and optical spectral evidence that is discussed in the original literature) (Herskovitz *et al.*, 1972), it appears that a striking structural and electronic similarity exists between the Fe_4S_4 clusters of the synthetic anions $[Fe_4S_4(SR)_4]^{2-}$ and those of the oxidized forms of the bacterial ferredoxins and the reduced form of HIPIP. The anion undergoes both one-electron oxidation and one-electron reduction, although to date neither of these two latter forms have proven sufficiently stable for isolation and characterization (Herskovitz *et al.*, 1972). Nevertheless, at this stage it would seem reasonable to expect that the *reduced* form of the anion will resemble the *reduced* form of the bacterial ferredoxins, and the *oxidized* form of the anion will resemble the *oxidized* form of HIPIP.

On the basis of the above, it is instructive to consider the formal valence status of the four component iron atoms of the synthetic analogue. Formally, the charge on the anion would be accounted for by the presence of two ferric and two ferrous irons. However, the X-ray, Mössbauer, NMR, and photoelectron spectroscopic results concur in assigning a structural and electronic equivalence to the four iron atoms of the analogue (Herskovitz *et al.*, 1972). A better description might then be four ferric ions and two more or less delocalized, spin-paired electrons. Reduction of the analogue, and, presumably, the Fe_4S_4 clusters of the bacterial ferredoxins, would simply increase the number of delocalized electrons to three; oxidation of the analogue and, presumably, also the Fe_4S_4 cluster of the reduced form of HIPIP, would result in a decrease of the number of delocalized electrons from two to one. In this connection, the qualitative resemblance between the contact-shifted spectra of the reduced bacterial ferredoxins (Fig. 9) and the oxidized HIPIP (Fig. 12) is worth noting.

VII. ^{13}C NMR STUDIES OF *C. acidi-urici* FERREDOXIN

A striking feature of the bacterial ferredoxins is that of the 55 (or 54) amino acid residues, only two are aromatic, and these generally are phenylalanine or tyrosine. From their X-ray studies, Sieker *et al.* located each of the two tyrosine residues of the ferredoxin from *M. aerogenes* adjacent to faces of each of the two component Fe_4S_4 clusters (Sieker *et al.*, 1972). The ferredoxin from *C. acidi-urici* contains also two tyrosine residues, and because of similarities of sequence and electronic properties with the ferredoxin from *M. aerogenes*, the two tyrosine residues of the ferredoxin from *C. acidi-urici* probably are similarly positioned with respect to two Fe_4S_4 clusters. Strong evidence for this as well as an indication that aromatic residues may be involved in the redox reactions of the ferredoxins derive from a recent ^{13}C NMR study of *C. acidi-urici* ferredoxin.

Packer, Sternlicht, and Rabinowitz have examined the ^{13}C NMR spectra of both oxidized and reduced (partially) forms of the ferredoxin from *C. acidi-urici* (Packer *et al.*, 1972). ^{13}C NMR spectra of proteins generally are badly overlapped, but the ^{13}C resonances of the phenyl carbon atoms of the two tyrosine residues of the ferredoxin appear in a window of the spectrum where resonances of saturated carbon atoms are absent. Upon reduction, the ^{13}C resonances of the 2′, 6′-ring carbon atoms of both tyrosine residues of the protein are shifted substantially down field. This shift was attributed to a contact interaction origin. On the basis of these results, it was not possible to decide whether the observed ^{13}C shifts derived from pseudocontact interaction, hyperfine contact interaction, or a combination of the two. If hyperfine contact interaction is at least a contributing factor, implying spin density transfer from the Fe_4S_4 clusters to the tyrosine rings, an important clue may be at hand with regard to the mechanism of electron transport in the bacterial ferredoxins (Packer *et al.*, 1972).

VIII. TWO-IRON FERREDOXINS

Aspects of the PMR spectra of the two-iron ferredoxins from plant sources are discussed in Chapter 8 of this volume and will not be detailed further here.

IX. VALIDITY OF THE PMR RESULTS

Physical studies of the iron–sulfur proteins have been plagued by the relatively low temporal and thermal stabilities of the molecules, particularly in unfrozen aqueous solution. Even with the active participation of biochemists, results of physical studies frequently have been misleading because of at least partial decomposition of the protein to apoprotein and "adventitious" iron prior to or during the course of a physical measurement. Because of the relative ease of oxidation and reduction of these materials, failure to maintain given redox states sometimes has led to difficulties unsuspected during the course of an experiment.

In many respects, PMR studies of the iron–sulfur proteins are made under conditions least likely to ensure integrity of the molecular species and its redox state, namely, in aqueous solution and at temperatures in the 4° to about 50°C range. Frequently the samples must be maintained at temperature for an hour or longer to permit signal-to-noise enhancement of the weak, broad contact-shifted resonances. Even though applications of PMR spectroscopy to the iron–sulfur proteins are at an early stage, it is fair to consider validities of claims that given sets of experimental results can be associated with particular intact molecular species in assumed redox states.

Hong and Rabinowitz recently have carried out extensive studies of the reconstitution of apoferredoxin from $C.$ $acidi$-$urici$ to the ferredoxin, and the decomposition of $C.$ $acidi$-$urici$ ferredoxin in the presence of the iron chelating agent α, α'-bipyridyl (Hong and Rabinowitz, 1970). From the reconstitution experiments carried out in the presence of limiting amounts of sulfide or iron, they arrived at the important conclusion that no ferredoxin molecules containing less than full complements of eight iron and eight sulfur atoms were formed in substantial quantities. Similarly, in the presence of α, α'-bipyridyl, the reduced eight-iron ferredoxin appeared to decompose to the apoferredoxin without appreciable buildup of intermediate states with iron complements of one to seven atoms (Hong and Rabinowitz, 1970).

From PMR studies, we concur completely in the "all or nothing" nature of the decomposition process of the eight iron ferredoxins from $C.$ $acidi$-$urici$ and $C.$ $pasteurianum$. Distinctly different and characteristic contact shift spectra are observed for each of the oxidized and reduced forms of these two ferredoxins. For freshly prepared solutions of ferredoxins with absorbance ratios (A_{390}/A_{280}) indicating preparations of the highest quality, integrated intensities of resolved contact-shifted resonances correspond to single protons per ferredoxin molecule. At intermediate stages of reduction, corresponding to less than a two-electron transfer per ferredoxin molecule, "averaged" spectra intermediate between those of the fully oxidized and fully reduced ferredoxin are observed. As was discussed earlier, this averaging reflects "fast" intermolecular electron exchange. Once the titration with dithionite is complete, further additions of the reducing agent are without effect on the PMR spectrum of reduced ferredoxin. Upon exposing the sample of reduced ferredoxin to air, the contact shift spectrum of the oxidized form is reestablished, usually with an overall decrease in intensity and a dramatically increased paramagnetic susceptibility. The redox cycle of the ferredoxins can be accomplished a number of times, each cycle being accompanied with the same spectral changes indicated above, including the diminution in overall intensity of the contact-shifted resonances and increase in paramagnetic susceptibility.

The contact-shift spectra reviewed earlier for the various iron–sulfur proteins are reversible in temperature with respect to numbers, positions and *relative* intensities of resolved contact-shifted resonances. There is, however, an overall decrease in absolute intensity of the contact-shifted resonances with time. In this connection it is important to note that as the contact-shifted resonances decrease in overall intensity, new resolved contact-shifted resonances do not appear.

The above observations on defined PMR contact shift spectra for the oxidized and reduced forms of the eight-iron clostridial ferredoxins and effects of redox cycling and prolonged exposure to temperatures above 0°C on overall spectral intensities apply equally to the two-iron plant ferredoxins and the four-iron *Chromatium* HIPIP.

Resolution of contact-shifted resonances in the PMR spectra of the iron–sulfur proteins probably depends on the reduction of the effective magnetic moments of the iron atoms through antiferromagnetic exchange coupling. Where such exchange coupling is not present, as in the one-iron rubredoxin, the widths of the few contact-shifted resonances that are observed are so broad as to be almost undetectable. Thus, the all-or-nothing loss in intensity of the contact-shift resonances of the iron–sulfur proteins as the protein decomposes appears attributable to a cooperative destruction of exchange coupling between component iron atoms. It cannot be determined from the PMR results alone whether the destruction of exchange coupling on decomposition in turn implies a cooperative release of iron from the protein or whether the iron remains at least partially bound to the protein, but in a high spin state. It does not appear, however, from the PMR results that once the iron–sulfur moieties of the clostridial ferredoxins and the *Chromatium* HIPIP starts to come apart that any appreciable concentrations of lower, exchange-coupled species exist. Such species presumably would give rise to different but detectable contact-shift spectra.

It does appear clear, therefore, from the PMR results to date that readily identifiable and characteristic contact shift spectra can be obtained for both redox forms of the two-, four-, and eight-iron ferredoxins. Because of the unique resonance characteristics conferred by the exchange coupling of the component iron atoms, the experimental results would seem to be relatively free of artifacts arising from degradation and the presence of "adventitious" iron.

REFERENCES

Bartle, K. D., Jones, D. W., and Maricic, S., (1968). *Croatica Chemica Acta* **40**, 227.

Bartsch, R. G. (1963). *In* "Bacterial Photosynthesis" (H. Gest, A. San Pietro, and L. P. Vernon, eds.), p. 315. Antioch Press, Yellow Springs, Ohio.

Bernal, I., Rieger, P. H., and Fraenkel, G. K. (1962). *J. Chem. Phys.* **37**, 1489.

Bloembergen, N., and Morgan, L. O. (1961). *J. Chem. Phys.* **34**, 842.

Bloembergen, N., Purcell, E. M., and Pound, R. V. (1948). *Phys. Rev.* **73**, 679.

Carter, C. W., Jr., Freer, S. T., Xuong, Ng. H., Alden, R. A., and Krant, J. (1971). *Cold Spring Harbor Symp. Quant. Biol.* **36**, 381.

Chesnut, D. B. (1958). *J. Chem. Phys.* **29**, 43.

de Boer, E., and van Willigen, H. (1967). *Progr. Nucl. Magn. Resonance Spectrosc.* **2**, 111.

Dickinson, W. C., (1951). *Phys. Rev.* **81**, 717.

Dus, K., De Klerk, H., Sletten, K., and Bartsch, R. G. (1967). *Biochem. Biophys. Acta* **140**, 291.

Eaton, W. A., and Lovenberg, W. (1970). *J. Amer. Chem. Soc.* **92**, 7195.

Eaton, D. R., and Phillips, W. D. (1965). *Advan. Magn. Res.* **1**, 103.

Eaton, D. R., Josey, A. D., and Benson, R. E. (1967). *J. Amer. Chem. Soc.* **89**, 4040.

Glickson, J. D., McDonald, C. C., and Phillips, W. D., (1969). *Biochem. Biophys. Res. Commun.* **35**, 492.

Herriott, J. R., Sieker, L. C., Jensen, L. H., and Lovenberg, W. (1970). *J. Mol. Biol.* **50**, 391.

Herskovitz, T., Averill, B. A., Holm, R. H., Ibers, J. A., Phillips, W. D., and Weiher, J. F. (1972). *Proc. Nat. Acad. Sci. U.S.* **69**, 2437.

Hong, J. S., and Rabinowitz, J. C. (1970). *J. Biol. Chem.* **245**, 4982.

Hong, J. S., and Rabinowitz, J. C. (1970). *J. Biol. Chem.* **245**, 6574, 6582.

Horrocks, W. D., Taylor, R. C., and LaMar, G. N. (1964). *J. Amer. Chem. Soc.* **86**, 3031.

Johnson, C. E., Rao, K. K., Cammack, R., Evans, M. C. W., and Hall, D. O. (1970). *Abstracts, Int. Conf. Magn. Resonance Biolog. Syst., 4th, Oxford, U.K.*

Knight, W. D. (1949). *Phys. Rev.* **76**, 1259.

Lovenberg, W., and Sobel, B. E. (1965). *Proc. Nat. Acad. Sci. U.S.* **54**, 193.

Lovenberg, W., Buchanan, B. B., and Rabinowitz, J. C. (1963). *J. Biol. Chem.* **238**, 3899.

McConnell, H. M., and Chesnut, D. B. (1958). *J. Chem. Phys.* **28**, 107.

McConnell, H. M., and Robertson, R. E. (1958). *J. Chem. Phys.* **29**, 136.

McDonald, C. C., and Phillips, W. D. (1969). *Biochem. Biophys. Res. Commun.* **35**, 43.

McDonald, C. C., and Phillips, W. D. (1969). *J. Amer. Chem. Soc.* **91**, 1513.

McDonald, C. C., and Phillips, W. D. (1970). *Biolog. Macromol.* **4**, 1.

McDonald, C. C., Phillips, W. D., and Glickson, J. D., (1971). *J. Amer. Chem. Soc.* **93**, 235.

McLachlan, A. D. (1958). *Mol. Phys.* **1**, 233.

Mortenson, L. E., Valentine, R. C., and Carnahan, J. E., (1962). *Biochem. Biophys. Res. Commun.* **7**, 448.

Moss, T. H., Petering, D., and Palmer, G., (1969). *J. Biol. Chem.* **244**, 2275.

Orme-Johnson, W. H., and Beinert, H. (1969a). *Biochem. Biophys. Res. Commun.* **36**, 337.

Orme-Johnson, W. H., and Beinert, H. (1969b). *J. Biol. Chem.* **244**, 6143.

Overhauser, A. W. (1953a). *Phys. Rev.* **91**, 476.

Overhauser, A. W. (1953b). *Phys. Rev.* **92**, 411 (1953).

Packer, E. L., Sternlicht, H., and Rabinowitz, J. C. (1972). *Proc. Nat. Acad. Sci U.S.* **69**, 3278.

Palmer, G., Sands, R. H., and Mortenson, L. E. (1966). *Biochem. Biophys. Res. Commun.* **23**, 357.

Palmer, G., Brintzinger, H., Estabrook, R. W., and Sands, R. H. (1967). *In* "Magnetic Resonance in Biological Systems" (A. Ehrenberg, B. G. Malmstrom, and T. Vanngard, eds.), p. 159. Pergamon, Oxford.

Patel, D. J., Kampa, L., Shulman, R. G., Yamane, T., and Fujiwara, M. (1970). *Biochem. Biophys. Res. Commun.* **40**, 1224.

Phillips, W. D., and Poe, M. (1972). *In* "Methods in Enzymology" (A. San Pietro, ed.), Part B, Vol. XXIV, p. 304. Academic Press, New York.

Phillips, W. D., Poe, M., Weiher, J. F., McDonald, C. C., and Lovenberg, W. (1970a). *Nature (London)* **227**, 574.

Phillips, W. D., Poe, M., McDonald, C. C., and Bartsch, R. G. (1970b). *Proc. Nat. Acad. Sci. U.S.* **67**, 682.

Poe, M., Phillips, W. D., McDonald, C. C., and Lovenberg, W. (1970). *Proc. Nat. Acad. Sci. U.S.* **65**, 797.

Poe, M., Phillips, W. D., McDonald, C. C., and Orme-Johnson, W. H., (1971). *Biochem. Biophys. Res. Commun.* **42**, 705.

Rall, S. C., Bolinger, R. E., and Cole, R. D., (1969). *Biochemistry* **8**, 2486.

Roberts, G. C. K., and Jardetzky, O. (1970). *Advan. Protein Chem.* **24**, 447.

Schunn, R. A., Fritchie, C. J., Jr., and Prewitt, C. T. (1966). *Inorg. Chem.* **5**, 892.

Sieker, L. C., Adman, E., and Jensen, L. H. (1972). *Nature (London)* **235**, 40.

Stone, E. W., and Maki, A. H. (1967). *J. Chem. Phys.* **37**, 1326.

Wei, C. H., Wilkes, G. R., Treichel, P. M., and Dahl, L. F. (1966). *Inorg. Chem.* **5**, 900.

Wüthrich, K. (1970). *Structure Bonding* **8**, 53.

CHAPTER 8

Current Insights into the Active Center of Spinach Ferredoxin and Other Iron–Sulfur Proteins

GRAHAM PALMER

The preceding chapters of Volumes I and II of this treatise are ample testimony to the intense interest and imaginative experimentation that has been generated by the iron–sulfur proteins. This phenomenon has its origins in two diverse circumstances. First, and foremost, it is abundantly clear that the iron–sulfur proteins are vital constituents of many fundamental biochemical processes. Second, they have proved to be particularly amenable to investigation by physicochemical techniques (see Chapters 9 and 10 in Volume I and Chapters 1–7 of Volume II), and the anticipation that the active site(s) of these proteins are polynuclear clusters of iron and sulfur has stimulated the imagination not only of the biochemist, but of inorganic chemists working in the areas of metal–metal bonds and "sulfur-rich" iron–dithiolene chemistry (McCleverty, 1968) and of physicists interested in applying the powerful new spectroscopic techniques to biological problems.

The simplest of the iron–sulfur proteins are those that contain only one iron atom, that is, the rubredoxins, and these are also the best understood members of this class, for not only do we have an X-ray structure for one rubredoxin (see Chapter 4 of this volume), but, in addition, the spectroscopic and magnetic properties of iron in environments such as found in rubredoxins have been thoroughly investigated on low molecular weight compounds and other proteins (Blumberg, 1967).

The basic geometry of rubredoxin is depicted in structure I; the detailed chemical and physical properties of rubredoxin are discussed in Chapter 3 of this volume, and it is assumed the reader is familiar with the contents

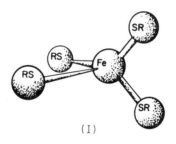

(I)

of that chapter. For our purposes, oxidized rubredoxin can be considered as a high-spin ($S = \frac{5}{2}$) ferric ion coordinated to four cysteine sulfur atoms tetrahedrally disposed with respect to the metal atom. On reduction the iron is converted to the ferrous high-spin ($S = \frac{4}{2}$) state with little or no change in coordination geometry. We will assume that the tetrahedron with a sulfur atom at each vertex and an iron atom in the middle is the basic unit of the iron–sulfur proteins and that the active centers of the poly-iron proteins are aggregates of these tetrahedra sharing either an edge or a face. The sulfur atoms, which occur at the vertices of the tetrahedra, may be contributed either completely by cysteine residues, as in rubredoxin, or by a combination of cysteine residues and labile sulfides: in the latter case the sulfide ions are presumed to function as ligands bridging adjacent metal irons. These structural features have been documented with two iron–sulfur proteins: the high-potential protein from *Chromatium* (Carter *et al.*, 1972) and the eight-iron ferredoxin from *M. aerogenes* (Sieker *et al.*, 1972) (see below). The simplest example of these principles is structure II which is a popular model for the structure of the active center of spinach ferredoxin (Brintzinger *et al.*, 1966). It consists of two tetrahedra sharing an edge, the common bridging atoms being labile sulfides, whereas the exterior sulfur atoms are designated as originating from cysteine. Much of this chapter will be devoted to examining to what extent structure II is consistent with the available physical and chemical data.

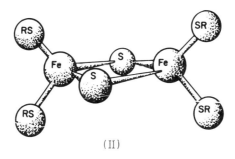

(II)

The outstanding physical consequence of this aggregation of iron and sulfur is the potential for antiferromagnetic interactions between the metal ions. The nature of this interaction will be foreign to most biochemists, and thus the first part of this chapter is devoted to a discussion of this phenomenon in terms of a simple model with emphasis on the consequences of the antiferromagnetic coupling on the physical properties of the active centers of these proteins.

I. EXCHANGE INTERACTIONS AND ANTIFERROMAGNETIC COUPLING

The exchange interaction is a mysterious, quantum-mechanical phenomenon that, formally, is a consequence of the requirement that molecular wave functions conform to certain symmetry conditions. In effect the electrons on adjacent atoms are constrained so that they can only occupy the same space if their spins are antiparallel, a constraint which will be familiar from the application of the Pauli exclusion principle in assigning electrons to the atomic orbitals of the elements of the Periodic Table and to the molecular orbitals of polyatomic species.

The relevance of this phenomenon and the mechanism by which it leads to antiferromagnetic coupling may best be appreciated by a simple example. Figure 1 depicts the symmetry relationships between metal ion d orbitals and ligand p orbitals for a linear (180°) metal–ligand–metal system. The $p_\sigma(p_x)$ orbital of the ligand has a finite overlap with $d_{x^2-y^2}$ on each metal atom but is orthogonal (zero net overlap) with the respective d_{xy} orbitals. On the other hand, the p_π orbital (p_y) has some overlap with

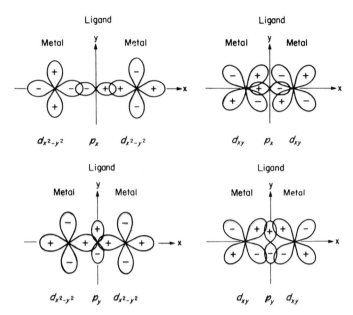

Fig. 1. Diagrammatic representation of overlap patterns between d (metal) orbitals and p (ligand) orbitals.

d_{xy} but is orthogonal to $d_{x^2-y^2}$ (note that by symmetry d_{z^2} and $d_{x^2-y^2}$ behave the same, as do d_{xy}, d_{xz}, and d_{yz}).

We can use these symmetry relations to understand what can happen in the system Fe^{3+}—O^{2-}—Fe^{3+}, with the iron in the high-spin octahedral state.

The formation of a bond between the O^{2-} and say the Fe^{3+} on the left of Fig. 2, involving the p_σ orbital and $d_{x^2-y^2}$, requires some transfer of a p_σ

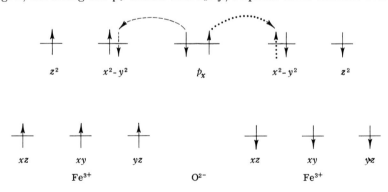

Fig. 2. Diagrammatic representation of the superexchange mechanism.

electron into the $d_{x^2-y^2}$ orbital. However, by the Pauli principle, the transferred electron will be oriented antiparallel to the five $3d$ electrons of the Fe^{3+} on the left. This p electron is strongly coupled to the second p_σ electron which is then forced to be parallel to the d electrons of the left-hand Fe^{3+}. But this second p electron is partially transferred, via bonding, into the $d_{x_2-y_2}$ orbital of the right-hand Fe^{3+}, "forcing" the five $3d$ electrons of this iron atom to be antiparallel to the second p electron and hence also antiparallel to the electrons on the first (left-hand) iron atom. We thus have a coupling of the electrons spins of the two iron atoms so that they are antiparallel to each other. This antiparallel coupling is called antiferromagnetic exchange, and in this instance the interaction was transmitted via the bonding electrons of the intervening ligand. The above linear arrangement is called 180° exchange; when there are two bridging ligands, e.g., as in structure II, which should exhibit a Fe—L—Fe angle of about 90°, then we have 90° exchange. With 90° exchange and tetrahedral geometry about each metal ion, the overlap pattern of metal and ligand orbitals becomes quite complicated, and a visual representation is not readily communicated (for more examples of this kind, see Martin, 1968).

TABLE I

CONSEQUENCE OF ANTIFERROMAGNETIC EXCHANGE INTERACTION ON THE
MAGNETIC AND OPTICAL PROPERTIES OF IRON-SULFUR PROTEINS

Parameter measured	Technique	Physical consequence	Experimental implication
g Tensor	EPR	Measured g value weighted sum of g values of each iron atom	None (without additional information)
A Tensor	EPR, ENDOR, Mössbauer	A tensor of ferric and ferrous ions have opposite sign	Antiferromagnetic coupling established
Bulk susceptibility	Magnetic susceptibility	Non-Curie behavior observed	Antiferromagnetic coupling established; J determined
Contact-shifted proton resonances	PMR	Ferric protons have different temperature dependence from ferrous protons	Discriminates ferric and ferrous protons
Visible spectrum	Optical spectroscopy	Possible enhancement of intensity of d–d transitions	Independent measure of J? Identification of d–d bands

The strength of the exchange interaction can vary over a wide range depending on the chemistry of the system. For compounds of the form Fe^{3+}—O^{2-}—Fe^{3+} this energy of interaction (called J) is fairly large, about 0.3 kcal (100 cm^{-1}); thus the energy of interaction is small compared to typical bonding energies, about 100 kcal, but large compared with the energies associated with the magnetic properties of the electron (1 cal). Consequently, in systems which exhibit antiferromagnetic coupling, one anticipates very substantial modifications of those physical quantities which are associated with electron magnetism and hence to observe rather unusual behavior in those techniques which measure these quantities (e.g., EPR, ENDOR, Mössbauer, magnetic susceptibility). Conversely, phenomena associated with higher energies, e.g., optical spectroscopy should, in the first approximation, be unaffected by the exchange interaction. These considerations are outlined in Table I and will be discussed in detail.

II. CONSEQUENCES OF THE EXCHANGE INTERACTION

A. Magnetic Susceptibility

In the limit of a large exchange interaction, the system (Fig. 2) that formally contains two Fe^{3+} ions and a total of ten unpaired electrons is actually diamagnetic, for the magnetic moment of each iron atom is equal in magnitude but opposite in sign to the other. However this interaction can be broken down by thermal energies (room temperature = 0.6 kcal), and at temperatures very much greater than J the two irons are maximally decoupled and one will detect magnetism close to that of ten unpaired electrons. However, the totally coupled ($S = 0$) and totally uncoupled ($S = \frac{10}{2}$) configurations are not the only magnetic states allowed. Rather, quantum mechanics teaches us that there is a ladder of states available to the coupled system which runs from $S_1 + S_2(=\frac{10}{2})$ to $S_1 - S_2(=0)$ in steps of unity, that is, the available states are 0, 1, 2, 3, 4, and 5 (Fig. 3). (S_1 and S_2 are the spin states of the two separated iron atoms.) In the antiferromagnetic case, the state represented by $S = (S_1 - S_2) = 0$ has the lowest energy, whereas the states with $S = 1, 2, 3, 4,$ and 5 are at $2J, 6J, 12J, 20J,$ and $30J$ to higher energy.*†

---

* There is no general agreement on the formalism used to describe exchange interactions. The quantum-mechanical representation is of the form $-2J\ S_1 \cdot S_2$, and this is the form generally used in the work on iron–sulfur proteins. If the value of $J < 0$ then the systems behave antiferromagnetically; the value of the exchange energy J that is reported is one-half the separation to the first excited state that is at $2J$ in this example. Further complications arise because some chemists and physicists pre-

$$\frac{S = 5}{} E = 30\,J_{ox}$$

$$\frac{S = 9/2}{} E = 24\,J_{red}$$

$$\frac{S = 4}{} 20\,J_{ox}$$

$$\frac{S = 7/2}{} 15\,J_{red}$$

$$\frac{S = 3}{} 12\,J_{ox}$$

$$\frac{S = 5/2}{} 8\,J_{red}$$

$$\frac{S = 2}{} 6\,J_{ox}$$

$$\frac{S = 1}{} 2\,J_{ox}$$

$$\frac{S = 3/2}{} 3\,J_{red}$$

$$\frac{S = 0}{} 0$$

$$\frac{S = 1/2}{}$$

$$S_1 = 5/2 \sim S_2 = 5/2 \qquad\qquad S_1 = 5/2 \sim S_2 = 4/2$$

Fig. 3. Ladder of magnetic substates produced as a result of antiferromagnetic coupling of two high-spin ferric ions (oxidized spinach ferredoxin) (left-hand side) and one high-spin ferric ion with a high-spin ferrous ion (reduced spinach ferredoxin) (right-hand side). Each substate is associated with an effective or resultant spin (S) and is located at an energy nJ above the lowest state. J_{ox} and J_{red} are used to emphasize the fact that the magnitude of J is usually different in the two cases.

At very low temperatures ($T \ll J$) all of the molecules will be found in the state of lowest S (0 and $\frac{1}{2}$, respectively, for the examples in Fig. 3) and exhibit the magnetic properties of that state. As the temperature approaches J, an increasing number of molecules populate the higher excited states, and the observed magnetic properties then have contributions from all occupied states, the contribution from each state being determined by its intrinsic magnetism weighted by the fraction of molecules in that state. Because the fraction of molecules in each state is a continuously varying function of temperature, the magnetic properties vary

---

fer to replace $2J$ by J or to drop the minus sign. It is consequently crucial to establish which convention is in use when reading the literature on exchange interactions.

† The energy of each of the spin states relative to the lowest is given by $-J[S(S + 1)]$ where S is the total spin of each state. With J negative the relative energies for $S = 0, 1, 2, 3, 4$, and 5 are 0, $2J$, $6J$, $12J$, $20J$, and $30J$, respectively. When $S_1 = \frac{5}{2}$, $S_2 = \frac{4}{2}$ (e.g., reduced spinach ferredoxin), S can take the values $\frac{1}{2}$, $\frac{3}{2}$, $\frac{5}{2}$, $\frac{7}{2}$, and $\frac{9}{2}$ and the relative energies are 0, $3J$, $8J$, $15J$, and $24J$, respectively (Fig. 3).

in manner different from that exhibited by a system with a well-defined electron spin.

B. Electron Paramagnetic Resonance

This anomalous behavior is not confined to the bulk magnetic susceptibility. Thus, for instance, the very characteristic electron paramagnetic resonance (EPR) spectrum that one observes with reduced spinach ferredoxin is completely unexpected for a mononuclear iron species but can very easily be understood on the basis of a ferric and ferrous species coupled antiferromagnetically (Gibson et al., 1966), and, indeed, all of the magnetic methods give curious results which can be rationalized rather simply in terms of this model.

An alternative physical picture, and one which is useful for understanding the spectroscopic ramifications of this process, can be formulated in a manner analogous to the Landé coupling scheme of atomic spectroscopy whereby orbital (L) and spin (S) angular momenta are coupled to yield a total angular moment J. It is convenient to develop this model in terms of the magnetic moments μ of the spin system, where $\mu = g|\mathbf{S}|$ [in units of μ_β (the Bohr magneton)].* When the magnetic moments of high-spin ferric $(g_1|\mathbf{S}_1|)$ and high-spin ferrous $(g_2|\mathbf{S}_2|)$ are coupled antiferromagnetically, the resultant moment is $g|\mathbf{S}|$, and it is this quantity that is observed by EPR, for example. However, it is in the nature of this coupling that S has contributions from both S_1 and S_2 as illustrated in Fig. 4 in which the antiferromagnetic coupling of S_1 and S_2 are represented as a precession of the two spin moments about a common axis, the direction of S, at a frequency J ($\sim 10^{13}$ Hz for $J = 100$ cm^{-1}). In this way S_1 and S_2 generate cones of different heights and amplitudes and of opposite orientation. The heights of these cones represent the respective contribution of S_1 or S_2 to S. For the ground state of reduced spinach ferredoxin $(S = \frac{1}{2})$, S_1 contributes $\frac{7}{3}|\mathbf{S}|$,* while S_2 contributes $-\frac{4}{3}g_2|\mathbf{S}|$, the minus sign being an obvious reflection of the fact that S_2 is antiparallel to S_1 (Fig. 4).

Because of the precessional motion of S_1 and S_2, the magnetic moments of these spins can be separated into two parts, the components parallel to and thus contributing to S, and the components perpendicular to S. The perpendicular components of both S_1 and S_2 average to zero over one cycle around the cone and thus *cannot be observed by experiment*, and it is only the components of S_1 and S_2 parallel to S that we can observe experimentally. In an applied magnetic field, S precesses around H at a much lower frequency (10^{10} Hz at 3 kG). However, the energy of the Zeeman interaction is very small (1 cal) and cannot break the coupling between

---

* $|\mathbf{S}| = [S(S + 1)]^{1/2}$ is the magnitude of the quantum-mechanical vector **S**.

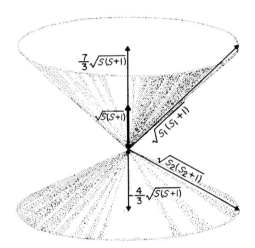

Fig. 4. Vector coupling of two spins S_1 and S_2 with magnitude $S_1(S_1 + 1)^{1/2}$ and $S_2(S_2 + 1)^{1/2}$ to yield a resultant S of magnitude $S(S + 1)^{1/2}$. Note that the projection of S_1 along the direction of S is parallel to S, whereas the direction of S_2 is antiparallel to S. The contribution of S_1 to S is $\frac{7}{3}[S(S + 1)^{1/2}]$, and of S_2 is $-\frac{4}{3}S[(S + 1)^{1/2}]$.

S_1 and S_2. Consequently, S_1 and S_2 precess rapidly about S which is itself slowly precessing about $\mathbf{H}$; thus our double cone of Fig. 4 also executes precessional motion about the applied field.

In an EPR experiment, one observes $g|\mathbf{S}|$ and indirectly $g_1|\mathbf{S}_1|$ and $g_2|\mathbf{S}_2|$; in fact

$$g|\mathbf{S}| = \tfrac{7}{3}g_1|\mathbf{S}| - \tfrac{4}{3}g_2|\mathbf{S}| \qquad \text{and} \qquad g = \tfrac{7}{3}g_1 - \tfrac{4}{3}g_2.$$

If the g value is anisotropic, $g_x = \tfrac{7}{3}g_{1_x} - \tfrac{4}{3}g_{2_x}$,* etc.; however, without additional information, one cannot determine g_1 and g_2 separately (see Chapter 5 of this volume for a more formal presentation of this topic).

C. ENDOR and Mössbauer

In an applied magnetic field (H), the total spin S is aligned along H and thus the unpaired electrons on the Fe^{3+} (S_1) are also aligned along H (Fig. 4). Consequently, the Fe^{2+} electrons are aligned against H. These unpaired electrons produce a magnetic field at their own nucleus, the so-called hyperfine interaction,† and it, therefore, follows that the field at

* The coefficient $\tfrac{7}{3}$ is obtained by simply evaluating the component of $\mathbf{S}_1$ along $\mathbf{S}$; in vector notation $= \mathbf{S}_1 \cdot \mathbf{S} = (\mathbf{S}^2 + \mathbf{S}_1{}^2 - \mathbf{S}_2{}^2)/2\mathbf{S}^2$, where $\mathbf{S}^2 = S(S + 1)$. For $\mathbf{S}_2 \cdot \mathbf{S} = -\tfrac{4}{3}$, simply interchange the subscripts.

† The existence of hyperfine structure in EPR spectra is due to the presence of a (hyperfine) magnetic field produced at a nucleus by its unpaired electron. One d elec-

the ferric nucleus is of opposite sign to that at the ferrous nucleus. Both
the magnitude and sign of these fields can be established from a combination of ENDOR and Mössbauer experiments, and a demonstration that
the hyperfine fields at the two iron nuclei are of opposite sign is direct
proof that the iron atoms are coupled antiferromagnetically.

D. NMR Contact Shifts

In Chapter 7 of this volume, devoted to the PMR of iron–sulfur proteins, Phillips and Poe have described the phenomenon called the "contact
shift" by which proton resonances are observed at abnormal positions
because the paramagnetism of the material results in a small amount
of unpaired spin density from the paramagnetic center being present at
the proton in question. The position of the observed lines (σ) thus has
two contributions, the normal diamagnetic contribution (σ_D) and the
paramagnetic one (σ_p).

$$\sigma = \sigma_D + \sigma_p$$

The paramagnetic contribution is the product of two terms, A, the hyperfine interaction between the proton nuclear moment and the magnetic
field induced at the proton by the unpaired electron spin density and,
χ, the magnetic susceptibility of the sample.

$$\sigma_p \propto A \cdot \chi$$

---

tron produces about 10^5 G worth of magnetization at its own nucleus. (Likewise if the
nucleus has a nuclear moment then it produces a magnetic field at the electron; for
^{57}Fe this is about 10 G.) The internal magnetic field H_N produced by an electron at its
own nucleus has three contributions H_C, H_D, and H_L (Johnson, 1967). H_C, often called
the core polarization (Watson and Freeman, 1961), produces an isotropic field at the
nucleus. Each unpaired d electron contributes about 10^5 G to H_C; thus for high-spin
Fe^{3+}, $H_C \approx 500$ kG. The sign of H_C is negative which means that the direction of H_C is
opposite to that of the electron magnetic moment. The magnitude of H_C may be
reduced by covalency which transfers electron spin density onto the ligands. H_D is
the magnetic field produced at the nucleus by a dipolar mechanism. It is anisotropic
and, in contrast to H_C, is characteristic of the orbital containing the unpaired electron;
this asymmetry is identical with that responsible for the electric field gradient (see
Table I in Lang, 1970). In spherical electron distributions (e.g., t^3, e^2, t^3e^2) $H_D = 0$
as is obvious from that table. H_L is the magnetic field produced by the orbital magnetism of the electron. Because this orbital magnetism is anisotropic (= anisotropic g
factor), it also produces an asymmetric hyperfine field at the nucleus. For compounds
with only a small g anisotropy the contribution of H_L is small and $H_N = H_C + H_D$.
For high-spin d^5 $H_N = H_C$. For high-spin d^6, four electrons contribute to H_C; however,
the contribution to H_D is effectively that of one electron for d^6 is one electron added
to the spherical d^5 configuration.

For normal Curie paramagnets $\chi \propto S(S + 1)/T$ and

$$\sigma_p = A \cdot S(S + 1)/T$$

Thus $\sigma = \sigma_D + \text{const} \times (A/T)$. If we know σ and σ_D, we can calculate A; alternatively, knowing σ and the dependence of σ on T, we can calculate σ_D and, in principle, identify to which class a given proton belongs.

Contact-shifted resonances can occur to both high- and low-field sides of the "normal" diamagnetic region (Chapter 7 of this volume). However, if the system follows Curie behavior, the resonances move closer *toward* the diagmagnetic region as T is increased (χ goes to zero as T approaches infinity).

The ferredoxins exhibit strikingly unusual behavior (see Chapter 7 of this volume) in that resonances exhibit both normal and anti-Curie behavior (resonances moving *away* from the diamagnetic region as T increases) which can be explained rather simply as follows (Dunham *et al.*, 1971b). We have seen (Fig. 4) that the two metal ions make qualitatively and quantitatively different contributions to the magnetic ground state ($S = \frac{1}{2}$) of the reduced protein ($\frac{7}{3}$ for the Fe^{3+}, $-\frac{4}{3}$ for the Fe^{2+}). For the excited states these contributions change; for instance, for the first excited state ($S = \frac{3}{2}$) they are $\frac{13}{15}$ and $\frac{2}{15}$ for Fe^{3+} and Fe^{2+}, respectively, and their contributions get even closer in the higher states. Thus the contribution of each iron atom to the total magnetism exhibits a complicated temperature dependence reflecting the changes in thermal population of the ladder of magnetic states, each of which has unique contributions from both the ferric and ferrous ions. These contributions are shown in Fig. 5 for relevant values of quantum mechanical parameters. The first thing to notice about the figure is the qualitatively different behavior for Fe^{3+} and Fe^{2+}, and this explains the observation of the different temperature dependencies for the different protons. This has diagnostic value, for it identifies the Fe^{3+} protons* as those that move upfield (towards 0 ppm) with increasing temperature, whereas Fe^{2+} protons are those moving downfield as the temperature is increased. The second thing to notice is that the *sign* of S_z for Fe^{2+} depends both on the value of J and on the temperature (Fig. 5). Thus if the sign of A is the same for both the Fe^{3+} and Fe^{2+}, it follows that the position of the Fe^{2+} protons can be the same as (low J, high T) or opposite to (high J, low T) the position of the Fe^{3+} protons. Using this, it is possible to obtain an approximate estimate of J. (If one accepts that the quantum-mechanical description of these iron–sulfur proteins is best provided by molecular orbitals, then it is, in principle, possible for a given proton to "feel" spin density from both the ferric

---

* The term "Fe^{3+} protons" and Fe^{2+} protons is used to mean those protons which are most affected by the paramagnetism of the Fe^{3+} ion and Fe^{2+} ions, respectively.

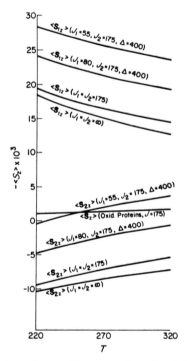

Fig. 5. Temperature dependence of the magnetism of each iron atom ($\langle S_{1_z} \rangle$, $\langle S_{2_z} \rangle$) in an antiferromagnetically coupled system. S_1 = high-spin Fe^{3+}, S_2 = high-spin Fe^{2+}. Applied field = 51.5 kG. (From Dunham *et al.*, 1971b.)

and ferrous ions, although presumably one of the metal ions will make the dominant contribution. As a consequence, estimates of J using the procedure of Fig. 5 may be somewhat in error. For an up to date discussion of this problem see La Mar *et al.*, 1973.)

E. Optical Spectra

For high-spin d^5 ions, optical transitions between the d orbitals can only occur with simultaneous pairing of electrons. This is forbidden by the selection rules for electric dipole transitions. Further, the intensity of d–d transitions are intrinsically low for reasons of symmetry (Laporte selection rule). Thus for d^5 ions the d–d transitions are extremely weak; for instance, the extinction coefficients for Mn^{2+} can be as low as 0.01 M^{-1} cm^{-1}. The antiferromagnetic exchange coupling between vicinal d^5 ions presents a mechanism for overcoming the intrinsic spin-forbidden quality of these bands (Fig. 6) (Lohr and McClure, 1968).

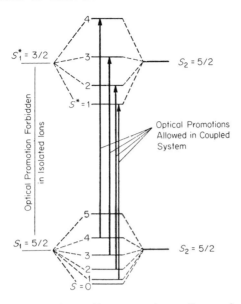

Fig. 6. A mechanism whereby antiferromagnetic coupling can increase the intensity of optical transitions which are very weak in single iron atoms.

Transitions from the $S = 1, 2, 3$, and 4 magnetic sublevels of the electronic ground state to the corresponding levels of the electronic excited state can proceed without violating the spin selection rule for the total system, and these bands should appear with an enhanced intensity. However, the distribution of molecules among the magnetic substates ($S = 0, 1, \ldots$) is determined thermally; thus by lowering the temperature low, all of the molecules will occupy the $S = 0$ state, and the allowed transitions will disappear, i.e., on lowering the temperature such bands should decrease in intensity with a temperature dependence related to the magnetic susceptibility. We are currently trying to identify these transitions.

With this background to the problem we can now consider the experimental data available on these proteins and discuss to what extent these data support one or another model for their active center. Because the detailed backgrounds to many of these experiments are discussed in previous chapters, I need only summarize the salient features of these results:

III. PHYSICAL DATA

These proteins do not exhibit any EPR in the oxidized state, but reduction elicits an intense EPR spectrum of the $g = 1.94$ type (i.e., $g_{av} < 2$,

$g_x, g_y < g_z$; Chapter 5 of this volume). The techniques of EPR and ENDOR have established that both iron atoms are components of the paramagnetic center (Chapter 5 of this volume). Likewise, by using protein in which the labile sulfide has been replaced by selenide, it has been shown that the selenide ions bear unpaired spin density, and thus probably function as ligands to the metal ion. By inference the labile sulfide plays the same role in the native protein. Both *Azotobacter vinelandii* and *Pseudomonas putida* have been grown on ^{33}S and their respective 2 Fe—S* proteins isolated. The EPR spectra of these proteins are broader than the isotopically normal proteins, and some of this broadening is produced by sulfur atoms other than the labile sulfide, that is, by either cysteine or methionine sulfur.

Oxidized spinach ferredoxin is diamagnetic from 1.4° to 77°K (Moss *et al.*, 1969); at higher temperatures it becomes increasingly paramagnetic (Palmer *et al.*, 1971) thus establishing the existence of an antiferromagnetic interaction between two equivalent spin systems (Fig. 7). The data could be fitted well assuming that the interaction was between two high-spin $(S = \frac{5}{2})$ ferric ions, with a value of -182 cm^{-1} for J, the exchange constant. With this value of J only the first two excited states $(S = 1,2)$ have appreciable occupation even at the highest temperature of the experiment, and thus an equally good fit to the data can be obtained by coupling two $S = 1$ (or $\frac{3}{2}$ or $\frac{4}{2}$) ions. Naturally the protein exhibits no EPR at low temperature and there has been no report of anyone observing EPR from one of the excited states, although this is possible (Okamura and Hoffman, 1969).

The reduced protein exhibits Curie behavior from 1.4° to 77°K (Moss *et al.*, 1969) with a slope appropriate to a $S = \frac{1}{2}$ system with the g values of spinach ferredoxin. At higher temperatures, deviations from Curie behavior are observed [Fig. 7 (Palmer *et al.*, 1971)], the paramagnetism of the protein disappearing less rapidly than is normal. Again, the data can be fitted well by assuming an antiferromagnetic interaction, this time between $S = \frac{5}{2}$ and $S = \frac{4}{2}$ ions, that is, between high-spin ferric and ferrous ions, respectively. In this instance, it is possible to introduce certain complications into the theoretical analysis. In the simplest case, a value for $J = -110$ cm^{-1} fits the data best.† However, by making allowances for complications suggested by other data, for example Mössbauer, it was concluded that J could be as small as -80 cm^{-1} (Dunham *et al*, 1971b).

The above data were all taken in the solid (frozen) state, and one might wonder what is the situation in solution at room temperature. Cer-

---

† The value is 10 cm^{-1} larger than the value originally recorded, a consequence of employing the experimental g values in the susceptibility equation (Palmer *et al.*, 1971).

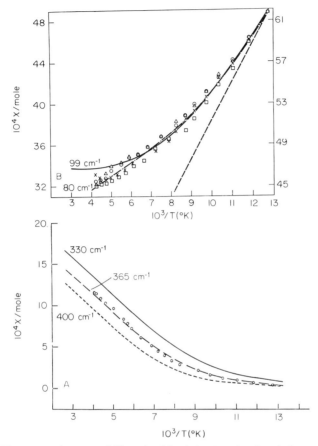

Fig. 7. The magnetic susceptibility of oxidized (top) and reduced (bottom) spinach ferredoxin. The several lines represented theoretical curves calculated according to the model of Fig. 3 using the values of J indicated. The dashed line in the bottom is the result expected for a single unpaired electron. (From Palmer *et al.*, 1971.)

tainly, both oxidized and reduced forms of the protein are paramagnetic at room temperature. This was first established by proton relaxation enhancement measurements (Mildvan *et al.*, 1967) and subsequently verified by single temperature solution susceptibility measurements (Ehrenberg, 1966) and from the observation of contact-shifted PMR (see Chapter 7 of this volume). The susceptibility measurements are the most useful to us: Ehrenberg (1966) has measured the susceptibility at room temperature of oxidized and reduced spinach ferredoxin using samples of protein prepared in the United Kingdom and the United States. The agreement between both samples was quite good, and the measured values are 1920 ± 120 and 4120 ± 200 10^{-6} cgs units/mole protein for the oxidized and reduced protein, respectively. Extrapolation of the low-temperature data (Palmer et al., 1971) to room temperature yields values of 1300×10^{-6} and 3400×10^{-6} cgs units/mole protein for the oxidized and reduce protein, respectively, which is reasonably close to Ehrenberg's data. Conversely, the values of J needed to account for the solution results are -143 cm and -85 cm^{-1}, respectively: the implication is that there is not a fundamental change in properties of the site in passing through the freezing point.

The Mössbauer results can be summarized briefly (Chapter 6 of this volume): In oxidized spinach ferredoxin, one observes a simple quadrupole doublet at all temperatures. Thus by this criterion the two iron atoms in the oxidized protein are equivalent. However, it should be appreciated that in this instance the Mössbauer parameters do not provide a stringent criterion for equivalence. Thus the isomer shift of high-spin ferric ion is very insensitive to its coordination geometry, and, consequently, the centroid of absorbtion for each iron atom should be very close together. The observation of a quadrupole doublet rather than a singlet anticipated if the high-spin Fe^{3+} were in a truly cubic (i.e., accurately octahedral or tetrahedral) environment is evidence for some distortion at each iron site. But, again, the magnitude of the quadrupole splitting is not a sensitive discriminant of the character of the distortion, and it is quite conceivable that the two iron atoms actually suffer significantly different distortions of some common geometry. Indeed, in no case has it been possible to accurately reproduce the observed Mössbauer line shape by computation (Dunham et al., 1971a; Munck et al., 1972); although the agreement between experiment and calculation is rather good, a somewhat better fit is to be expected assuming that both iron sites are identical and that no other complications exist.

For the reduced protein (Fig. 2 of Chapter 6 of this volume), the shape of the observed Mössbauer spectrum depends on the temperature of the measurement. The spectrum is easiest to interpret at high temperature when electron spin relaxation is fast enough to average away all magnetic interactions between the electron and the nucleus. Under these conditions, one observes two quadrupole pairs, a narrow pair having the same Mössbauer parameters observed in the oxidized protein and can be interpreted as one of the original iron atoms which had remained unchanged, and a very wide quadrupole pair, with Mössbauer parameters typical of high-spin ferrous iron. At very low temperatures where electron spin relaxation becomes long, the Mössbauer spectrum changes dramatically, because under these conditions the electron magnetism exerts a substantial magnetic field at the iron nucleus. The analysis of this spectrum is extremely complicated, but by using the Mössbauer parameters from the high-temperature experiment together with the EPR g values and the magnitude of the electron–nucleus interaction (**A** tensors) for each iron atom as determined by ENDOR (Fritz et al., 1971), it is possible to compute the observed spectrum. Among the free parameters in this computation are (1) the *sign* of the electric field gradient (efg), a quantity which is obtained from the quadrupole splitting and (2) the relative signs of the **A** tensors for the ferric and ferrous ions. From the sign of the efg, it can be deduced that the sixth (reducing) electron is in a d_{z^2} orbital which requires that the coordination geometry at this ion to be either tetrahedral-like or a trigonally distorted cubic structure.

ENDOR experiments on several 2 Fe—S* proteins which have been substituted with ^{57}Fe are impressively consistent (Chapter 5 of this volume). Two sets of ^{57}Fe hyperfine interactions were observed. One set is characterized by values for the hyperfine tensor which are almost equal (viz., -19, -17, and -15 G),[†] as expected for high-spin ferric ion. The hyperfine tensor for the second iron atom show three greatly different components (viz., 4, 5, and 12 G)[†]; this is characteristic of high-spin ferrous ion. The result (Dunham et al., 1971) that the signs of the **A** tensors for the ferric and ferrous ion are opposite requires that the iron atoms be coupled by an antiferromagnetic interaction as was discussed earlier: this, of course, is consistent with the magnetic susceptibility results.

IV. OPTICAL SPECTRA

The point has already been made that the optical spectra of the iron–sulfur proteins are the phenomena least likely to be perturbed by existence of an exchange interaction, and thus it is with the optical spectra that we might expect to see the strongest similarities between rubredoxin and, say, the plant-type ferredoxins. Figure 8 presents the optical spectra of oxidized and reduced rubredoxin and spinach ferredoxin in the visible and the near UV regions. Both oxidized proteins exhibit relatively intense spectra that are presumed to be ligand-to-metal charge transfer bands (Fee and Palmer, 1971) on the basis of their intensity, relatively

† Note that these are the values obtained for the antiferromagnetically coupled system: when corrected for the effects of the exchange interaction (Chapter of this volume), the values for the isolated ions are -7, -6.6, -6 and -3.5, -8 G for the ferric and ferrous ions, respectively. These compare a value of about 12 G for purely ionic ^{57}Fe (Locher and Geschwind, 1965), imp that the d electrons of the metal ions are substantially delocalized onto the li that is, the bonding is very covalent in character.

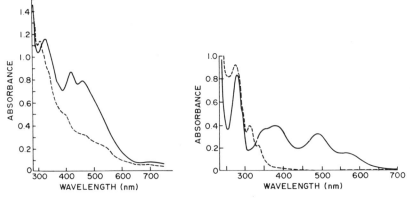

Fig. 8. The optical spectra of oxidized (——) and reduced (----) spinach ferredoxin (left-hand side) and rubredoxin (right-hand side). (Left-hand figure from Palmer *et al.*, 1967b; right-hand figure reprinted from B. E. Sobel and W. Lovenberg, *Biochemistry* **5**, 6. Copyright 1967 by the American Chemical Society. Reprinted by permission of the copyright owner.)

weak circular dichroism, and on the changes observed when the labile sulfide is replaced by selenide.

Jorgensen (1968) has rationalized the electron transfer spectra of many inorganic compounds using the concept of optical electronegatives in an empirical relationship

$$\nu_{corr} = (30 \text{ kK})(\chi_{L_{opt}} - \chi_{M_{opt}})$$

is given by the energy of the longest wavelength (lowest energy)
ɔn transfer band corrected for crystal field and electron repulsion
χ_{opt} are the optical electronegativities of the metal and ligand
·nd the proportionality constant is 30,000 cm⁻¹ (1 kK = 1000

ʰredoxin has its longest wavelength transition at 700 nm with
coefficient of 350 (Eaton *et al.*, 1972), so $\nu_{obs} = 13,300$ cm⁻¹.
˙tra of tetrahedral ferric halides one can calculate that
ɔn contributes about 9300 cm⁻¹ to the electron transfer
ˑ, 1968), so ν_{corr} is 4000 cm⁻¹ (in this particular example
ʌl field corrections). Jorgensen has deduced that χ_{opt}
ˑnd that for Fe (II) is 1.8 (Jorgensen, 1968), so that
˞ about 2.5 and is comparable to the value for S²⁻
-2.6 has been reported.
essentially colorless in dilute solution, although
ʟˑ is quite yellow. Using values for χ_{opt} of 2.5
ˑd Fe (II), respectively, and assuming an

electron repulsion term of 10,900 cm^{-1} as found for FeBr$_4{}^{2-}$ (Jorgensen, 1968), it is found that the longest wavelength charge transfer band should appear at 305 nm, and, further, the remainder of the electron transfer bands should be shifted into the ultraviolet. Spectra of the reduced protein show the longest wavelength band to be at 330 nm, and new bands can be seen down to 250 nm (Fig. 5 of Chapter 3 of this volume).

Spinach ferredoxin differs from rubredoxin in that the absorbance per Fe is decreased by about 40% and that the individual components of the spectra have substantially different intensities in the two proteins (Fig. 8). Furthermore, on reduction only about one-half of the visible absorbance is lost. Whereas the interpretation of absolute intensities of optical spectra is extremely difficult, the loss of only 50% of the color can have a simple explanation. According to our thesis, spinach ferredoxin (structure II) is a polymer of the basic rubredoxin structure I. Thus the oxidized protein should contain two high-spin ferric ions, one of which should be converted to high-spin ferrous ion on reduction, and the intensity of the visible optical spectrum should decrease, for as we saw, reduced rubredoxin has no visible color, the ligand → Fe (II) charge transfer bands moving into the near UV. Consistent with this interpretation is the demonstration that reduced spinach ferredoxin shows very little decrease in the 300–350 nm region (Fig. 8), where the lowest energy ligand → Fe (II) bands are anticipated to contribute intensity and replace the contribution to the absorbance of the reducible ferric ion. The residual absorbance in the visible region is thus attributed to the ferric ion that remains oxidized: Although the optical spectrum has no prominent features, it is clear from circular dichroism (CD) measurements (Palmer *et al.*, 1966) that there are a large number of unresolved bands contributing to this spectrum.

Because the optical electronegativities of sulfide and mercaptide sulfur are so similar (see above), we would anticipate that the lowest energy ligand → metal charge transfer band in spinach ferredoxin would also appear at about 700 nm, and indeed there is a band at 750 nm with a molar absorbance of 750. However, whereas the intensity of the low-energy band rapidly falls to zero in rubredoxin, the oxidized two-iron iron–sulfur proteins exhibit absorption out of 1 μm, with a clearly resolved band at about 950 nm. The origin of this band is unknown, one possibility being that it is an exchange-enhanced ferric d–d transition as was discussed earlier.

The utility of near-infrared optical and CD measurements in assigning d–d transitions was discussed earlier by Eaton and Lovenberg (Chapter 3 of this volume) who have used these methods to characterize the ^5E–^5T transitions of high-spin ferrous ion in a tetrahedral ligand field of cys-

teine residues–the examples is rubredoxin. An obvious extension of that
work was to examine the two-iron proteins in the same spectral range
and by the same techniques in the hope that some parallels could be
observed between rubredoxin and, say, spinach ferredoxin. Indeed, qualitatively, and even semiquantitatively, both proteins behave in a strikingly similar manner [Fig. 9 (Eaton *et al.*, 1972)]. Thus neither protein
exhibits absorption to wavelengths longer than 1.0 μm when oxidized,
while on reduction both proteins exhibit bands at about 1.6 and 2.5 μm
with extinction coefficients 50–100; in both cases these bands are intensely
optically active with g factors ($\Delta A/A$) of about 0.05 (Chapter 3 of this
volume). These similarities are good reason to believe that the reduced
two-iron proteins also contain a high-spin ferrous ion in a tetrahedral
ligand field provided by four sulfur atoms. However, it is obvious that
the spectra exhibited by these proteins are not identical: For instance,
the 1.6 μm band is much better resolved in rubredoxin than in the spinach
protein, while the ratio of intensities at 2.5 and 1.6 μm is about 3 for
spinach ferredoxin and only 1 for rubredoxin.

Presumably, these differences reflect significant structural dissimilarities
between the two proteins. Thus rubredoxin is significantly distorted away

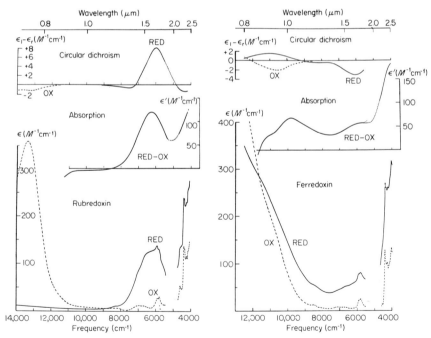

Fig. 9. A comparison of the infrared optical and circular dichroism spectra of
rubredoxin and spinach ferredoxin. (From Eaton *et al.*, 1971.)

from a tetrahedron and, in reality, the symmetry of the chromophore is no higher than C_{3_v}. The inequivalence of the inner and outer sulfurs in the hypothetical ferredoxin structure II imply that in this latter system the symmetry be no higher than D_{2_d}.

V. CHEMICAL DATA

It is ironic that some chemical experiments performed over ten years ago (Fry et al., 1963) characterized the formal valence of each iron atom in both oxidized and reduced spinach ferredoxin, and yet, because of the distrust of chemical determination of metal valences in proteins prevalent at that time (Singer and Massey, 1957), the early results were largely ignored. In those experiments the iron atoms were released from ferredoxin by mercurial treatment and their valence determined using colorimetric reagents. With oxidized ferredoxin the iron analyzed as being completely in the ferric state. When the ferredoxin was reduced using chloroplast fragments, 50% of the iron was then reduced in the ferrous form. Similar experiments have also been performed using dithionite as reductant (Palmer and Brintzinger, 1966). Today, of course, those experiments have become "respectable."

A classical approach for determining whether all of the five cysteine residues are involved in metal chelation is to try and react some or all of the cysteines with a chemical reagent without perturbing the active center. With spinach ferredoxin this has not been possible. In normal solvents, certain SH reagents completely destroy the active center in a rapid and monophasic manner (e.g., mercurials), while alkylating agents (e.g., iodoacetate) are completely unreactive. If the protein is "loosened" with 5 M urea, carboxymethylation does occur, but, apart from a possible initially rapid reaction of one sulfhydryl group, the reaction appears to proceed in an all-or-none manner (Petering and Palmer, 1970). It thus seems that at least four of the five cysteine residues are involved in metal coordination.† Furthermore, the 2 Fe–S* ferredoxin from horsetail (Agarwal et al., 1971) and cotton (Newman et al., 1969) each contain only four cysteine residues—implying that this is the minimum number necessary for a viable active center.

† The interpretation of chemical experiments of this kind are always subject to what might be called the "uncertainty principle of chemical modification of proteins," for the effect of modifying any given amino acid residue can be either a direct one, such as involved here, or a secondary consequence of changes in the configuration of the protein by the modifying agent. The resolution of this ambiguity is almost always difficult, if not impossible.

The stoichiometry of reaction with mercurials is a significant analytical datum. It is found that the ferredoxins consume just enough mercurial to satisfy the cysteine and sulfide contents of the protein assuming 1 mole of monovalent mercurial is required per mole cysteine and 2 moles mercurial per mole sulfide (Petering and Palmer, 1970). Under these conditions, the iron is liberated in the ferric valence, irrespective of whether the reaction is carried out in presence or absence of oxygen. Thus the stoichiometry and formal oxidation states of the iron and sulfur is four (or five) RS⁻, two S^{2-} and two Fe^{3+}. A similar conclusion is reached from titration of spinach ferredoxin with a mild oxidant such as potassium ferricyanide (Petering *et al.*, 1971), where a stoichiometry of 9 moles ferricyanide per mole ferredoxin is also found.

The significance of this result is that it eliminates possible structures for the active center involving disulfide or persulfidelike species. For instance, Bayer and Josef (1970) have proposed five possible structures with these features; each of these postulated structures predict that 7 moles of mercurial should be consumed by the protein, substantially less than the observed value of 9.

VI. THE STRUCTURE OF THE ACTIVE CENTER

Accepting then, the formal description of the active center as four RS⁻, two S^{2-}, and two Fe^{3+}, the possible structures that can be written are severely limited. Indeed there is only one chemically reasonable way to dispose of the sulfide ions and that is to locate them as ligands bridging the two iron atoms (structure III).

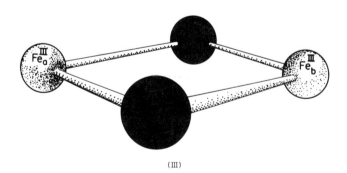

(III)

In structure III both iron atoms are in the high-spin ferric state and interact via a moderately strong exchange interaction. On reduction, an electron is added to Fe$_b$ which is then converted into the high-spin ferrous configuration. This still interacts with the ferric ion (Fe_a), but the strength of the interaction is significantly reduced, though still substantial. The bridging sulfide ions are very polarizable and thus provide a reasonable explanation for the strength of these exchange interactions.

The arrangement of ligands around the "ouside" of the iron atoms is more difficult to establish. For that iron atom which becomes reduced (Fe_b), there are several lines of spectroscopic evidence (optical and Mössbauer) that suggest that the coordination geometry at this site is essentially tetrahedral and that the four ligands are sulfur atoms. We thus dispose of two of the cysteines in the following way (structure IV).

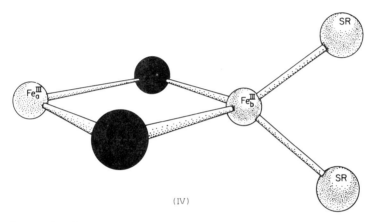

(IV)

These data exist for the reduced protein, but, in the absence of data to suggest otherwise, it is reasonable to suppose that the coordination geometry at Fe_b is also tetrahedral in the oxidized state.

The disposition of the ligands at the second iron center (Fe_a) cannot be specified. It is certainly true that in many binuclear complexes the coordination geometry at each metal ion is identical, and this is an aesthetically pleasing arrangement. However, there are no compelling reasons to believe that this is always true and indeed with spinach ferredoxin there are data to suggest that Fe_a may be coordinated to ligands other than sulfur and that there may be more than four ligands at the ferric site (Salmeen and Palmer, 1972). Thus the conclusion from NMR spectra that there are ferric protons originating from other than cysteine residues is evidence for this alternative. For this reason a more realistic representation of the facts representing our current understanding of the structure of spinach ferredoxin is shown in structure V, in which the uncertainty with regard to the geometry at Fe_a is represented by the underemphasis.

It must be emphasized that structures I–V are depicted using formal oxidation states, whereas, in reality, the complexes are highly covalent, and it must also be emphasized that the real charges on the component atoms will be much lower than is represented in the drawings.

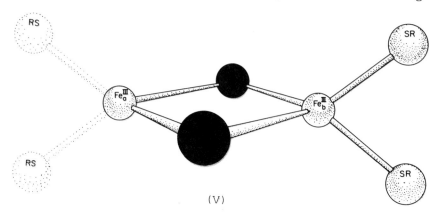

(V)

The contact-shifted NMR spectra of oxidized and reduced spinach ferredoxin have been presented (Chapter 7 of this volume).* Recently several additional resonances have been observed (Fig. 10), and an attempt has been made to assign some of the observed resonances in the context of the model just described. The bases for the assignments were severalfold: (1) The procedure of Dunham et al. (1971b) was used to differentiate between ferric and ferrous protons. (2) Spin density is assumed to be attenuated tenfold by a C—C single bond (Eaton et al., 1967). (3) The hyperfine interaction constants of the ferric and ferrous protons remained unchanged on reduction. (4) The resonances at 13–21 ppm observed in reduced ferredoxin are the β-CH$_2$ protons of the ferrous ion [cf. (1)]. (5) There are no pseudocontact contributions to the chemical shift. The bases for these assumptions are presented in the paper (Salmeen and Palmer, 1972).

With these assumptions, the following assignments were made. In the oxidized protein, (i) the broad resonance at 37 ppm is due to the eight β protons of four coordinated cysteines; (ii) the resonance at 14.7 ppm is not from cysteine; (iii) the α protons of cysteine lie in the "diamagnetic" region. In the reduced protein, (iv) the ferric β protons are very far downfield (about 450 ppm); (v) the resonance at 43 ppm is from the two α-CH cysteine protons of the ferric ion; (vi) the resonances at 13–21 ppm are ferrous β-CH$_2$ protons; (vii) the ferrous α protons are in the "diamagnetic" region; and (viii) the resonances at 10 and 18 ppm are

_____

* It should be noted that all the published data have been taken in D$_2$O: Thus the only resonances observed are from nonexchanging protons. Additional resonances may well be observed in H$_2$O from readily exchanging protons.

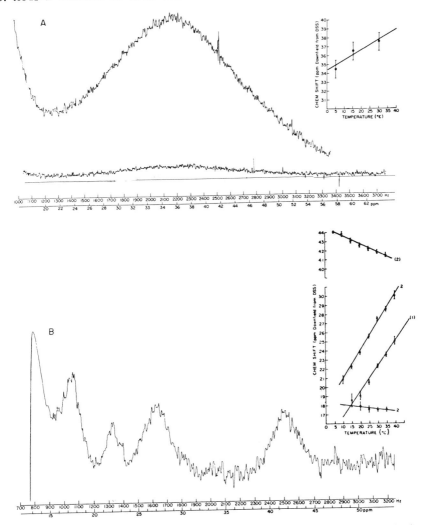

Fig. 10. NMR spectra of oxidized (A) and reduced (B) spinach ferredoxin in D₂O at 60 MHz. The insets give the temperature dependence of the resonances. (From Salmeen and Palmer, 1972.)

from other amino acid residues "coupled" to the ferric ion. An analysis of the observed linewidths in terms of the Solomon–Bloembergen equations (Carrington and McLachlan, 1967) yielded distances from the various protons to the paramagnetic center which fell within range permitted by measurements on space-filling (CPK) models (2.6–4.3 Å for β protons, 2.3–5.5 Å for α protons) indicating an internal consistency for the assignment and providing circumstantial support for the validity of the model.

VII. THE RELATIONSHIP BETWEEN THE STRUCTURE OF SPINACH FERREDOXIN AND OTHER 2 Fe–S* PROTEINS

Many of the data that have been obtained for spinach ferredoxin are also available for other 2 Fe–S* proteins, and one can, therefore, inquire to what extent the structure V is valid for such proteins as adrenodoxin (Ad) and putidaredoxin (Pd). From a statistical analysis of the amino acid sequences of spinach ferredoxin and adrenodoxin, it has been concluded that these two proteins are greatly separated on the evolutionary tree (Barker et al., 1972), and indeed this can be surmised just by visual inspection of the respective sequences. For instance, in adrenodoxin the four cysteine residues are clustered in two groups of the general sequence cys-X-X-cys with about 39 residues between the two groups (Tanaka et al., 1970). In spinach only one of these groupings is found the remaining cysteine residues being distributed throughout the polypeptide chain. Nevertheless, one is struck more by the similarities in the physical properties between adrenodoxin (Ad) and spinach ferredoxin (SFd) than in the differences that exist. A comparison of the physical properties of SFd, Ad, and Pd is shown in Table II from which one might conclude that the variations between the proteins reflect quantitative rather than quali-

TABLE II

COMPARISON OF PHYSICAL PROPERTIES OF SPINACH FERREDOXIN (SFD) AND ADRENODOXIN (AD)

Method	Result
Optical spectra	No significant difference from 0.3–2.5 μm in either redox form
CD spectra	No significant difference from 0.3–2.5 μm in either redox form
Magnetic susceptibility	SFd shows non-Curie behavior in both redox forms above 77°K; no anomalous behavior reported for Ad
EPR	SFd shows rhombic g tensor, EPR only well resolved below 77°K; Ad exhibits axial g tensor; EPR well resolved to 150°K
Mössbauer	No differences in oxidized state; 4.2°K spectrum of reduced SFd collapses to two quadrupole pairs by about 100°K, reduced Ad still exhibits complex spectrum at 300°K
ENDOR	No major differences noted
NMR contact shifts	SFd exhibits contact-shifted resonances in both redox states; no published data on Ad
Proton relaxation rates	No significant differences detected in either redox state
E_0'	SFd, −0.42 V; Ad, −0.36 V; Pd, −0.24 V

tative differences in the active center. For instance, the strength of the exchange interaction appears to be at least 50% stronger in adrenodoxin ($J_{ox} \geq 350$ cm^{-1}, $J_{red} \geq 250$ cm^{-1}) than in SFd with the consequence that no significant deviations from Curie behavior have been detected by low-temperature magnetic susceptibility (Kimura et al., 1970; Moleski et al., 1970). This is probably the reason that the EPR of the reduced protein is preserved to much higher temperatures than is the case with SFd, for thermal promotion into the exchange-coupled excited states is the most likely mechanism for electron spin relaxation in these proteins.

The most conspicuous difference between the two proteins is to be found in the magnitudes of their respective g tensor. Spinach ferredoxin exhibits a rhombic EPR ($g_x \neq g_y \neq g_z$), whereas the spectrum of adrenodoxin is axial ($g_x = g_y \neq g_z$) (Fig. 8 of Chapter 5 of this volume). In mononuclear species the g tensor can be used to determine the microsymmetry at the coordination center. Thus an axial g tensor implies axially symmetric coordination geometry [e.g., square planar Cu (II)], while a rhombic g tensor indicates that the local symmetry is less than axial. [Sometimes the fact that the symmetry is lower than axial is not immediately obvious. Low-spin ferrihemoproteins, e.g., cytochromes, exhibit rhombic EPR because the orientation of the axial (fifth and sixth ligands) is asymmetric with respect to the four pyrole nitrogens.] However, in polynuclear species the simple correlation between site symmetry and g anisotropy does not exist a priori. In the simplest form of the theory presented by Gibson et al. (1966), the ferric ion was assumed to have an isotropic g value; then the observed g tensor reflects the symmetry at the ferrous site. However, Munck et al. (1972) have pointed out that this assumption does not hold in compounds such as [FeS$_3$Se] and [FeS$_2$Se$_2$] (Schneider et al., 1968) and give a more general form for the g-tensor relationship

$$g_i = \tfrac{7}{2}g_{1i} - \tfrac{4}{3}g_{2j}$$

where i, $j = x$, y, x and i may equal j. In this situation the observed g tensor represents a weighted average of the g tensors of each iron atom and thus any deductions concerning the site symmetry from the g anisotropy are precluded.

The Mössbauer properties of putidaredoxin have been extensively investigated by Munck et al. (1972). For the most part, the protein behaves like spinach ferredoxin, though there is one significant experimental difference. Both reduced proteins exhibit the same complex spectrum at 4.2°K: As the temperature is increased, this spectrum broadens, and, in the case of spinach ferredoxin, finally collapses to a simple pair of quadrupole doublets at about 250°K. With putidaredoxin a similar process occurs except that the temperature ($>300°K$) required to produce the collapsed spectrum is not experimentally accessible because of the instability of the proteins. Further, the temperature at which this complex transition begins is higher for the bacterial protein ($20°K$ for SFd, $80°K$ for Pd). This difference in behavior is a reflection of the longer electron spin lattice relaxation time (T_1) of putidaredoxin; T_1 is presumably longer because the exchange interaction is larger.

VIII. THE PROPERTIES OF THE 4 Fe–S* IRON–SULFUR PROTEINS

At this time there appear to be two classes of single-center 4 Fe–S* iron–sulfur proteins. These are (1) the high-potential proteins (HIPIP) found in *Chromatium* and other photosynthetic purple bacteria (Dus *et al.*, 1967), (2) a ferredoxin found in *Bacillus polymyxa* (Shethna *et al.*, 1971). Of these, the HIPIP from *Chromatium* is by far the best characterized, and the structure of the active center of this protein has been deduced from an electron density map (Carter *et al.*, 1972).

The X-ray data show that the four iron atoms are arranged in a tetrahedron with an average Fe–Fe separation of 3.1 Å. The iron atoms are coordinated to the polypeptide chain via the mercaptide sulfur's of residues 43, 46, 63, and 77. The labile sulfides are located outside each face of the tetrahedron so that each iron atom is coordinated to four sulfur atoms, three inorganic, and one mercaptide, which are also tetrahedrally disposed with respect to the iron atom. The mean bond lengths are 2.35 and 2.01 Å for the Fe–S$_{inorganic}$ and Fe–S$_{cysteine}$, respectively (Fig. 11). The precision of these bond lengths was only about ±0.2 Å and thus the interpretation of these distances must be made circumspectly. However, it does appear that the mean Fe–S distance of 2.28 Å is typical of an iron–sulfur covalent

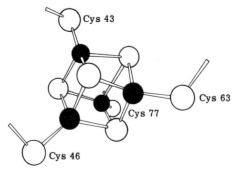

Fig. 11. The structure of the active center of *Chromatium* high-potential protein. (From Carter *et al.*, 1972.)

single bond. It may be significant that the Fe–S$_{inorganic}$ bond length of 2.35 Å is close to the mean bond length observed with three of the Fe∼S$_{cysteine}$ bonds in rubredoxin (Chapter 4 of this volume) (Watenpaugh et al., 1972), while the one Fe–S$_{cysteine}$ bond in HIPIP and Fe ∼ S$_{cys42}$ in rubredoxin have a bond length close to 2.0 Å. There is no evidence for any changes in electron diffraction on oxidation of the reduced protein: However, once again it is wise to note that the data refinement is still at a relatively crude stage.

With these details of the structure of the active center, it might be hoped that the interpretation of the available physical data would be straightforward; unfortunately, this does not seem to be the case.

In contrast to the 2 Fe∼S* proteins which are diamagnetic in the oxidized form (at cryogenic temperatures) HIPIP is diamagnetic in the reduced form at low temperatures as determined by magnetic susceptibility though a value of $(600 \pm 800) \times 10^{-6}$ cgs units/mole has been reported (Ehrenberg and Kamen, 1965) for room temperature. Because of the large error, this datum is consistent with the protein being diamagnetic or containing as much as one unpaired electron per mole. However, the demonstration of contact-shifted NMR in the reduced protein (Phillips et al., 1970) establishes that the reduced protein does indeed have some paramagnetism at room temperature and indicates that the low-temperature diamagnetism is a consequence of antiferromagnetic exhange interactions. The Mössbauer spectrum of the reduced protein exhibits but one quadrupole pair with a small isomer shift but a fairly large quadrupole splitting (Evans et al., 1970). This spectrum does not change on cooling to 4.2°K and on applying an external magnetic field to the sample, thus confirming that the iron atoms do not have a net magnetic moment.

The result that the reduced protein is diamagnetic has certain elementary consequences, viz., the formal valences of the iron atoms are either four Fe^{2+}, two Fe^{2+} plus two Fe^{3+} or four Fe^{3+}, for the total number of metal electrons must be even. Oxidation of the last alternative (4 Fe^{3+}) requires either that we invoke the formation of Fe^{4+} or the involvement of the ligand(s) as the redox center, both of these possibilities seem rather unlikely. The other alternative will be considered later.

One electron oxidation of reduced HIPIP, for instance by addition of stoichiometric amounts of potassium ferricyanide, produces a spin.one-half paramagnet as judged by low-temperature magnetic susceptibility (Moss et al., 1969) and EPR (Palmer et al., 1967a). The EPR spectrum of oxidized HIPIP is rather complicated; at first sight it appears to be a simple axial spectrum with $g_\perp = 2.04$, $g_\parallel = 2.12$. However, there are several additional features present in the spectrum which are not consistent with a simple $S = \frac{1}{2}$ system (Figure 13 of Chapter 5 of this volume).

Furthermore, in contrast to spinach ferredoxin, it should be noted that the g values for oxidized HIPIP are all > 2.00. The room-temperature magnetic susceptibility of oxidized HIPIP is $3600 \pm 400 \times 10^{-6}$ cgs units/mole (Ehrenberg and Kamen, 1965) a value comparable to that obtained with spinach ferredoxin, and which indicates that a significant fraction of excited states are occupied at 25°C.

It is worth pointing out that the analysis of the magnetic susceptibility of a tetrahedron of antiferromagnetically coupled iron atoms can be complicated. In the simplest case all iron atoms are equivalent, and a single electron is "plucked" from the active center; then the susceptibility can be described by a single interaction parameter (J). However, in extreme contrast, if all four iron atoms are inequivalent, then six such interaction parameters are required $(J_{1,2}; J_{2,3},$ etc.). As the susceptibility is a relatively monotonic function of temperature, it will be well-nigh impossible to discriminate between the many possibilities by this technique.

The high-temperature (77°K) Mössbauer spectrum of oxidized HIPIP is very similar to the reduced protein (Evans *et al.*, 1970): Once more one observes a single quadrupole pair with both quadrupole splitting and isomer shift slightly less than was observed for the reduced protein. Thus we have the surprising result that the iron atoms appear to be equivalent in both the oxidized and reduced protein, a result which is most simply interpreted by assuming that the four irons are equivalent in the reduced protein and, on oxidation, the electron is removed from an orbital which is centered on all four iron atoms, i.e., a molecular orbital; however, the reality may be more complicated. When the oxidized protein is cooled to 4.2°K, its Mössbauer spectrum changes radically as the electron relaxation rate becomes slow. Evans *et al.* (1970) were unable to interpret this low-temperature spectrum in terms of a single species and attempted to rationalize the features of the spectra using stick spectra. Their assignments, however, are far from convincing and do not explain several prominent features of the spectrum. It would be worthwhile to attempt a full computer simulation of these spectra starting first from the premise that the iron atoms are equivalent and allowing for moderately large anisotropies in the hyperfine interactions.

The high-resolution NMR spectrum of HIPIP has also been interpreted as showing the inequivalence of the iron atoms at the active center (Phillips *et al.*, 1970). Thus in oxidized HIPIP there are four contact-shifted resonances of unit intensity at 26, 32, and 42 ppm (5°C) that move to higher field as the temperature is increased while there is one resonance at 24 ppm (5°C) of intensity corresponding to three protons which moves in the opposite direction (Fig. 5 of Chapter 7 of this volume).

The early suggestion (Phillips *et al.*, 1970) that these two classes of protons could be assigned to different "ends" of the four-iron structure, only one of which was redox active, seems unwarranted in view of the possible alternative. In particular, the experience with spinach ferredoxin shows that those resonances observed in the -10 to -45 ppm region are not solely the β-CH_2 protons of cysteine, for with spinach ferredoxin a good case can be made for cysteine α protons and protons from other amino acid residues having resonances in this region. Furthermore, if two of the four iron atoms were isolated from the paramagnetic center, then they should exhibit an unchanged quadrupole doublet in the low-temperature Mössbauer spectrum, comprising 50% of the total intensity. There is no evidence for this quadrupole doublet.

These NMR data are in fact analogous to those which we discussed earlier for spinach ferredoxin and, in that instance, they were readily rationalized by the antiferromagnetic exchange interaction. However, this interpretation required that one be able to discriminate between the iron atoms (e.g., Fe^{3+} and Fe^{2+}), and there is no basis for this discrimination in the high-temperature Mössbauer spectrum of oxidized HIPIP.

A further prominent difference between HIPIP and the 2 Fe–S* proteins is found in their optical spectra. Whereas the 2 Fe–S* proteins has relatively well-defined maxima at about 320, 420, and 460 nm in the oxidized form, HIPIP exhibits an extremely bland spectrum, the only features being several inflections between 300 and 450 nm superimposed on a steep-end absorption (Fig. 12); the absorbance per iron was typical (about 5 mM^{-1} cm^{-1}). On reduction the absorbance decreases throughout the whole visible range and a relatively prominent maximum appears at 390 nm. There is no evidence for any increase in absorption at wave-

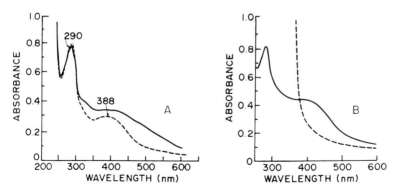

Fig. 12. The optical spectra of oxidized (——) and reduced (----) high-potential protein (A) and the ferredoxin from *B. polymyxa* (B). (From Dus *et al.*, 1967; Shethna *et al.*, 1971.)

lengths less than 350 nm associated with the appearance of sulfur $\rightarrow Fe^{2+}$ charge transfer bands.

The ferredoxin from *B. polymyxa* has a rather similar optical spectrum with a pronounced shoulder at about 400 nm (Fig. 12) and comparable extinction coefficients. Reduction with hydrogenase is accompanied by some loss of visible absorbance and additional features appear in the range 350–390 nm. [Somewhat similar spectra are obtained with a ferredoxin obtained from *Azotobacter* (Yoch *et al.*, 1969) which thus can be predicted to be a four- (or eight-) iron protein rather than a six-iron protein as reported.] At this point the similarities in physical chemistry of this protein with HIPIP stops. The EPR spectrum of oxidized *polymyxa* ferredoxin shows an intense isotropic resonance at $g = 2.0$. On one electron reduction with dithionite, this resonance disappears and a simple rhombic EPR spectrum of the $g = 1.94$ type replaces it (Fig. 14 of Chapter 5 of this volume). The intensity of the spectrum accounts for one electron per mole protein. From the published data (Shethna *et al.*, 1971), one can estimate that the intensities of the signals in both oxidized and reduced protein are comparable.

We thus have two classes of proteins each with similar chemical composition and optical spectra but with quite different EPR characteristics; HIPIP has an approximately axial spectrum when oxidized and is diamagnetic when reduced, *polymyxa* ferredoxin exhibits an isotropic EPR signal in the oxidized form and a classical $g = 1.94$ spectrum when reduced. These results lead to two clear deductions: First, the optical spectra are poor indicators of the magnetic characteristics of these sites, and second, that we are a long way from understanding the complex interactions which are characteristic of these compounds.

IX. PROPERTIES OF THE 8 FE–S* IRON–SULFUR PROTEINS

The elucidation, by X-ray crystallography, of the structure of an 8 Fe–S* (bacterial) ferredoxin from *Micrococcus aerogenes* has revealed that, in these, the most complicated of the ferredoxins, there are in fact two active centers, each of which resembles the structure observed in HIPIP, separated by 12 Å [Fig. 13 (Sieker *et al.*, 1972)].

That there might be more than one active center in these proteins had already been anticipated from several lines of evidence. Thus, although the complete reduction of the 8 Fe–S* ferredoxins required two electrons (Mayhew *et al.*, 1969; Evans *et al.*, 1968) the oxidation–reduction behavior conformed well to the Nernst equation for $n = 1$, that is, with the electrons being transferred one at a time (Eisenstein and Wang,

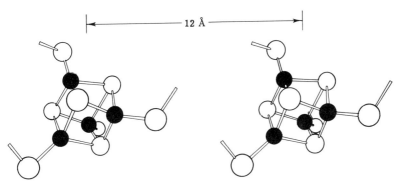

Fig. 13. The active centers of the ferredoxin from *M. aerogenes*. (After Sieker *et al.*, 1972.)

1969). The difference in reduction potentials reported for the two sites was simply that anticipated on statistical grounds which lead to the suggestion that two redox active sites did not interact (Eisenstein and Wang, 1969). Heterogeneity in both the Mössbauer spectrum of an oxidized bacterial ferredoxin (Blomstrom *et al.*, 1964) and in the EPR spectrum of the reduced protein (Palmer *et al.*, 1966) also prompted the suggestion that these systems were more complex than was anticipated for a single center.

A direct demonstration that there were indeed two paramagnetic centers in *C. pasteurianum* ferredoxin was provided by Orme-Johnson and Beinert (1969) who showed that the EPR spectrum of this protein partially reduced by addition of 0.2 electron equivalents/mole was almost a pure axial species with $g_{\parallel} \approx 2.06$, $g_{\perp} \approx 1.94$ and that further addition of reducing equivalents produced an increase in intensity of this species and the appearance of a second narrower signal in the middle of the axial spectrum (Fig. 15 of Chapter 5 of this volume). Both signals were fully developed by the addition of two reducing equivalents per mole protein. The simplest interpretation of this experiment* is that the axial species is characteristic of the site with the more positive reduction potential, for it is this site that will trap the reducing equivalents during the early part of the titration.

---

* The redox potentials of the two sites do not differ by more than a statistical factor (Eisenstein and Wang, 1969)—in just the same way that the pK's of the carboxyl groups in COOH—(CH₂)₆—COOH differ by a factor of log₁₀ 4 (Wold, 1971). There is thus no evidence from redox potentials that the sites are inequivalent. However, the observation that the two sites have different EPR spectra make it likely that the two sites are indeed inequivalent. The possibility of a site–site interaction which allowed the first site reduced to have an axial spectrum with subsequent conformational change so that the second site had the narrower spectrum seems to be ruled out by the redox potential data.

318

In view of the apparent similarity between the structures of HIPIP and the *M. aerogenes* ferredoxin, one would anticipate many similarities in the physical properties. Certainly, the optical spectra show some similarities, for instance, the existence of the maximum around 400 nm in the spectrum of the oxidized protein though the pronounced peak seen at 400 nm in the reduced HIPIP has no counterpart in the reduced ferredoxin. Indeed, the most striking fact is the marked similarity in optical properties between reduced HIPIP and oxidized ferredoxin from 340–750 nm (Fig. 14), a fact to be discussed further.

The magnetic properties of bacterial ferredoxin are poorly documented. There are no reported measurements of the magnetic susceptibility of either the oxidized or reduced proteins at low temperatures. Just as with the ferredoxin from *B. polymyxa* the oxidized bacterial ferredoxins exhibit a slightly asymmetric resonance at $g = 2.0$, but the intensity of this signal varies significantly from protein to protein, and in one instance (*M. lactylyticus*) (Mathews and Palmer, unpublished) is ≪1% as intense as the resonance in the reduced protein. The reduced protein from *M. lactylyticus* exhibits very complex EPR in the $g = 1.94$ region; spectra recorded at 35 GHz on samples progressively reduced with sodium dithionite exhibit changes which suggest that the EPR spectra of the individual iron–sulfur clusters are similar and that the complex EPR spectra exhibited in the fully reduced protein may be a consequence of a

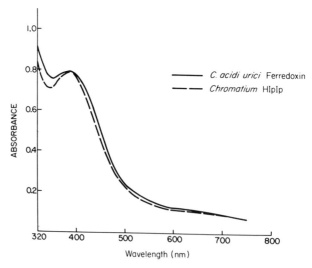

Fig. 14. A comparison of the optical spectra of oxidized bacterial ferredoxin with reduced high-potential protein. The spectra were adjusted to give the same absorbance at 390 nm. (From G. Palmer and S. Mayhew, unpublished.)

magnetic coupling between the two paramagnetic centers. The simplest source of this coupling is dipolar, but if this is the major mechanism then it is probable that reduction produces a major change in the conformation of the protein which results in a movement of the iron–sulfur clusters toward one another.

Room-temperature susceptibility measurements have been made using NMR (Chapter 5 of this volume) (Poe *et al.*, 1970) and substantial paramagnetism found in both redox states. In the oxidized protein, the susceptibility per Fe was about half that anticipated for one spin per Fe and increased with temperature, strongly implicating an antiferromagnetic exchange process. On reduction, the susceptibility increases and is reported to behave normally (it is proportional to T^{-1}).

The bacterial ferredoxins exhibit a wealth of contact-shifted NMR lines (Chapter 7 of this volume); all those in the oxidized protein show anti-Curie behavior, whereas in the reduced both positive and negative temperature dependences have been observed (cf. above discussion of spinach ferredoxin). Although it was earlier proposed that the majority of these resonances were due to the β-protons of cysteine, this conclusion should be considered tentative in light of the earlier discussion on spinach ferredoxin.

The Mössbauer spectra on these proteins have been unenlightening. The asymmetric quadrupole pair observed previously in the oxidized form has been confirmed (Chapter 6 of this volume). This asymmetry was originally interpreted as due to two overlapping species, but as there are a large number of physical interactions monitored by a Mössbauer spectrum, it is possible that this asymmetry has an alternative origin. Relatively little change in the Mössbauer spectrum occurs on reduction (Chapter 6 of this volume). Qualitatively then, the Mössbauer properties of bacterial ferredoxin resemble HIPIP—but the analysis of both proteins is still in a very preliminary stage and this conclusion could easily change.

Are there any conclusions that we can draw with regard to the electronic configuration in the 8 Fe–S* proteins? To do so requires many assumptions. Thus we first assume that the oxidized protein is diamagnetic at low temperature. Then the formal valences of the iron atoms in each center are either 4 Fe^{3+}, 4 Fe^{2+}, or 2 ($Fe^{3+} + Fe^{2+}$). We next assume that the electronic configurations at both active centers are the same. Then we use the result that liberation of the iron atoms from these proteins by mercurial† give 50% Fe^{3+} and 50% Fe^{2+} (Palmer *et al.*, 1966;

---

† The mercurial prevents artifactual reduction of the iron by cysteine or S^{2-}. From the X-ray structure and the value of the mercurial titer, there is no reason to suspect protein oxidizing equivalents at the active center, so both sources of error appear to be eliminated.

Sobel and Lovenberg, 1966) which establishes the last of the above alternative as the likely configuration. Thus one can deduce that the electronic configuration in oxidized ferredoxin is 2 Fe^{3+} plus 2 Fe^{2+}. Reduction then produces 1 Fe^{3+} plus 3 Fe^{2+} which can couple antiferromagnetically to yield $S = \frac{1}{2}$: Chemical analysis of the iron liberated from photosynthetically reduced protein establishes that 75% Fe is in the ferrous valence (Sobel and Lovenberg, 1966).

From the similarities in the optical spectrum referred to above (reduced HIPIP = oxidized ferredoxin) (Fig. 13), we would then anticipate that reduced HIPIP will contain 2 Fe^{3+} plus 2 Fe^{2+}; on oxidation this would be converted to 3 Fe^{3+} plus 1 Fe^{2+},† which could again couple antiferromagnetically to yield a net spin of $\frac{1}{2}$. Bacillus polymyxa ferredoxin should behave like the 8 Fe–S* protein. The formal oxidation states of the metal and ligand components in these proteins are thus predicted to be 2 Fe^{3+}, 2 Fe^{2+}, 4 RS^-, 4 S^{2-}, net charge = -2 (reduced HIPIP, oxidized bacterial ferredoxin) Fe^{3+}, 3 Fe^{2+}, 4 RS^-, 4 S^{2-}, net charge = -3 (reduced bacterial ferredoxin), and 3 Fe^{3+}, Fe^{2+}, 4 RS^-, 4 S^{2-}, net charge = -1 (oxidized HIPIP).

Adding an electron to the HIPIP system reduces the net charge from -1 to -2, while adding an electron to bacterial ferredoxin will reduce the net charge from -2 to -3. The latter process would require much more work than the former and provides an explanation for the much lower redox potential observed with the ferredoxin. Furthermore, it may be no coincidence that HIPIP is a very basic protein while ferredoxin is very acidic. The strongly positive environment in HIPIP will stabilize the -2 state relative to the -1 while the negative charge on ferredoxin will destabilize the -3 state to -2. Thus in both proteins the -2 state would be more stable, and HIPIP would be expected to be an oxidizing agent while ferredoxin would function as a good reductant. The determination of whether the 2 ($Fe^{3+} - Fe^{2+}$) unit can be oxidized or reduced may well depend on subtle differences in bond angles and lengths not yet resolved by X-ray crystallography, and there is an urgent need that the X-ray analysis of these proteins be carried to the highest possible resolution.

The Mössbauer data, however, show that this is too simplistic an approach. The observation of a single quadrupole doublet in both redox states *plus* the unusual values for these quadrupole doublets point to an interpretation that the reduced protein contains a cluster of 4 Fe^{3+} plus two electrons which are paired in a molecular orbital encompassing all

† One would hope that this could be tested chemically. Unfortunately, the release of Fe from HIPIP by mercurials is a very slow process and indeed may not go to completion.

four Fe atoms, and that oxidation consists of removing one electron from that molecular orbital; the decrease in the quadrupole splitting is consistent with this alternative. The discrimination between the iron atoms which is seen in the temperature dependence of the NMR contact shifts then requires that there be thermally accessible molecular orbitals which are centered predominantly on only part of the iron cluster. A more detailed analysis of this Mössbauer data together with an ENDOR analysis is required to resolve this problem.

X. CONCLUSIONS

It is now seven years since the first Symposium on Non-Heme Iron Proteins held at Antioch College in Yellow Springs. A comparison of the proceedings of that volume (San Pietro, 1965) with this book reveals the remarkable progress that has occurred in the interim. The emphasis at that meeting was on the biological and biochemical properties of these proteins, and relatively few of the presentations were physical in nature. The similarities between "bacterial" and chloroplast ferredoxin were widely accepted while, for instance, the mitochondrial proteins, which had the then unique property of exhibiting the $g = 1.94$ signal, were suspected of being a separate species. The physical and structural bases of these properties were completely obscure though even then there had been at least two suggestions that the active center of these proteins were poly-iron complexes (Blomstrom et al., 1964; Beinert et al., 1962).

By contrast, one volume of this treatise is devoted to the physical and chemical properties of these proteins. X-Ray structural data are available for rubredoxin, HIPIP, and the eight-iron ferredoxin from M. aerogenes, and many features of the active center of the two-iron ferredoxins have been deduced from physical measurements. Ironically the physical and X-ray data have not yet complemented each other. Those poly iron proteins which have been solved crystallographically are a mystery physicochemically; conversely, the two-iron proteins are well understood physicochemically, but detailed X-ray information is needed to secure the physical data, and it is in these two areas that future efforts are sure to be concentrated.

One of the properties of the ferredoxins is their unusually low reduction potential, an attribute which is obviously of profound biological significance. However, it may be questioned whether there is any unique feature of these proteins which can account for this. The essential identity of the active centers of HIPIP and the M. aerogenes ferredoxin despite the large (>0.7 V) difference in reduction potential, implies that these differences will be found in rather subtle variations in bond lengths and bond angles of the Fe–S cluster variations which can hardly be interpreted at our present level of chemical intuition. Further, it should be remembered that at least two cytochromes have been reported to have comparably low reduction potentials (Waterman and Mason, 1972; Deeb and Hager, 1962).

A much more fundamental problem is the reluctance of the individual iron–sulfur clusters to participate in two-electron transport. Both the 2 Fe and the 4 Fe centers will only accept one electron even though there is no obvious mechanism restricting the addition of a second electron. In the case of spinach ferredoxin, it is possible to obtain complete bleaching of the protein using photochemical reductants (B. Hosein and G. Palmer, unpublished); presumably both iron atoms are reduced under these conditions. However, the product appears to be destroyed under these conditions, for the admission of air to the sample does not restore the spectrum of the native protein. Clearly, complete reduction is a lethal process in this one case, but why this should be so is obscure.

In the event that the reader has made it to this point, I would like to remind him that the justification for this and the immediately preceding chapters is to be found in the obvious biological importance of these proteins and to urge him to return to the early chapters and review that material, for it is there that he will find the definition of new and, as yet, unexplored territory. In particular, he should be aware of recent developments in mitochondrial electron transport (cf. Orme-Johnson et al., 1972; Ohnishi et al., 1972; Albracht et al., 1972) which point to a very real possibility that the iron–sulfur proteins may be involved in oxidative phosphorylation—still the least understood of the fundamental cellular processes.

Clearly, the iron–sulfur proteins offer a rich area for future experimental research, and the next decade should provide answers to many of the questions posed or implicit in this book.

ACKNOWLEDGMENTS

The properties of the iron–sulfur proteins involve phenomena that are strange to most biochemists, and can only be accurately described in the language of physics. Nevertheless, it is important that the biochemist be given some physical insight into these phenomena without necessarily being overwhelmed by the quantum mechanical formalism. As a "card-carrying" biochemist, I can appreciate the demands of my colleagues in biochemistry for these physical pictures—the same demands that I have made on my co-workers over the past decade—and I trust that some of these have been answered in this chapter. Obviously, my own education in this given area has benefited from prolonged interaction with colleagues of different backgrounds and talents and it is to these colleagues and friends that I express my appreciation: A. Bearden, H. Beinert, W. E. Blumberg, H. Brintzinger, W. Eaton, I. Salmeen, and R. H. Sands. The preparation of this chapter and much of the work described in it was supported by a Research Grant from the National Institutes of Health, Grant No. GM-12176.

REFERENCES

Aggarwal, S. T., Rao, K. K., and Matsubara, H. (1971). *J. Biochem.* **69**, 601.

Albracht, S. J., Deerikhuisen, H. V., and Slater, E. C. (1972). *Biochim. Biophys. Acta* **256**, 1.

Barker W. C., McLaughlin, P. J., and Dayhoff, M. O. (1972). *Fed. Proc.* **31**, 837.

Bayer, E., and Josef, D. (1970). *Hoppe-Seyler's Z. Physiol. Chem.* **351**, 537.

Beinert, H., Heinen, W., and Palmer, G. (1962). *Brookhaven Symp. Biol.* No. 15, p. 249.

Blomstrom, D. C., Knight, E., Jr., Phillips, W. D., and Weiher, J. F. (1964). *Proc. Nat. Acad. Sci. U.S.* **51**, 1085.

Blumberg, W. E. (1967). *In* "Magnetic Resonance in Biological Systems" (A. Ehrenberg *et al.*, eds.), p. 119. Pergamon, Oxford.

Brintzinger, H., Palmer, G., and Sands, R. H. (1966). *Proc. Nat. Acad. Sci. U.S.* **55**, 397.

Carrington, A., and McLachlan, A. (1967). "Introduction to Magnetic Resonance," p. 228. Harper, New York.

Carter, C. W., Jr., Freer, S. T., Xuong, Ng H., Alden, R. A., and Kraut, J. (1972). *Cold Spring Harbor Symp. Quant. Biol.* **36**, 381.

Deeb, S., and Hager, L. P. (1962). *Fed. Proc.* **21**, 49.

Dunham, W. R., Bearden, A. J., Salmeen, I. T., Palmer, G., Sands, R. H., Orme-Johnson, W. H., and Beinert, H. (1971a). *Biochim. Biophys. Acta* **253**, 134.

Dunham, W. R., Palmer, G., Sands, R. H., and Bearden, A. J. (1971b). *Biochim. Biophys. Acta* **253**, 373.

Dus, K., DeKlerk, H., Stetten, K., and Bartsch, R. G. (1967). *Biochim. Biophys. Acta* **140**, 291.

Eaton, D. R., Josey, A. D., and Benson, R. E. (1967). *J. Amer. Chem. Soc.* **89**, 4040.

Eaton, W., Palmer, G., Fee, J. A., Kimura, T., and Lovenberg, W. (1972). *Proc. Nat. Acad. Sci.* **68**, 3015.

Ehrenberg, A. (1966). personal communication.

Ehrenberg, A., and Kamen, M. D. (1965). *Biochim. Biophys. Acta* **102**, 333.

Eisenstein, K., and Wang, J. H. (1969). *J. Biol. Chem.* **244**, 1720.

Evans, M. C. W., Hall, D. O., and Johnson, C. E. (1970). *Biochem. J.* **119**, 289.

Evans, M. C. W., Hall, D. O., Bothe, H., and Whatley, F. R. (1968). *Biochem. J.* **110**, 485.

Fee, J. A., and Palmer, G. (1971). *Biochim. Biophys. Acta* **245**, 175.

Fritz, J., Anderson, R., Fee, J., Palmer, G., Sands, R. H., Tsibris, J. C. M., Gunsalus, I. C., Orme-Johnson, W. H., and Beinert, H. (1971). *Biochim. Biophys. Acta* **253**, 110.

Fry, K. T., Lazarini, R. A., and San Pietro, A. (1963). *Proc. Nat. Acad. Sci. U.S.* **50**, 652.

Gibson, J. F., Hall, D. O., Thornley, J. F., and Whatley, F. (1966). *Proc. Nat. Acad. Sci. U.S.* **56**, 987.

Johnson, C. E. (1967). *Proc. Phys. Soc.* **92**, 748.

Jorgensen, C. K. (1968). *In* "Halogen Chemistry" (V. Gutman, ed.), Vol. 1, p. 303. Academic Press, New York.

Kimura, T., Tasaki, A., and Watari, H. (1970). *J. Biol. Chem.* **245**, 4450.

La Mar, G. L., Eaton, G. R., Holm, R. H., and Walker, F. A. (1973). *J. Amer. Chem. Soc.* **95**, 63.

Lang, G. (1970). *Quart. Rev. Biophys.* **3**, 1.

Locher, P. R., and Geschwind, S. (1965). *Phys. Rev.* **139**, A991.

Lohr, L. L., and McClure, D. S. (1968). *J. Chem. Phys.* **49**, 3516.

Martin, R. L. (1968). *In* "New Pathways in Inorganic Chemistry" (E. A. V. Ebsworth, A. G. Maddock, and A. G. Sharpe, eds.). Cambridge Univ. Press, London and New York.

Mathews, R., and Palmer, G. (1973). unpublished.

Mayhew, S. G., Petering, D., Palmer, G., and Foust, G. P. (1969). *J. Biol. Chem.* **244**, 2830.

McCleverty, J. A. (1968). *Progr. Inorg. Chem.* **10**, 49.

Mildvan, A., Palmer, G., and Estabrook, R. W. (1967). *In* "Magnetic Resonance in Biological Systems" (A. Ehrenberg *et al.*, eds.), p. 157. Pergamon, Oxford.

Moleski, C., Moss, T. H., Orme-Johnson, W. H., and Tsibris, J. C. M. (1970). *Biochim. Biophys. Acta* **214**, 548.

Moss, T. H., Petering, D., and Palmer, G. (1969). *J. Biol. Chem.* **244**, 2275.

Munck, E., Debrunner, P. G., Tsibris, J. C. M., and Gunsalus, I. C. (1972). *Biochemistry* **11**, 855.

Newman, D. J., Ihle, J. N., and Dure, L. (1969). *Biochem. Biophys. Res. Commun.* **36**, 947.

Ohnishi, T., Wilson, D. F., Asakura, T., and Chance, B. (1972). *Biochem. Biophys. Res. Commun.* **46**, 1631.

Okamura, M. Y., and Hoffman, B. M. (1969). *J. Chem. Phys.* **51**, 3128.

Orme-Johnson, W. H., and Beinert, H. (1969). *Biochem. Biophys. Res. Commun.* **36**, 337.

Orme-Johnson, N. R., Orme-Johnson, W. H., Hansen, R. E., Beinert, H., and Hatefi, Y. (1972). *Biochem. Biophys. Res. Commun.* **44**, 446.

Palmer, G., and Brintzinger, H. (1966). unpublished.

Palmer, G., Sands, R. H., and Mortenson, L. E. (1966). *Biochem. Biophys. Res. Commun.* **23**, 357.

Palmer, G., Brintzinger, H., Estabrook, R. W., and Sands, R. H. (1967). *In* "Magnetic Resonance in Biological Systems" (A. Ehrenberg, T. Vanngard, and B. Malmstrom, eds.), p. 159. Pergamon, Oxford.

Palmer, G., Brintzinger, H., and Estabrook, R. W. (1967). *Biochemistry* **6**, 1658.

Palmer, G., Dunham, W. R., Fee, J. A., Sands, R. H., Iizuka, T., and Yonetani, T. (1971). *Biochim. Biophys. Acta* **245**, 201.

Petering, D. H., and Palmer, G. (1970). *Arch. Biochem.* **141**, 456.

Petering, D., Fee, J. A., and Palmer, G. (1971). *J. Biol. Chem.* **246**, 643.

Phillips, W. D., Poe, M., McDonald, C. C., and Bartsch, R. G. (1970). *Proc. Nat. Acad. Sci. U.S.* **67**, 682.

Poe, M., Phillips, W. D., McDonald, C. C., and Lovenberg, W. (1970). *Proc. Nat. Acad. Sci. U.S.* **65**, 794.

Salmeen, I., and Palmer, G. (1972). *Arch. Biochem. Biophys.* **150**, 767.

San Pietro, A. (1965). "Non-Heme Iron Proteins: Role in Energy Conversion" (A. San Pietro, ed.). Antioch Press, Yellow Springs.

Schneider, J. Dischler, B., and Rauber, A. (1968). *J. Phys. Chem. Solids* **29**, 451.

Shethna, Y. I., Stombaugh, N. A., and Burris, R. H. (1971). *Biochem. Biophys. Res. Commun.* **42**, 1108.

Sieker, L. C., Adman, E., and Jensen, L. H. (1972). *Nature (London)* **235**, 40.

Singer, T. P., and Massey, V. (1957). *Rec. Chem. Progr.* **18**, 201.

Sobel, B. E., and Lovenberg, W. (1966). *Biochemistry* **5**, 6.

Tanaka, M., Haniu, M., and Yasunobu, K. T. (1970). *Biochem. Biophys. Res. Commun.* **39**, 1182.

Watenpaugh, K. D., Sieker, L., Harriott, J. R., and Jensen, L. H. (1972). *Cold Spring Harbor Symp. Quant. Biol.* **36**, 359.

Waterman, M., and Mason, H. S. (1972). *Arch. Biochem. Biophys.* **150**, 57.

Watson, R. E., and Freeman, A. J. (1961). *Phys. Rev.* **123**, 2027.

Wold, F. (1971). *In* "Macromolecular Structure and Function," p. 78. Prentice-Hall, Englewood Cliffs, New Jersey.

Yoch, D. C., Benemann, J. R., Valentine, R. C., and Arnon, D. I. (1969). *Proc. Nat. Acad. Sci. U.S.* **64**, 1404.

Author Index

Numbers in italics refer to the pages on which the complete references are listed.

A

Aasa, R., 198, 208, 210, 211, 213, 234, *235*
Abragam, A., 196, 199, 203, 204, *235*
Adman, E. T., 38, 44, 45, 47, 50, 59, 64, 77, 81, 107, *123*, *125*, *129*, 192, *193*, *194*, 227, *238*, 239, *253*, 277, 280, *284*, 316, 317, *325*
Aggarwal, S. J., 32, 67, 122, *123*, 305, *323*
Akagi, J. M., 6, *24*, 32, 37, 41, 121, 122, *123*, *125*, *129*, *130*
Albracht, S. J., 322, *323*
Alden, R. A., *59*, *125*, 251, *252*, 269, 274, 277, 312, *283*, *323*
Aleman, V., 230, 234, *235*
Alger, R. S., 196, *235*
Allison, R. G., 101, *125*
Allkins, J. R., 156, *161*
Anderson, A. W., 122, *125*
Anderson, R., 200, 201, 205, 207, 218, 220, 221, 234, *236*, 246, 248, *252*, 301, *323*
Ando, K. J., 242, *252*
Andrew, I. G., 121, *124*
Anfinsen, C. B., 101, *124*
Arnon, D. I., 2, 3, 6, 7, 8, 10, 11, 13, 23, *23*, *24*, *25*, *26*, 29, 36, 52, 53, 59, 60, 82, 83, 84, 121, 122, 123, *124*, 127, *129*, *130*, 233, *238*, 316, *325*
Aronson, A. E., 121, *128*
Asakura, T., 231, *237*, 322, *324*
Atherton, N. M., 5, 6, *23*, 148, 151, *160*, 211, *235*
Averill, B. A., 277, 278, 279, *283*
Ayscough, P. B., 196, *235*
Azari, P., 32, 37, 38, 41, *124*

B

Bachmayer, H., 32, 33, 122, *124*, 132, 133, 134, 135, 148, *160*, 180, 181, *193*

Bachofen, R., 2, 10, *23*, 52, 53, 59, 122, *124*
Baird, J. C., 196, *235*
Bale, J., 226
Ballhausen, C. J., 138, 141, *160*
Baptist, J. N., 89, *124*, *126*
Barker, W. C., 310, *323*
Barnes, E. M., 32, 37, *129*
Bartholomaus, R. C., 21, *25*, 217, 219, *236*, *237*
Bartle, K. D., 261, *283*
Bartsch, R. G., 2, 5, 10, 11, 17, *23*, *24*, 30, 32, 77, 78, 79, 81, 115, 123, *124*, *125*, *128*, *236*, 245, 249, 250, 251, *251*, *252*, 260, 274, *283*, *284*, 312, 313, 314, 315, *323*, *324*
Basu, D., 88, 89, 123, *128*, 132, *162*
Bayer, E., 9, 21, *24*, 99, *124*, 306, *323*
Bearden, A. J., 78, *124*, *128*, 217, 218, 221, *236*, 240, 245, 247, 249, 251, *251*, *252*, 295, 296, 298, 300, 308, *323*
Behringer, J., 156, *160*
Beinert, H., 2, 11, 21, 22, *25*, 60, 70, 72, 82, 83, 84, 123, *124*, *125*, *129*, *130*, 200, 201, 205, 207, 209, 214, 215, 217, 218, 219, 220, 225, 226, 228, 229, 230, 231, 234, 235, *236*, *237*, *238*, 245, 246, 247, 248, *252*, *253*, *284*, 300, 301, 317, 321, 322, *323*, *324*
Bendall, D. S., 122, *124*
Bendall, F., 29, 122, *126*
Benemann, J. R., 2, *26*, 82, 83, 84, 123, *130*, 233, *238*, 316, *325*
Benfield, G., 245, *252*
Benson, A. M., 6, 7, *24*, *26*, 32, 33, 37, 38, 62, 90, 120, 122, *124*, *129*, 133, *160*
Benson, R. E., *283*, 308, *323*
Bernal, I., 259, *283*
Bersohn, M., 196, *235*
Birktoff, J., 180, *193*
Black, C. C., 122, *124*, *129*

327

Subject Index

A

Molecular Biology

An International Series of Monographs and Textbooks

Editors

BERNARD HORECKER

Department of Molecular Biology
Albert Einstein College of Medicine
Yeshiva University
Bronx, New York

NATHAN O. KAPLAN

Department of Chemistry
University of California
At San Diego
La Jolla, California

JULIUS MARMUR

Department of Biochemistry
Albert Einstein College of Medicine
Yeshiva University
Bronx, New York

HAROLD A. SCHERAGA

Department of Chemistry
Cornell University
Ithaca, New York

Molecular Biology

An International Series of Monographs and Textbooks

WALTER W. WAINIO. The Mammalian Mitochondrial Respiratory Chain. 1970

LAWRENCE I. ROTHFIELD (Editor). Structure and Function of Biological Membranes. 1971

ALAN G. WALTON AND JOHN BLACKWELL. Biopolymers. 1973

WALTER LOVENBERG (Editor). Iron-Sulfur Proteins. Volume I, Biological Properties — 1973. Volume II, Molecular Properties — 1973

Volume II, Molecular Properties — 1973

A. J. HOPFINGER. Conformational Properties of Macromolecules. 1973

R. D. B. FRASER AND T. P. MACRAE. Conformation in Fibrous Proteins. 1973

In preparation

OSAMU HAYAISHI (Editor). Molecular Mechanisms of Oxygen Activation